PSYCHOLOGY
OF JUDGMENT
AND CHOICE

PSYCHOLOGY OF JUDGMENT AND CHOICE:
a theoretical essay

FRANK RESTLE

Department of Psychology, Michigan State University

New York · London, John Wiley & Sons, Inc.

Preface

The theory presented in this book is mathematical in structure, is based on thinking and research already completed mainly by other workers, and is in a sense a general theory for some topics of experimental psychology. Each of these characteristics merits some introductory discussion, to clarify what is and what is not intended.

It is important to be clear as to the reason for using mathematics before we begin actual work, for the application of mathematics to social science is a new and popular parlor game with many interpretations. Some discussions make us feel that it is morally good to use mathematics in scientific discourse, but the ethical base is left unspecified. It may be said that mathematics is rigorous, and after all that is what we psychologists wish to be; hence we should use mathematics. The validity of this argument depends on whether mathematical and psychological rigor are really the same, and whether psychological rigor is actually a good thing. The use of mathematics in psychological theory can, I think, be justified by a proper statement of the aims of theory, the material with which we can work, and the state of our art at present.

If we seek specific and precise agreement between theory and data there are two reasons for using mathematics. First, we must have some way of telling whether our ideas do agree with fact.

v

We must know exactly what the theory does and does not predict before we can test it, and this in turn requires a systematic method of checking complicated deductions. Mathematics serves as a structure for valid deduction. Second, besides permitting such an accurate check of reasoning, mathematics often makes it possible to deal with quantitative relationships. It is usually easier to test a supposed quantitative relationship than a qualitative distinction in the laboratory.

The material of psychological theory is the accumulation of experimental and observational findings. Although the first study of a new area is often descriptive and qualitative, much of psychological experimentation and observation has already been reduced to quantitative form. In a few cases measurements in the physical sense have been made, but more often the psychologist has counted the frequencies of various interesting events. He may count the frequency of errors in a study of visual detection, the frequency of bar-presses in a study of rat performance, the frequency of idiosyncratic responses to a Rorschach ink blot, or the number of items on an attitude questionnaire to which the subject changes responses after viewing a propaganda film. A little consideration will show that the vast mass of psychological data is in the form of frequencies of particular events, often corrected as relative frequencies or frequencies per unit time (rates).

One is not prepared from physics or psychological imitations of physics to consider frequencies as the natural basis of a quantitative theory; one is inclined to consider measurable continuous variables like position, mass, or energy as the foundations of a quantitative theory. The approach taken in this book is that the psychologist usually and most naturally begins a theoretical discussion by classifying his materials in some qualitative fashion, and then counting the frequency with which the various categories occur.

The kind of mathematics used in this book begins with qualitative distinctions and the formation of sets or categories. The measures of sets, which in general correspond to the frequencies of occurrence, are then introduced, and the theory is made predictive by treating the measures as probabilities. Although the resulting theory is not complete, it is, I think, broader and more relevant to the genuine psychological problems than would be a theory which attempted to work mainly on continuous variables just as classical physics does. If we agree to concentrate on frequencies, the data with which the psychological theorist works are numerical and fitted for mathematical analysis.

If this argument is accepted, then we can use mathematics. One may ask what advantages may be expected, for one does not do everything that is possible merely because it is possible. In this study mathematical methods are not added to a theory which is intrinsically of some other sort, but are a natural part of the whole line of thinking.

As psychologists we work under certain self-imposed handicaps. Our professional choice is to work on the hard problems of perception, learning, personality, and social behavior. We may seek physiological mechanisms which underlie behavior, but we leave the detailed investigation of mechanisms to the physiologist and instead plunge into the broader and more involved problem of integrating the parts into a picture of total behavior. We study, not the eye, but the perceiving organism; not the reflex, but the whole process of learning and adjusting; not the formal structure of the group, but the actions of men in harmony or in conflict. This means that we always deal with complexity, and our every problem requires the delicate articulation of many data and concepts. It is difficult to deal with anything as complex as behavior while doing all the thinking in our heads—we need to turn reasoning into routine whenever possible.

Mathematics is useful as a way of stating reasoning problems so that they are easily solved. Everyone remembers the elementary algebra problem: Car A starts at 11 o'clock going 30 miles an hour and car B starts from the same place at 3 o'clock going 45 miles an hour. When car B overtakes car A, how far have they gone? Conceptually, the problem is simple and straightforward, but it is not easy for the unaided intuition to arrive at the correct answer. Once we see that the distance covered by car A is $30h$ and the distance covered by car B is $45(h - 4)$ and that these are equal, we have the equation $30h = 45h - 180$. Then $15h = 180$, and $30h = 360$ is the number of miles traveled.

The formulation of the problem is not too difficult, though it requires a little thought and some understanding of the factors involved. Once the formulation is set, the reasoning process uses the standard simplifying devices of elementary algebra—devices which are readily learned and have properties which have been intensively studied by mathematicians. The final advantage is that the answer can be checked, and one can prove that the answer is correctly reasoned.

The sources of error in solving such problems, besides careless errors in calculation, center around errors in formulating the problem. These are failures in theory, which may be consistently avoided in elementary algebra examples but which will be with us throughout our study of psychological problems. However, the ability to separate failures in understanding of psychology from errors of deduction will help us remedy our lacks.

Some of the same methods used in the simple problem of two cars moving at steady rates can be generalized to deal with larger collections of cars and with cars that change their rates of movement. When the problem is sufficiently enriched, it has applications in matters as practical as the analysis of highway traffic and the calculation of how many lanes should be built in a new thruway. Thus, even when a problem can be treated without mathematics, it may be advantageous to push through a mathematical analysis to see what complications could then be handled. The treatment of the complications may be very difficult mathematically, in which case it is likely that an intuitive approach would be impossible; and it may turn out that the development of the theory into complex cases makes obvious some flaw in the formulation. If this happens we may be able to correct an error in thinking which would not be noticeable in any of the simple cases of which we have immediate understanding.

The theory developed in this essay depends heavily on the research and thinking of other psychologists. No reasonable alternative presents itself, and yet it is sometimes argued that a theory developed on the basis of published data is so contaminated that its validity and even its value are seriously compromised. On the basis of this opinion psychologists prefer or even require that hypotheses be stated before an experiment is performed. Explanations after the fact must be stated with extreme caution and are even then barely tolerated. Since the chapters to follow are almost entirely *post hoc*, it is perhaps sensible to defend the procedure.

First, it must be conceded that predictions have a peculiar power to either overthrow or support a theory. Most of us are, I think rightly, impressed when a theory is shown to predict an experimental result that subsequently occurs. The result is not, however, conclusive. In fact, if the prediction is sufficiently obvious and in accord with a variety of theories, then a successful prediction is not of very great moment at all. A theory which predicts that rats can solve T-mazes is not very much strengthened by an experimental demonstration, since the fact is already well known and almost all learning theories make the same prediction. The power of a prediction arises as much from its disconfirmation of alternative theories as from its confirmation of the theory being studied. This disconfirming function of an experiment is not affected by whether it is a new or an old one, and does not depend on there being a prediction a priori.

If we inquire into the exact reason for the superiority of prediction over postdiction, we find two major arguments: (1) When a theory is checked against published data there is a tendency to select favorable evidence and disregard or explain away unfavorable findings. (2) A theory may give a *post hoc* "explanation" of an experiment when the same theory could not have made a prediction.

It is true that a theorist who bases his argument on published data will tend to select favorable results. One might suppose that if new findings are predicted and then studied experimentally, the evidence is unbiased. However, an experimenter may modify and "improve" his laboratory technique until he obtains results in accord with his theory. It is not entirely clear what analyses of the data are most important, so one may select those analyses which agree best with theory. Furthermore, unsuccessful predictions yield data that are difficult to interpret and which may, for that reason, not be published. Thus it is possible to select evidence in favor of a theory even when one proceeds by pure prediction, and no entirely decisive advantage of this sort can be given to prediction.

The possibility of a spurious "explanation" which would not support a prediction must, especially in an ill-formed science like psychology, be given serious attention. This possibility by its very nature is peculiar to postdiction and cannot apply to prediction, hence is a sound basis for preferring predictions in general. However, it is useful to consider how spurious explanations arise, so that the real bearing of the argument is clear.

When will a theory advance an explanation which could not be a prediction? There seem to be two major cases to examine: (1) that in which the logical structure of the theory is incompletely understood, so that one imagines that the experimental result follows from the theory when logically it does not; and (2) that in which one must know something about the experimental results before the rest of the results can be predicted. For example, in studying the solution of word problems, one might construct a problem which presents the subject with two distinct kinds of difficulty. If one can measure separately, in part of the experiment, the distribution of times required to complete the two difficulties separately, one may be able to make a theoretical prediction of the distribution of times to solve the compound problem. Without such advance information, there is no hope of predicting performance on the compound problem.

Certainly the simplest way to show that prediction is possible is to predict. However, careful attention to the formal structure of the theory can ensure that an explanation has the necessary logical ingredients to permit prediction. If we are to work a posteriori we must be careful of our logic, but the use of a sound mathematical argument ensures that explanations are not spurious. If predictions are possible only on the basis of "calibration," the use of some of the data, then explanations like predictions are contingent and we must be clear as to the conditions of the argument. Whether we are predicting or postdicting, it is essential to show some interdependence between the data used and the data predicted, to show that the explanation is substantial and not a mere tautology. Again, the problem is mainly logical and can be solved by precision of theoretical statement.

I do not wish to conclude, from this, that predictions are unnecessary or that postdictions are quite as good as predictions. Certainly, in fact, one must have both; for imagine a theory that makes an unbroken string of correct predictions but when applied postdictively to other results is found to be in error. One would, I think, try to improve the theory. The ideas in this book give ample opportunity for predictions, some of which have been tested. Most of the empirical checks are, however, based on the vast volume of published data and theory. I have tried to make the theoretical statements clear and complete enough to ensure that the explanations of old data are genuine and that predictions could have been made in advance. It must be admitted that the theory is but imperfect in form and that the data have been hand-picked, so that all conclusions are necessarily tentative. However, the real reason for writing the book is not to arrive at final conclusions but to help stimulate deeper and more complete analysis of the experimental topics treated.

It has seemed natural and, indeed, necessary to express the theoretical ideas of this book in mathematical form. Since many psychologists and students of psychology have in recent years been at some pains to acquire a working knowledge of ordinary mathematics, this should present no grave difficulties in communication. However, I have made several efforts to make the book accessible to readers whose current technical skill in mathematics is not at a high level. As nearly as possible I have made the book self-contained by devoting the first chapter to the topics of set theory and probability theory, the main mathematical ideas used in the book. Throughout the book I have tried to keep the notation simple and to place each argument firmly on its theoretical foundations. The same equation

is repeated in each section in which it is used, so that the reader
need not remember or refer back to other chapters. Most of the
deductions are performed with ordinary high-school algebra or
elementary set theory, and the reader is also helped by verbal discussions of the hypotheses and conclusions. I have attempted to make
the mathematical arguments complete and rigorous, but to supplement
them as is done in lectures or discussions with students, so that lack
of a particular mathematical fact does not make the point inaccessible.
The book is easier the more mathematics the reader knows, but most
of the arguments should be intelligible to students with some talent
for abstract thinking even if they are not already familiar with the
mathematical system used.

It must be admitted that the mathematical arguments
become more difficult and complex as the book advances. If this were
not so, the use of mathematics at all would be unjustified. In the
last few chapters some problems arise which are not tractable with
the elementary methods used in the rest of the book, so more advanced
methods are brought in. The reader is advised, however, to continue
beyond any sections which present difficulties, for the hard mathematical points are not assumed in sections which follow them.

As a final aid to the reader, I have resisted the temptation
to state problems and theorems in the most general form possible and
have instead limited the mathematics to concrete and special cases.
An elegant procedure is to prove a very general theorem and then
produce the remainder of the needed results as corollaries, or to
generate a very general equation and then develop other equations by
inserting the restrictions which apply. These approaches, although
convincing, are often not very enlightening to the student, who cannot
hold the general idea firmly in mind or grasp exactly what it means
in a specific application. The crucial step from experimental method
to results must pass through a general theoretical equation which is
not fully understood. To avoid these difficulties, I have proved the
same points over and over again in different contexts. In some cases,
to preserve an intuitive basis for the argument, formal precision and
niceties of mathematical expression have been sacrificed. I trust the
more sophisticated readers will suffer these indignities with good
grace, and will enjoy their opportunities to extend and improve the
arguments.

The various ideas and analyses used in this book have been
collected over a number of years, but the opportunity to bring them
together was afforded by my tenure as a Faculty Research Fellow of
the Social Science Research Council, 1959–1962. Preparation for this

essay was greatly aided by a fellowship at the Center for Advanced Study in the Behavioral Sciences, 1955–1956, by membership in a workshop held by the Social Science Research Council in 1957, and by the patient cooperation of my students, Department, and University.

A study of this sort draws on the whole of psychology, and calls for an acknowledgment to all those who developed and brought forward the ideas of psychology to the author. I have borrowed most shamelessly from a few teachers and friends: Robert R. Bush, William K. Estes, Douglas H. Lawrence, R. Duncan Luce, and Patrick Suppes. Professor Luce read the entire book, and his suggestions led to many corrections and improvements and the removal of a large volume of irrelevant discussion, for which the reader may well be grateful.

FRANK RESTLE

East Lansing, Michigan
May, 1961

Contents

Part I   Theory

1. Set Theory and Theory of Probability   3
2. Theory of the Probability of a Response   25
3. The Concepts of Order and Distance on Sets   38

Part II   Applications

4. Choices and the Measurement of Utility   59
5. Recognition and the Effects of Frequency   94
6. Patterns of Events and Responses in Prediction
   Experiments   107
7. Detection and the Notion of Homogeneous Classes   135
8. Theory of Compound Responses   164
9. Complex Systems of Response—Judgments and
   Estimations   188

   References   221

   Index   225

xiii

PART I Theory

CHAPTER ONE

Set Theory and Theory of Probability

A large part of psychological fact consists of recorded observations of what a certain subject did in a certain situation under given conditions. Responses to a multiple-choice test, choices in a learning experiment, expressions of preference, and attempts to detect or distinguish stimuli are all examples of discrete responses. These responses are recorded, classified in various ways, and then counted. The mathematical operations corresponding to classification are expressed in set theory; counting finds its mathematical counterpart in measure theory; and these two operations together, along with attempts to predict what will happen next, are reflected in probability theory. This chapter introduces the concepts of set, measure, and probability, and discusses in a general way how they may be applied in psychological contexts.

Elementary Set Theory

A set is any arbitrary collection of things. The things may be objects, abstract entities like numbers, or anything else. A set of sets is often called a "family," and when one works with a variety of different families of sets alternative words for "set" are available; these include "space," "collection," "range," and "domain." Special kinds of sets may have names, such as "group" and "ring." These special names correspond to sets over which certain abstract conditions, of general interest, hold.

A set may be designated by giving it a name like A (capital letters are used in this book) or by listing its members inside braces. The set whose only members are the numbers 1, 2, and 3 is written $\{1, 2, 3\}$.

A set may also be defined in terms of a defining property, $\underline{a}$. Consider, for example, a set of people and let the property $\underline{a}(x)$ mean "person x has red hair." Then the set of redheads can be written $\{x: \underline{a}(x)\}$, which is read "the set of all x such that $\underline{a}(x)$" or, in the example, "the set of all x such that x has red hair." Thus a set may be designated by a name, A, by enumeration of its elements, or by its defining property.

In discussing sets in general it is customary and convenient to illustrate general notions with sets of *numbers*—there are always plenty of numbers available and they have concise and unambiguous names. In abstract set theory these numbers are often thought of as mere entities with no special properties. When working with sets developed from defining properties, special properties of numbers may be used as an example of the principle involved. Talking about integers, for example, there is a set of integers $\{x: 0 < x < 10\} = \{1, 2, 3, 4, 5, 6, 7, 8, 9\}$.

Two sets are equal or identical provided they have exactly the same members. Just above, for example, we had the two expressions about integers, $\{x: 0 < x < 10\}$ and $\{1, 2, 3, 4, 5, 6, 7, 8, 9\}$. These two expressions are equivalent because the sets have exactly the same elements. Two listings of the same elements are equal even if the order of listing is different; for example, $\{1, 2\} = \{2, 1\}$.

One distinction which is crucial in set theory is between members and subsets of a set. Consider the set $\{1, 2, 3\}$. Its members are 1, 2, and 3. A subset is a set all of whose members are also members of the parent set. Thus, the set $\{1, 2\}$ is a subset of $\{1, 2, 3\}$. Also, $\{1\}$ is a subset of $\{1, 2, 3\}$. However, 1 is not a subset but a member of $\{1, 2, 3\}$. We must distinguish between 1 and $\{1\}$. Here, 1 is a number and $\{1\}$ is a set whose only member is the number 1.

This does not mean that a set cannot be the member of another set. A set is any collection of things; hence one can form a set of sets. Things sometimes get a trifle complicated; for example, consider the set $\{1, \{1\}\}$. Here, $\{1\}$ is both a member and a subset. It is a member by virtue of being the second element in the set, and a subset by virtue of the fact that its only member, 1, is also the first member of the parent set. Fortunately there are no such sets in the discussion to follow, but consideration of the possibilities clarifies the distinction between members and subsets.

The common notation of set theory is as follows. To say that a is a member of the set B, write $a \in B$. It is equivalent to say that a is an element of B. To say that a set A is a subset of B, write $A \subset B$. It is equivalent to say that A is contained in B. To say that $A \subset B$ is equivalent to saying that for any x, if $x \in A$, then $x \in B$. Now it follows that $B \subset B$.

The main operations on sets are union, intersection, and complementation. They correspond directly to the logical words OR, AND, and NOT, and are similar to the operations of addition, multiplication, and subtraction of numbers.

The union of sets A and B, written $A \cup B$, is a set which has in it all the members of A and all the members of B and no others. For example, if $A = \{1, 2, 3\}$ and $B = \{3, 5\}$, then $A \cup B = \{1, 2, 3, 5\}$. Note that although 3 appears in both A and B it is written only once in $A \cup B$. This is an example of the rule that each element is written (and counted) only once in a set.

The correspondence to the logical word OR is seen by writing the set in terms of a defining property. Suppose that A is the set of things which have property $\underline{a}$ and B is the set of things which have property $\underline{b}$, i.e.,

$$A = \{x \colon \underline{a}(x)\} \quad \text{and} \quad B = \{x \colon \underline{b}(x)\}$$

Then

$$A \cup B = \{x \colon \underline{a}(x) \text{ or } \underline{b}(x)\}$$

For example, restrict the discussion to the integers from 1 to 10. Let A be the set of odd integers, so that $\underline{a}(x)$ is "x is odd." Let B be the set of integers less than 5, so that $\underline{b}(x)$ is "x is less than 5." Writing out all the members,

$$A = \{1, 3, 5, 7, 9\} \quad \text{and} \quad B = \{1, 2, 3, 4\}$$

whence

$$A \cup B = \{1, 2, 3, 4, 5, 7, 9\}$$

Now construct the set $\{x \colon \underline{a}(x) \text{ or } \underline{b}(x)\}$. The numbers 1, 2, 3, and 4 satisfy this relationship because they have property $\underline{b}$, and the numbers 5, 7, and 9 satisfy the relationship because they have property $\underline{a}$. The numbers 1 and 3 have both properties, hence a fortiori have property $\underline{a}$ or property $\underline{b}$. Thus this set is $\{1, 2, 3, 4, 5, 7, 9\}$, which is equal to the other expression for $A \cup B$. Whenever the elements of A and B can be written out the two ways of constructing the union $A \cup B$ must give the same answer. In the case of an infinite set there is only the logical operation on properties as a foundation, but this gives us an exact set theory because the rules of usage of the word OR are precise in logic.

The intersection of sets A and B, written $A \cap B$, is the set which has as members all elements common to A and B and no otheres. It is also called the "set product" or the "overlap," and relates to the word "joint" in probability theory. In the example where $A = \{1, 2, 3\}$ and $B = \{3, 5\}$, $A \cap B = \{3\}$. Note the braces around 3, indicating that the intersection is a set and not the element itself.

The operation of intersection corresponds to the logical word AND. If $A = \{x: \underline{a}(x)\}$ and $B = \{x: \underline{b}(x)\}$, then $A \cap B = \{x: \underline{a}(x)$ and $\underline{b}(x)\}$. Using the previous example where $\underline{a}(x)$ is "x is odd" and $\underline{b}(x)$ is "x is less than 5," the set $A \cap B$, is $\{x: x$ is odd and x is less than 5$\}$, which is the set $\{1, 3\}$. Writing out A and B as $A = \{1, 3, 5, 7, 9\}$ and $B = \{1, 2, 3, 4\}$, the common elements are found to comprise $\{1, 3\}$.

The complement of a set, written $\overline{A}$, is defined in terms of the universe of discourse U. In set theory as in any other logical or mathematical argument, one must decide on the scope of study. The examples above use the universe consisting of the first 10 positive integers. In psychological applications the universe may be the set of responses, the set of stimulus situations, the set of cues, the set of people involved in a group discussion, the set of possible total outcomes of an experiment, etc. In every case a well-defined universe is needed for deductive analysis.

The complement of A, $\overline{A}$, is the set which contains all the elements of U except those in A. For example, in the universe of numbers from 1 to 10, if A are the odd ones, then $\overline{A} = \{2, 4, 6, 8, 10\}$. In terms of a property $\underline{a}(x)$,

$$\overline{A} = \{x: \text{not } \underline{a}(x)\}$$

so that complementation corresponds to the use of the logical word NOT.

One of the advantages of using set theory in psychological theory is this correspondence of union, intersection, and complementation with OR, AND, and NOT. The general strategy is to try to state the psychological ideas in simple language that brings out the logical structure. Then it is possible to make a direct translation of the ideas in ordinary language into set theory, and the mathematical structure of the situation mirrors psychological intuition.

Consider the following intuitive description of group problem-solving, similar to a mathematical model developed by Lorge and Solomon (1955). Four persons are working on a problem. The psychological statement is: "Either some member of the group can solve the problem alone, or the group cannot solve the problem." The universe of discourse is all groups of four people working on this problem. Consider the following sets of groups:

$$A = \{x: \text{someone in group } x \text{ can solve the problem}\}$$

$$B = \{x: \text{group } x \text{ can solve the problem}\}$$

The logical form of the argument comes out clearly when this is written with briefer descriptions of the two properties, letting $\underline{a}(x)$ be "someone in group x can solve the problem" and $\underline{b}(x)$ be "group x can solve the problem." Then

$$A = \{x: \underline{a}(x)\}$$

$$B = \{x: \underline{b}(x)\}$$

The logical statement is then: either $a(x)$ or not $b(x)$. The statement means that throughout the universe U of groups, every element is in either A or $\bar{B}$, which is to say that

$$U = A \cup \bar{B}$$

Thus a psychological hypothesis is translated directly into set-theoretic terms in a straightforward way. What is more, this can be shown by set algebra to mean that $B \subset A$, i.e., that the set of groups which can solve the problem is a subset of the set of groups which have a solver in them.

This single hypothesis does not lead to a rich deductive system; the point here is merely to show that a hypothesis, stated in ordinary language, can be translated directly into set theory.

The algebra of sets requires one further notion, that of the empty set. Two sets are equal if and only if they have the same members. Now consider the following two sets:

$$A = \{x: x > 7\}$$

$$B = \{x: x < 5\}$$

Obviously, $A \cap B$ has no members at all.

Now consider the set

$$C = \{x: x \text{ is a living personal acquaintance of Plato}\}$$

Evidently, C has no members. Since the sets $A \cap B$ and C have exactly the same members, they must be equal: $A \cap B = C$.

All sets which have no members are equal, or, to put it another way, there is just one empty set. This unique set is given a particular name, and it is called $\emptyset$ in this book.

The Algebra of Sets

The power of a mathematical system resides in the ability to transform particular expressions into other equivalent ones, showing that two quite different-appearing expressions may have the same meaning or that one expression is a consequence of others. The rules by which such transformations can be made define the logical properties of the system. The minimum set of rules or axioms of set theory is very small, for from a few rules one can deduce others. We shall not investigate these fundamental questions, but merely take as given a large set of useful rules. The following are taken from Kemeny, Snell, and Thompson's (1957) elementary book.

Rules governing union and intersection:

A1. $A \cup A = A$
A2. $A \cap A = A$
A3. $A \cup B = B \cup A$
A4. $A \cap B = B \cap A$
A5. $A \cup (B \cup C) = (A \cup B) \cup C$
A6. $A \cap (B \cap C) = (A \cap B) \cap C$
A7. $A \cap (B \cup C) = (A \cap B) \cup (A \cap C)$
A8. $A \cup (B \cap C) = (A \cup B) \cap (A \cup C)$
A9. $A \cup U = U$
A10. $A \cap \emptyset = \emptyset$
A11. $A \cap U = A$
A12. $A \cup \emptyset = A$

Axioms A1 and A2 are useful for reducing entirely redundant sentences. Axioms A3 and A4 show that the order of two sets combined by union or intersection is immaterial, which permits useful rearrangements. Axioms A5 and A6 show that parentheses can be rearranged around a set of sets connected by union or intersection signs. In practice this means that the parentheses are not used, and one writes expressions like $A \cup B \cup C$ or $A \cap B \cap C$. Axioms 7 and 8 are the "distributive" axioms, which are of great importance in simplifying expressions. Axiom 7 is like the axiom of algebra, $a(b + c) = ab + ac$, which permits "multiplying out" or factoring. Axiom 8 shows one of the differences between set algebra and numerical algebra. It would correspond to the assertion $a + (bc) = (a + b)(a + c)$, which is not true of numbers. Since it is true of sets, one can use a term like "adding out" to represent the operation intended. This axiom greatly simplifies calculations in set theory and makes it much easier than numerical algebra. The last four axioms, A9–A12, introduce the obvious but useful facts about the universe U and the empty set $\emptyset$.

Laws governing complements:

B1. $\bar{\bar{A}} = A$

B2. $A \cup \bar{A} = U$

B3. $A \cap \bar{A} = \emptyset$

B4. $\overline{A \cup B} = \bar{A} \cap \bar{B}$

B5. $\overline{A \cap B} = \bar{A} \cup \bar{B}$

B6. $\bar{U} = \emptyset$

Axiom B1 permits the canceling of double negatives. Axioms B2 and B3 relate complementation to the sets U and $\emptyset$. Axioms B4 and B5 are deMorgan's rules which make it possible to decompose the complement of a compound expression into the complements of elementary sentences. The general idea of axiom B4 may be expressed as follows: if an element is not in the set $(A$ or $B)$, it is not in A and it is not in B. Axiom B5 says: if the element is not in both A and B, then either it is not in A or it is not in B. These are perfectly simple ideas, but it helps that they can be expressed in simple algebraic form, for otherwise ordinary logic would involve constructing quite formidable sentences.

The Measure of a Set

The algebra of sets is useful in simplifying logical argument, but does not itself add more than ordinary language can provide. However, quantitative results can be obtained by considering the magnitude of a set, which in general terms is the "measure" of the set. The measure of a set A will be called $m(A)$.

The abstract concept of a measure may reflect any psychological notion of magnitude required in the particular context. An example of a measure is the number of elements in the set. If one set has 25 members and another has 100, the second is larger. In general, the magnitude of a set can be represented by the number of elements in it, except for two cases which may arise:

1. The elements may have different weights.
2. There may be an infinite number of elements.

In the first case of weighting of elements, it is true that all football teams have 11 members, but one team may be much "larger" because the players weigh 210 instead of 170 pounds. In this case the best measure of the magnitude of the team may be the sum of the weights of players rather than the mere number. In an experiment on memory it may be that different experiences, because they differ in importance, should receive different weights. The measure of a set of experiences would then be the sum of their weights rather than the mere number of experiences.

If there are infinitely many elements in a set, then there is no "number of elements." An example of the difficulties here is the following. Consider the set I of all positive integers, and the set E of all even integers. It would seem that I has a magnitude twice that of E. However, any element i of I can be paired with an element e of E with no duplication, as follows. Let $i = 5$. Pair this with $2i = 10$, an even integer in the set E. By this method it is apparent that every element of I has its pair in E. Since the even integers are never exhausted there is no end to the process, and all elements of I have their (unique) partners in E. This means that the two sets have exactly the same number of elements, for they can be put into one-to-one correspondence with no leftovers. It is characteristic of an infinite set that it can be put into one-to-one correspondence with a proper subset of itself. However, it is natural to say that the measure of the set of even integers plus the measure of the set of odd integers equals the measure of the set of all integers, even though "measure" cannot mean "number." In the general treatment of set theory, the abstract concept of a measure function is used.

The characteristics of a measure function can be stated in terms of axioms which regulate their manipulation. We shall deal with discrete sets, i.e., sets which have a finite number of elements or sets whose elements can be arranged in a simple order, $x_1, x_2, \cdots ,$. The axioms are

M1. $m(\emptyset) = 0$
M2. $0 \le m(X)$ for any set X
M3. If X and Y are mutually exclusive sets, i.e., $X \cap Y = \emptyset$ then $m(X \cup Y) = m(X) + m(Y)$

In the case of an infinite number of sets one has to add one formal axiom,

M4. If $X_1, X_2, \cdots$ are mutually exclusive, then $m(X_1 \cup X_2 \cup \cdots) = m(X_1) + m(X_2) + \cdots$

A basic and useful consequence of these axioms is

THEOREM: For any sets X and Y, $m(X \cup Y) = m(X) + m(Y) - m(X \cap Y)$.

Proof: Intuitively, the assertion is obvious for any finite set. If the measures of X and Y are added, certain elements will be counted twice, though they should be counted only once. The elements counted twice are just those in $X \cap Y$, and their measure should be subtracted once to correct.

A formal proof can be constructed using the technique of partitioning. To do this, two new words are introduced: A "partition" of a set X is a set of subsets $X_1, X_2, \cdots$, which are mutually exclusive and which exhaust X. The subsets are called the "cells" of the partition.

Now, it is possible to divide the universe into a partition as follows: $X \cap \bar{Y}$, $\bar{X} \cap Y$, $X \cap Y$, and $\bar{X} \cap \bar{Y}$. It is evident that $X \cup Y = (X \cap \bar{Y}) \cup (\bar{X} \cap Y) \cup (X \cap Y)$, and that these three subsets are mutually exclusive. Hence by axiom M3,

$$m(X \cup Y) = m(X \cap \bar{Y}) + m(\bar{X} \cap Y) + m(X \cap Y)$$

We now add and subtract $m(X \cap Y)$ and rearrange terms, to obtain

$$m(X \cup Y) = m(X \cap \bar{Y}) + 2m(X \cap Y) + m(\bar{X} \cap Y) - m(X \cap Y)$$

Now, $X \cap \bar{Y}$ and $X \cap Y$ are mutually exclusive, since the first is part of $\bar{Y}$ and the second is part of Y, and $Y \cap \bar{Y} = \emptyset$. Hence, $m(X \cap \bar{Y}) + m(X \cap Y) = m[(X \cap \bar{Y}) \cup (X \cap Y)] = m(X)$. Similarly, $m(\bar{X} \cap Y) + m(X \cap Y) = m(Y)$. Now we have

$$m(X \cup Y) = m(X) + m(Y) - m(X \cap Y)$$

which was to be proved.

The fact that the proof could be done formally shows that it holds generally for any measure function and any sets, even infinite ones.

It is in the introduction of measures that set theory goes beyond ordinary logic and becomes particularly useful to psychology. In logic, there are only three classes of sentences; those which are logically true (tautologies), those which are logically false (contradictions), and those which are neither. In "functional calculus" or the logic of properties, analogously, any property is either universal, so that every element of the universe has it, or impossible, so that no element of the universe has it, or somewhere between. For example, the property "is white or is not white" is universal. The property "is white and is not white" is impossible. The property "is white" is somewhere in between, applying to some things and not others.

Psychology is particularly interested in the cases which are in between—the attributes which some people have and others do not, the properties which some situations have and others do not, etc. Logic, which classifies sets as U, $\emptyset$, or "something else," is too weak, and cannot ask "how many" or "what part of the universe" has a property. Of a property $\underline{a}$ the psychologist may ask: What is the measure of the set $\{x:\ \underline{a}(x)\}$?

Merely counting the number of elements in a set leads to interesting and valuable conclusions, in cases where it is possible, for set-theoretic mathematics deals with just the process of counting which is so large a part of psychological measurement. Where the various things receive different weights, or where counting is impossible, the same mathematical apparatus which would be used if we were to count can still be applied. It will sometimes be possible to find a clear isomorphism between the measures of sets within the theory and the numbers of events of various types observed and counted in the experiment. When this happens, of course, the most serious problems of psychological measurement and the application of theory to experiment are solved in a simple and transparent way.

A further development may be indicated at this point. Much of psychological theory deals with probabilities of events. In fact, probabilities are the main theoretical quantities to be used, and much of the problem of applying theory to data is the question of estimation of probabilities or the parameters of probability distributions. It is a valuable fact that measure theory can be transformed into probability theory (as a mathematical discipline) by the addition of a single axiom:* namely,

Axiom P1. $m(U) = 1$

In the event that axioms M1–M4 and P1 are satisfied, the function m is called a "probability measure." It is conventional to write $P(X)$ as the probability of the set X, by which is meant a measure $m(X)$ which satisfies axiom P1. Thus, no important new apparatus is needed to enter into probability theory. However, some elaboration of this point is in order.

Elementary Theory of Probability

It is by no means a simple matter to decide just what is meant by the probability of a certain event. The classical approach argues that if, in a certain situation, there are n possible things which might happen and there is no way to know which will happen, each has probability $1/n$. A deductive theory develops by applying this approach, in the following way. Consider, for example, the probability of throwing a natural 7 with a pair of dice. This is a

* It is sufficient that $m(U)$ be finite, i.e., bounded from above.

compound event that may consist of a 1 and a 6, a 2 and a 5, etc., and any of these elementary events yields a 7. Classical theory says that any throw of the pair of dice is exactly as likely as any other; if the numbers on the two dice are written (x, y), x being the number on the first die and y on the second, then all the tosses $(1, 1)$, $(1, 2)$, $\cdots$, $(2, 1)$, $(2, 2)$, $\cdots$, $(6, 6)$ are equally likely. A little consideration shows that there are $6 \times 6 = 36$ possible throws, each of which has probability 1/36. Now we note that a 7 is obtained with six of these possibilities, namely $(1, 6)$, $(2, 5)$, $(3, 4)$, $(4, 3)$, $(5, 2)$, and $(6, 1)$. Hence the probability of getting a 7 is $1/36 + 1/36 + \cdots$, or $6/36 = 1/6$.

This approach to probabilities serves very well for the theoretical and practical analysis of gambling games. However, in scientific applications, equally likely elementary events may not exist, or it may be necessary to verify that certain events are equally likely. How would this be done?

To test a particular die to see if all its sides *are* equally likely to come up, a simple experiment would be to throw it a large number of times. Provided the die does not wear out, the six sides may appear about equally often in a million throws. However, even if the die is perfect, if the number of throws is large it becomes extremely unlikely that all sides will come up with exactly equal frequencies. Suppose that the die is tossed some multiple of six times, say, $6n$ times. The probability that it comes out with exactly n occurrences of each side is something like $6/n^5$ with a large number of tosses. With only 600 tosses, this would be $6/10,000,000,000$, which is very small.

Hence, a fair die must be identified even when the experiment does not come out exactly correctly. It is argued that if the experiment is run sufficiently long, the *relative* frequencies of the six sides will come very close to 1/6, so that in the limit, with an infinite number of trials, the relative frequencies will approach the true probabilities. This, then, is a definition of probability: The probability of an ace on a particular die may be defined as the relative frequency of aces in an infinite number of tosses, or, more exactly, the limit of the relative frequencies of tosses as the number of tosses increases without bound.

This definition escapes any assumption about the die, but requires, for definition, an infinite (and thereby impossible) experiment. Furthermore, nothing can be said about the probability of a particular, unique event, for that event cannot be repeated even once more, let alone an infinite number of times. Although it is generally agreed that the relative frequency of an event will converge to the probability in an endless sequence of trials, there is some question whether this should be taken as the defining property of probabilities.

A third approach attempts to avoid the difficulties of the above two approaches by stating that the probability of an event is how likely it seems, on the basis of evidence available. If there is nothing apparent which would make one side of the die more likely than another, then the sides are equally probable. Of course, if the die is then thrown 600 times and shows 500 aces, new information is available and the probability is different. This "subjective" approach is disconcerting, because it leaves probabilities to the judgment of some person, and because the probability of an event can apparently be changed simply by the process of gaining new information, even though the objective situation is in no way changed.

All of the above three definitions talk about the probability of a particular occurrence. A fourth approach retires a step from this question, and talks about the probability of a set of occurrences. The particular occurrence, such as an ace coming up the next time the die is thrown, is first classified by making it an element of some particular set of such occurrences, such as a particular set of 6000 tosses of the die. This set or "universe" is now divided into subsets, one of which (for example) is the set of all tosses in which an ace occurs. The probability of an ace is defined, now, as the relative frequency of aces in the universe of 6000 tosses, and it is understood that this definition is relative to the classification. The particular probability depends upon the set employed. For example, beginning with the set of possible tosses, the numbers 1 through 6, an ace is just one of these six, and the probability is 1/6. This would be the a priori probability of an ace. If the toss is related to some finite set of tosses, then the probability would be the relative frequency of tosses in that set, a number which may or may not be near 1/6 but ordinarily will not be exactly 1/6. If the toss is related to some hypothetical, infinite sequence of tosses, the relative-frequency definition applies. These are all different probabilities, for though they relate to the same particular toss they actually refer, not to the toss, but to the set of which it is a member, and the reference sets are different.

Whatever the other advantages or disadvantages of this last definition, it does avoid certain confusing cases in which it seems that the probability of an event changes for an inadequate reason. One example, discussed by Popper (1959), illustrates the issue nicely though it is a physical case. Imagine a mirror which transmits half the incident light and reflects the other half. As a particular photon approaches the mirror, it has a probability 1/2 of going through. The same photon, acted on in no way, as it comes out the other side of the mirror has a probability 1.0 of passing through. Such a change of probability is ordinarily thought to involve forces, but there are none here. Popper's analysis is, in essence, that the photon before it reaches the mirror is classified with all incident photons, half of which will go through. Hence, correctly, its probability relative to that set is 1/2, and always will be. However, when it emerges it may be classified anew with photons which have gone through. Since they all (by definition) have gone through, the probability associated with this new set is, correctly, 1.0. The change is not in the photon but in our classification of it, for as a finer classification becomes possible a new probability can be obtained. Notice that the ambiguity is removed if probabilities are considered as characteristics of sets, rather than of the specific events which make up those sets.

In practice, the true probabilities of individual occurrences are never exactly known, but are hypotheses to be used for prediction or to be rejected, as the facts may indicate. An infinite experiment is not needed to use probability theory, though it is sometimes useful to imagine that probabilities do characterize infinite sets of which some sample or subset is observed. To the extent that any scientific proposition is general in scope, the scientist tends to classify an interesting event with an infinite number of similar events which could exist and be like the observed one in all relevant ways. He classifies each particular observation as an example of an infinite set, and that infinite set has the probability—not the example.

The Basic Concepts of Probability

A probabilistic system involves some set Ω, the universe of discourse. All possible observations, i.e., all the possible ways the whole experiment can come out, are elements of Ω. These elements are often called "points," or, in other applications, "samples" or "observations," and Ω is often called the "sample space." A point corresponds to one particular way the experiment can come out.

Ordinarily, the center of interest is not the particular experimental outcome, but the *kind* of outcome. One would not hope to predict every response by every subject on every trial, but only some more general characteristic of the data, such as that the mean number of correct responses, per subject, is between 20 and 30. There are a great many particular experimental outcomes which satisfy this condition, though they differ among themselves in detail. Also, there are a great many particular observations which do not have a mean between

20 and 30. Every possible outcome would either be within the interval or outside it; hence the sample space is divided into two subsets. These subsets are called "events." Similarly, in the earlier example about throwing two dice for a 7, a sample space can be considered which consists of the 36 pairs of numbers (x, y). Of these, a set of six points (one event) all yield a score of 7, while the other 30 points (another event) do not. Alternatively, the total number on the two dice might be any number from 2 to 12, and all throws or points might be classified into these 11 categories or "events." An event, then, is a subset of the sample space.

The sample space consists of all possible outcomes of the experiment. Actually, in most probabilistic experiments, this means the set of all logical possibilities, of all observations which could arise without violating the formal conditions of the experiment. In many cases this sample space contains an astronomical number of numbers. For example, imagine that 100 students all take a 100-item, true-false test. What is the sample space?

First, any subject can answer any subset of the 100 items true, and the rest false. To determine the number of ways one person can answer the test, notice that the first item can be answered in either of two ways, the second separately in either of two ways, making four, the third in two ways irrespective of the first two, making eight, etc. In fact, there are 2^{100} ways any individual can answer the test; thus $2^{100} = (2^{10})^2 = (1024)^2$, which is somewhat over 1,000,000.

But, there are 100 subjects, and each may answer the test in any of 1,000,000 ways. This produces $(1,000,000)^{100}$ points in the sample space. This is a number represented by a 1 followed by 600 zeros. It can be seen at once how absurd it would be to attempt to single out a particular point in the sample space, for 10^{600} is an exceedingly large number. If one were to measure the distance a light ray goes in a year, using as a unit one-thousandth of an inch, the resulting number would be under 10^{20}. This number would have to be raised to the thirtieth power to obtain the number of points in the sample space of a modest experiment, which might be criticized as a trifle small for a master's thesis.

The mathematical treatment of probabilities rests on a more abstract treatment of probabilities. It is manifestly impossible to decide whether all of the 10^{600} points in the sample space have equal probability. However, consider that immense set of possibilities in which the mean number of correct answers, for the group of 100 subjects, lies between 40 and 50. Call this subset or event E_1. Now consider another set of possibilities, all those in which the mean score lies between

60 and 70, and call this event E_2. Now imagine that there are certain probabilities, p_1 that a given particular observation is in E_1, and p_2 that it is in E_2. What is the probability that a particular observation is in either E_1 or E_2? The answer is obviously $p_1 + p_2$. Now define an event E_3 in which the mean lies between 65 and 75. What is the probability that an event falls in both E_2 and E_3? Answer: Exactly the probability that it has a mean in the interval 70 to 75.

Although there is no direct way of evaluating these probabilities individually, there are many ways of combining probabilities so as to correspond to certain divisions or recombinations of events, or classifications of the data. The rules by which the probabilities of compound events are computed are simply those of measure theory. Events are sets; hence events can be combined by the operations of union, intersection, and complementation to define new events. The only further restriction arises from the fact that the probability of an event corresponds to that fraction of the sample space which is in the event. It is a "proportional" measure; hence, probabilities are always numbers between 0 and 1, and the measure of the whole sample space Ω is set equal to 1.

The main practical problem is to compute the probability of a certain compound event, knowing some simpler events. This turns out to hinge on the probability of the intersection of two events, what is called the "joint probability" of the two events. For consider: if the probability of an event A is $P(A)$, then the probability of the complement of A is known, for $P(\bar{A}) = 1 - P(A)$. Furthermore,

$$P(A \cup B) = P(A) + P(B) - P(A \cap B)$$

from the earlier general theorem of measure functions. Hence, if the probability of $A \cap B$ can be determined from knowledge of $P(A)$ and $P(B)$, the probability of any compound event can be computed from the probabilities of its component events. This follows because a complete logic can be built from the three logical words OR, AND, and NOT, so that all compound events can be built from the set-theoretic operations of union, intersection, and complementation.

It turns out, however, that knowledge of $P(A)$ and $P(B)$ is insufficient to determine $P(A \cap B)$. The reason is simply that the measure of the set $A \cap B$ is not determined by the measures of A and B. Consider the following abstract example which deals with the integers $0, 1, \cdots, 9$. Using a table of random numbers, one number is chosen at random, so that each number has probability $1/10$. There are several ways to define two events, A and B, such that $P(A) = .5$,

$P(B) = .5$, but $P(A \cap B)$ may vary. Table 1.1 shows examples which give all values of $P(A \cap B)$ from .5 to 0.

TABLE 1.1

SHOWING THAT $P(A \cap B)$ IS NOT DETERMINED BY $P(A)$ AND $P(B)$

Set A $(P(A) = .5)$	Set B $(P(B) = .5)$	Set $A \cap B$	$P(A \cap B)$
$\{0, 1, 2, 3, 4\}$	$\{0, 1, 2, 3, 4\}$	$\{0, 1, 2, 3, 4\}$	.5
$\{0, 1, 2, 3, 4\}$	$\{1, 2, 3, 4, 5\}$	$\{1, 2, 3, 4\}$	.4
$\{0, 1, 2, 3, 4\}$	$\{2, 3, 4, 5, 6\}$	$\{2, 3, 4\}$	.3
$\{0, 1, 2, 3, 4\}$	$\{3, 4, 5, 6, 7\}$	$\{3, 4\}$	.2
$\{0, 1, 2, 3, 4\}$	$\{4, 5, 6, 7, 8\}$	$\{4\}$	.1
$\{0, 1, 2, 3, 4\}$	$\{5, 6, 7, 8, 9\}$	$\emptyset$	0

In all these cases, $P(A) = P(B) = .5$, but $P(A \cap B)$ may be anything from .5 to 0 (in steps of .1, which are the smallest possible in this sample space).

In order to compute $P(A \cap B)$, hence $P(A \cup B)$, it is not sufficient to know the probabilities $P(A)$ and $P(B)$. In principle the events A and B might vary anywhere from maximum similarity (where the smaller is a subset of the larger or they are identical) to minimum similarity (where they are mutually exclusive). To obtain particular numerical solutions to problems, when the precise composition of the sets is not known in advance, requires some assumption about the relationship between the two sets A and B. The assumption is an empirical hypothesis or simplifying assumption which is tested experimentally.

One extreme assumption is that the two sets are as alike as possible. If so, and if $P(A) \leq P(B)$, then $P(A \cap B) = P(A)$. That is, the probability of the joint event is equal to the probability of the less probable individual event.

Another extreme assumption is that the two sets are as unlike as possible. This yields two solutions depending upon the individual probabilities. If $P(A) + P(B) \leq 1$, then $P(A \cap B) = 0$ and the two events are mutually exclusive, or incompatible. If $P(A) + P(B) > 1$, then $P(A \cap B)$ cannot equal zero. If it did, then it would follow that

$$P(A \cup B) = P(A) + P(B) - P(A \cap B)$$
$$= P(A) + P(B) - 0 > 1$$

which is impossible. No event can have a probability greater than 1. The minimum value which $P(A \cap B)$ can take is $P(A) + P(B) - 1$.

(It is useful to note that if two events A and B have probabilities which sum to more than 1, the two events cannot be incompatible.)

A third assumption, and one which is often invoked when the two events are neither very similar nor mutually exclusive but appear to have no connection with one another, is *independence*. Two events are said to be independent if and only if

$$P(A \cap B) = P(A)P(B)$$

The assumption of independence can be put in a form which more clearly brings out its intuitive meaning, and which yields the above equation as a consequence. For this purpose the notion of conditional probability is introduced.

Recall that probabilities can be defined only relative to some sample space, and that the sample space is the set of logical possibilities. After some observations are collected the sample space may be reduced—some of the possibilities did not happen, and are no longer possible. The most interesting probabilities are, in this case, those which apply to the possibilities which have not already been excluded.

For example, consider the toss of two dice, and in this case consider the probability of obtaining a total of 5 on the two faces. Originally there are four possibilities, $(1, 4)$, $(2, 3)$, $(3, 2)$, and $(4, 1)$, which constitute the event and its initial probability (usually called its "unconditional" probability) is 4/36. Now suppose that the first die has already been thrown and came up a 3. The only possible events, now, are $(3, 1)$, $(3, 2)$, $(3, 3)$, $(3, 4)$, $(3, 5)$, and $(3, 6)$. Of these one, $(3, 2)$, gives a 5, and therefore the probability of a 5 on the two dice is now 1/6.

The situation would be described this way. Let E_1 be the event that when the first die is thrown it comes up a 3. Let E_2 be the event that the total on the two dice is 5. The first computation showed that (for a perfect die) $P(E_2) = 4/36$. The second computation showed that, if E_1 has happened, the probability of E_2 is 1/6. This second probability is called "the conditional probability of E_2 given E_1," and written $P(E_2 \mid E_1)$.

Now, to say that some event B is independent of event A, is the same as saying that

$$P(B \mid A) = P(B)$$

that the conditional probability of B given A is equal to the unconditional probability of B. The prediction of whether B will occur or not is unaffected by whether A is already known to have occurred or not.

This would mean, in empirical applications, that the two events have no connection.

It can be shown that if A and B are independent, $P(A \cap B) = P(A)P(B)$. A probability is the relative measure of an event. Hence, an unconditional probability is relative to the measure of the sample space or universe. In other words, for a suitable measure function m,

$$P(B) = m(B)/m(U)$$

A conditional probability reduces the universe. When $P(B \mid A)$ is considered, the working universe is the event A, which is already known to have occurred. The two possible events, given A, are $B \cap A$ and $\bar{B} \cap A$, and their probabilities must add to 1. Thus

$$P(B \mid A) = m(B \cap A)/m(A)$$

If event B is independent of A,

$$P(B) = P(B \mid A)$$

Then,

$$\frac{m(B)}{m(U)} = \frac{m(B \cap A)}{m(A)}$$

Solving this for $m(B \cap A)$,

$$m(B \cap A) = \frac{m(B)m(A)}{m(U)}$$

Dividing both sides by $m(U)$,

$$\frac{m(B \cap A)}{m(U)} = \frac{m(B)m(A)}{m(U)m(U)}$$

which is equivalent to

$$P(B \cap A) = P(B)P(A)$$

which was to be shown.

The assumption of independence is, in psychological experiments, rather difficult to justify. There is a general opinion that every mental event affects every other one, so that no two events can be said to be independent. However, most probability problems are quite intractable without some assumption relating $P(A \cap B)$ to $P(A)$ and $P(B)$, and the assumption of independence is frequently of great value in simplifying computations. It corresponds, in general, to what psychologists mean by "randomness." The strategy followed in this book is to assume independence of events when it is useful. An attempt is made to define events so that they may be independent, or nearly so.

However, the assumption of independence is always put forward tentatively, as a hypothesis which must be tested by experiment.

One remark may be added to indicate how the assumption of independence may be used to find and specify actual interrelationships in psychological data. Recall that so far as probability theory is concerned, in its formal structure, the "events" are merely subsets of the set of logical possibilities. The scientist may define these events (select or invent defining properties) to suit himself. If certain definitions are proposed, the hypothesis of independence can be stated. If it turns out that for two such events, A and B, $P(A \cap B)$ is not equal to $P(A)P(B)$, it follows that the two events are not independent. Suppose that $P(A \cap B)$ is greater than $P(A)P(B)$. This may mean that the two events were so defined that they both always contain a certain set C, which had not been noticed before. New events, $A' = A \cap \bar{C}$ and $B' = B \cap \bar{C}$, might be defined, and the new hypothesis would be that A' and B' are independent. Similarly, if in another case $P(A \cap B)$ is smaller than $P(A)P(B)$, the definitions of A and B may involve a certain incompatibility in some cases. By segregating those special cases "purified" events, A'' and B'', which are in fact independent, might be found.

In a sense the analysis of any psychological or other scientific experiment into separate aspects or variables has, as its goal, the identification of variables which are unrelated to one another. When this criterion is applied to a probabilistic analysis, it seems natural to say that unrelated variables will turn out to be independent. In this way, by an inversion of the usual approach, it may be argued that independence as defined above is a criterion of a good probabilistic model. If so, it becomes natural to make the assumption of independence and see if it is tenable. If it is not, it is natural to turn to a revision which may make the events independent.

Regarding Probability Theory and Determinism

It has sometimes been argued that the application of probability theory to any empirical domain involves a surrender of the scientific ideal. If the best one can do is to estimate probabilities, it is said, then one is admitting that behavior is not determined. If behavior is not determined, no science of psychology is possible. Furthermore, if one merely accepts probabilistic laws one is in no wise motivated to purify one's experimental methods and observations so as to arrive at more specific, causal relationships.

This argument is without good logical foundation, but it does point to a certain danger in the indiscriminate use of probability theory in psychology. The first part of the argument, that a scientific psychology is impossible when probabilities are used, is manifestly erroneous, if only because some quite successful, and certainly scientific, theories of the probabilistic type exist. Actually, the argument hinges on an ambiguity in the word "determined." A probabilistic theory does not say that behavior is not determined, but merely admits that when a certain set of observations are classified together it happens that not all the observations are determined by exactly the same causes. Since the process of finding all causes for each observation is manifestly impractical, and would involve an infinite process of teasing out every tiny factor, science always deals with imperfect classifications. If this fact is faced, probability theory permits rigorous mathematical argumentation despite the imperfection of the data. If the fact of imperfection of data is not faced, a theory must call on "errors of observation" but cannot say anything very coherent about them, and scientific progress is accordingly retarded.

Though the first part of the argument is incorrect, the second part has considerable value. The best probabilities, from the point of view of prediction, are 1 and 0. If a probabilistic model for a set of data uses broad, inappropriate events, then the probability of an event may be of little use in predicting particular outcomes. Such a model may agree with results perfectly well, but the predictions are inconsequential. A constant pressure must be exerted to divide broad, ambiguous events (or categories, or concepts) into smaller, more precise ones, so that probabilities are driven toward one extreme or the other.

This amounts to saying that the analytic problem is best solved when the material is cut as finely and accurately as possible. However, this leaves the problem of reassembling these categories which have been analyzed. The problem of synthesis requires the ability to work with imperfect as well as perfect sets of categories, for rarely do perfect ones exist. Furthermore, some of the consequences of an analysis may be quite unclear until the behavior of certain mixed categories, or certain more complex combinations of categories, is determined. It sometimes happens that the simple cases can be handled by a determinate theory, but more complex cases require a probabilistic approach. An example from physics is the kinetic theory of gases. The interrelations of volume, pressure, and temperature are derived from a determinate theory about the rebounding of molecules from one another according to determinate laws. In an actual balloon full of gas, however, there are so many molecules in so complex an arrangement that the determinate laws cannot be used to predict anything. By passing to a probabilistic model one can derive average effects which turn out to be the gas laws familiar from elementary physics.

Similarly, Estes (1950) has developed a learning theory in which it is assumed that each stimulus element is attached to exactly one response in a determinate, all-or-none fashion. Furthermore, he assumes that if a certain element is perceived on a certain trial, and reinforcement for some response is administered, that element certainly becomes conditioned to that response. This is a very simple and entirely determinate model, very much like the earlier one of Guthrie (1946). However, with a great many stimulus elements in the typical situation, no clear predictions about actual behavior can be derived from this theory except in very special, highly controlled situations. Include the probabilistic hypothesis that stimulus elements are "sampled" at random in perception, as Estes does, and the theory produces an elegant and powerful set of predictions which have been studied in a great many experiments. Furthermore, the original deterministic theory is continuously being recast and improved on the basis of these experiments, as interpreted with the probabilistic model. The ideas of probability theory may be used to turn a deterministic but hardly applicable theory into a working tool for the analysis of data, and thereby bring data to bear on the assumptions of the theory.

Summary

In this chapter the mathematical foundations of the theory have been described. A *set* is in effect a category or a property of things. The operations on sets reflect, in an exact way, the logical words AND, OR, and NOT of ordinary logic, so that translation from ordinary discourse to mathematics is direct and systematic. The elements of the logic of sets were described and a few problems given. The concept of the *measure* of a set was introduced so as to give an account of properties which are neither universal nor impossible. Methods of calculating measures of complex sets from measures of more elementary sets were stated.

Probability theory was then introduced, with some remarks about its application to empirical problems, and it was emphasized that, so long as probabilities are assigned to *sets* and not to unique occurrences, most of the traditional difficulties evaporate. It was then noted that probabilities are closely related to measures—in fact, a probability is the ratio of the measures of two sets, the event and its universe.

It was found that the calculation of probabilities of compound events from probabilities of simpler events requires only ordinary algebra of sets, except that the joint probability of two events, A and B, cannot be calculated from knowledge of the probabilities of the events. The two extreme cases of maximum similarity and maximum separateness of events were discussed, and then the idea of independent events was stated, in the context of the important idea of conditional probabilities.

In the discussions to follow, two special simplifying assumptions will be made wherever they are of sufficient value: the *equal probability* hypothesis that each of a large set of observations is as likely as any other, and the *independence* hypothesis, that certain events which are not obviously related are, in fact, exactly independent of one another. The equal-probability hypothesis makes it possible to compute probabilities by the methods of counting combinations, permutations, etc., which have developed in probability theory. From this hypothesis, a number of predictions can be derived. The independence hypothesis makes it possible to derive numerical predictions of complex events from information about simpler ones. These two hypotheses are not part of probability theory, and instead (in applications) amount to empirical hypotheses. Their considerable power in developing definite predictions shows that they are not merely formal or trivial assumptions. In fact, the development of a strong mathematical psychology may involve only two steps: correct formulation of the events to which probabilities are assigned, and the judicious choice of the assumption of equal probability or independence. The resulting theories will be approximations, but good approximations are useful and poor approximations are suggestive of better hypotheses.

CHAPTER TWO

Theory of the Probability of a Response

Both behavior and mental life flow continuously, but the attention of the psychologist is turned to the choice-points or critical decisions which occur from time to time. At these points there are alternative acts or experiences, and the subject chooses one of them. In the development to follow, each choice is thought of as a discrete event, and more complex responses are considered as compounds of discrete events. The main question asked about a choice is, What are the probabilities of the several alternatives?

The question may be approached by examining the alternatives available, in a theory of responses; by considering the situation in which choice is made, taking a perceptual point of view; or by studying the past history of the subject, comparing the probability of a present choice with what the same person has done in the past in similar circumstances. Each of these approaches is essential, and it is not possible to settle for only one. If only the responses are considered, it often turns out that they cannot be clearly defined in an objective way—what is important are the alternatives as they appear to the subject. This in turn raises the perceptual problem. Within just the perceptual situation, neither the things perceived nor the responses which result from perception can be stated at all, for only the perceptual and not the objective term of the relationship is in hand. To interpret the past history is difficult if events in the past are not identical with the present case The relevance of a past event depends on whether the past and present situations are similar and the alternatives are comparable. The questions of the situation, the alternatives, and the history of the subject are completely interrelated and must all be discussed in the theory.

At any critical point in behavior there may be just two alternatives available or there may be many. The present theory will deal almost exclusively with the two-choice case, for a simple reason. When there are several alternatives, each should be studied, and this may be accomplished by redefining the alternatives as "the one we are interested in at the moment" and "all others." If there actually are five alternatives, this analysis may be performed five times, but each of the five analyses will be of a pair of alternatives, and the five analyses will use everything which is actually observed. Thus, the two-choice case may be used to analyze more complicated situations.

Situations and Their Aspects

What is the situation in which the individual finds himself at the time of choice? The problem is to avoid prejudging this question, and to answer it in the most general way. To describe the situation in terms such as "the individual is in his bedroom, sitting on the bed, with the overhead light on, facing a bureau, and thinking about international politics while tying his shoe," is certainly to give only part of the situation as it exists. The sentence above does not describe all the objects within the person's view, nor the sounds, nor the pressure of the bed, nor the temperature of the air, nor the chafing of his collar; in fact, it gives only a small sketch of the total situation. Furthermore, a more complete description would leave much unsaid, though what is unsaid may be immaterial.

For formal purposes it is not desirable to restrict the situation to some description of it. Let us begin with a fundamental set of situations within which the person might find himself, calling this set S^* and its elements (the particular situations) $s_1, s_2, \cdots$. These situations are not given any formal definition, and serve as the fundamental entities of all discussions. Thus S^*, the set of situations, is an undefined or primitive notion. The working rule is simple: Every situation is considered to be distinct from every other situation, and there is exactly one situation to be considered at each choice.

Situational Variables

Though a description of a situation does not exhaust its possibilities, we must describe situations in order to predict behavior.

The subject responds to a unique situation, but he is likely to do so by comparing it with other situations. One way to frame descriptions is by establishing a descriptive vocabulary, defining such terms as "brightness," "pitch," "compactness," "cooperativeness," which are used to describe situations. There is some intuitive agreement regarding the meaning of such words, so that experiments can be compared. The relative ease of communication may be misleading, however, unless it is remembered that nonpsychologists, students, and other people unacquainted with experimental procedures may not understand so easily. A more fundamental analysis asks how communications can be verified when they are in doubt; in other words, it asks for the epistemology of the description of situations.

To make clear to an inexperienced observer in a psychophysical experiment that he is to respond to brightness alone, not to any changes in hue or saturation of a color patch, the experimenter may discuss the matter with him, but when it gets to actual preparation for the experiment the observer is shown an array of situations which differ in brightness and trained to respond just to brightness. It would be natural to present some situations which differ in hue and not brightness (to the extent that this is technically feasible) and make it clear that a discrimination is not desired, so as to establish exact communication regarding a stimulus variable. The method is to present situations and teach a certain classification of them, the classification depending on the variable in question. To train an intern to rate expressions of hostility by mental patients, the supervisor exposes him to a variety of concrete situations and teaches a classification.

In summary, a situational variable can be communicated by showing a sufficient variety of situations and classifying them. This suggests that a "variable" is, fundamentally, a classification of situations. Technically, the classification should usually be into mutually exclusive and exhaustive categories, so that it is a partition. Hence it is natural to define:

DEFINITION: *A stimulus variable is a partition of the set S^* of situations.* With this definition it becomes apparent that a description of a situation is not complete. The reason is straightforward: Each variable employed classifies situations, but only 3 or 5 or 10 such variables cannot specify a *unique* situation. In fact, if S^*, the set of situations, is infinite, no finite vocabulary will be sufficient to identify exactly any but a negligible fraction of the possible situations. (Note that, if the unique situation is thought of as the "whole" and the descriptive variables as "parts," this gives a clear meaning to the

Gestalt slogan that "the whole is more [specific] than the sum of its parts.")

Stimulus Aspects

If a stimulus variable is a classification which may be used in description, then the categories of that variable are adjectives which apply to particular situations. For example, "brightness" is a variable, "very bright," "very dark," or "11 brils" are values of the variable and thus aspects that a situation may have. Within the present system, a stimulus variable is a partition, and a stimulus aspect corresponds to *a cell of that partition*.

To review the set-theoretic structure of this approach: The basic universe S^* is of situations. A stimulus aspect, a, corresponds to a subset of S^*. Most applications deal with families of aspects, i.e., with sets of sets of situations.

Now consider a reciprocal relationship which can be illustrated by a simple example of a basic set of people and some descriptive categories like "has brown hair," "is 6 feet tall," "is wearing shoes," etc. The people constitute the set S^* and the categories correspond to aspects. The aspect "has brown hair" identifies a certain set of people. However, any person also is related to a set of aspects, such as "has brown hair, is 6 feet tall, is wearing slippers," etc. A situation (an element of S^*) is associated with a set of aspects which pertain to it, and an aspect is associated with the set of people who have it.

In a more formal description, consider a set S^* of situations and a set A^* of aspects. Any aspect a is exactly equivalent to a subset S_a of S^*. Any situation s corresponds to a set A_s of aspects, a subset of A^*. A_s is the set of aspects a such that s has aspect a. In the set-theoretic notation of Chapter 1, this would be

$$A_s = \{a: a(s)\} \qquad (a \text{ an element of } A^*, s \text{ an element of } S^*)$$

which is read "A_s is the set of aspects a such that $a(s)$, i.e., s has attribute a."

Similarly, S_a would be defined as

$$S_a = \{s: a(s)\} \qquad (a \text{ an element of } A^*, s \text{ an element of } S^*)$$

It is necessary to keep these two kinds of sets quite distinct. The size or measure of the set S_a indicates how widespread the aspect a is in the set of situations. In this sense a "large" aspect is merely a common one. The measure of the set A_s indicates how many aspects situation s has. A complex display, such as a photograph of a crowded street scene, has a great many aspects and thus a large A_s, whereas a simple drawing of a circle has fewer aspects and a smaller A_s. The measure of a set A_s, therefore, corresponds to the complexity of a situation. This complexity cannot be defined in entirely external or objective terms, for it depends upon the subject as well as the objective situation, since aspects are characteristics attributed to the situation by the person.

Unfortunately, if the system as stated thus far is followed exactly, it can be proved that all situations are equally complex. The next point of discussion is to show how this is so, and to modify the definitions so as to permit, and at the same time to define, differences in complexity.

Recall that an aspect a is one cell of a partition of S^*. The set S^* is partitioned on some variable, and then a is one cell of that partition.

Now suppose that the set S^* of situations is cross-partitioned on some number N of variables. Since each variable is a partition, each element s of S^* appears in exactly one cell of each variable; hence, s appears in exactly N cells, or has N aspects. Without some arbitrary weighting of variables or aspects, which would be difficult to justify and even more difficult to apply in practice, all situations have N aspects and all situations are equally complex. This conclusion is intuitively absurd, and extremely inconvenient in practice.

The theory is applied at choice-points or moments of decision. Any aspect of a situation, to affect a choice, must somehow be relevant to the choice. It must, first, differentiate the choice situation from other situations in which no choice is made. For example, in the Primate Laboratories at the University of Wisconsin, a white noise of moderate intensity is sounded to mask any noises made by the experimenter or by animals and equipment elsewhere in the building. This noise is of constant intensity throughout the experiment. It is not an aspect to be considered in any choice within the experiment, because the noise is there whether choices are made or not. It is merely "background." In the same class are sensations from the myotatic (balancing) reflexes, heartbeat, any constant sources of illumination, incidental skin sensations, etc. Background stimuli do not contribute to complexity.

Consider the "Ganzfeld" of perceptual research—the completely homogeneous visual field, which can conveniently be produced by placing halves of ping-pong balls over the eyes. Under constant illumination every part of the field has a certain brightness, hue, saturation, etc., but the complexity of the field (barring hallucinations and other productions of the subject) would be set at 0. The observer does not see anything.

The aspects of a situation, as they are to be considered in any theoretical work, are only those cells of partitions which differentiate the situation from some "background." Spots, contours, or other inhomogeneities in the visual field; noises or silences, or unequal distributions of sound intensity in the auditory field; touches or releases, changes of temperature, changes of odor, etc., in the other senses; all these are aspects of the situation. A theory can only occupy itself with "discriminable" stimuli, and a subject cannot make a discrimination unless there is some inhomogeneity, in space or time, to be discriminated. Of course, the "background" is not constant from one experiment to another. Any physical energy or other external measurement of a situation must be considered, for psychological purposes, as a deviation from something. A 20-db noise may either be a sound (as when a subject is detecting sounds in silence) or may be a silence, as when a clock stops ticking, or when the signal in a reaction time experiment is the termination of a loud tone.

In the applications to follow, the aspects of a situation are just those in which the situation differs from its background. "Darkness," "quietness," "lightness" (of weights) and other such aspects will be considered, along with brightness, loudness, and heaviness. Since it is assumed that choices must depend on inhomogeneities, all aspects are contrasts with background, and other physical characteristics of the situation are not considered in the theory.

Situations can and do differ in complexity, for a situation which is almost exactly like the background will be assigned a small measure of aspects, and this will often mean low "complexity." (There is a possible paradox in using the term "complexity"; it would be possible to present a very complex stimulus field between trials and blank out some part of the field as a signal for choice. The measure of the set of aspects in such a "negative" stimulus would correspond to the fraction of the complex background removed, so that an entirely blank field would have the largest measure of aspects.)

Ideal Situations and Schemata

Merely describing a situation does not tell how the subject will react to it. Since each situation is unique, there is no guide from the past which can be applied directly to the new situation, and since each situation is a single entity, there is no way to analyze it so as to determine how it controls response, without recourse to aspects. Two distinct situations can be compared in terms of the aspects they have in common and the aspects in which they differ. The present theory of decision will develop from such comparisons.

From past experience, instructions, or inherited instinctive patterns of behavior the subject has a pool of situations to which response is fixed. Any new situation can be referred to one of these situations, and it is assumed that this is the characteristic way of making a choice.

Let these situation-response structures be called "schemata," and the reference situations themselves be "ideal situations." An example will serve to illustrate the ideas. A college man is about to call up a girl and make a date. His situation, in its relevant aspects, includes the appearance and personality of the girl as he knows them, his immediate financial situation, studies which he must complete, the various places he might take the girl, etc. He must decide whether to call the girl or not. There are situations in which he certainly would call the girl—she is beautiful and charming, he is well heeled and ahead in his studies, and an unusual and interesting movie is being shown downtown at reduced prices. This is an "ideal situation" and is part of a schema, "in this situation one calls for a date." A contrasting ideal situation might have the following aspects—the girl is fat and unpleasant, he is broke and far behind in his studies, and there is nothing to do. This is (in abstract terminology) another ideal situation, with a schema, "in this situation one does not call." The student may also, from experience, have a variety of other "ideal situations," differing from the ones stated above, in which calling for a date was a pleasant or unpleasant experience, or in which he lived to regret not having called.

Now, for the decision. The student considers his present situation and attempts to match it with one or another of his "ideal" situations. If he matches it with a situation in a schema, "in this situation one calls for the date," then he calls. If he matches his present situation with one in a schema, "in this situation one does not call," then he does not call.

A schema has the general form of a stimulus-response structure; it is rather like a habit. The term "schema" is used because schemata may arise not only from experience but from other sources: instructions from an experimenter, reading, communications from others, or the reflections of the individual. Ideal situations do not have to be ones which have actually been experienced. A schema may include not only the situation and indicated choice, but also some information about the consequences of that choice. It is a larger and more inclusive structure than a habit. However, it turns out that only the ideal situation itself (along with its aspects) and the response attached is needed to predict behavior.

Similarity

If there are two possible responses, 1 and 2, and two corresponding ideal situations S_1 and S_2, and the subject is in situation S, it seems apparent that the probability of response 1 depends on the similarity between S and S_1, whereas the probability of response 2 depends on the similarity of S to S_2.

Two situations are similar to the degree that they have aspects in common. The similarity between S and S_1 is the measure of the set of aspects $S \cap S_1$. For simplicity of notation, the situation and its set of aspects are here denoted by the same symbol, S. This is not a precise usage but it simplifies notation and leads to no serious complications.

The difficulty the subject has in deciding between two responses arises, usually, because S is similar to both S_1 and S_2. If S is more similar to S_1 than to S_2, then the probability of response 1 should be higher than the probability of response 2. Another factor arises, however, which complicates the problem. It is possible that the two ideal situations, S_1 and S_2, are similar to each other.

The aspects of the present situation S fall into four exhaustive and mutually exclusive categories, with respect to the ideal situations S_1 and S_2. These are: (1) the set which is common to S and S_1, but not S_2, and which contributes to response 1; (2) the set which is common to S and S_2 but not S_1; (3) the set which is common to S, S_1, and S_2 and which therefore constitutes part of the similarity of S_1 and S_2; and (4) the set which is in neither S_1 nor S_2. In the notation of set theory these four subsets are

$$(1) \quad S \cap S_1 \cap \bar{S}_2$$
$$(2) \quad S \cap \bar{S}_1 \cap S_2$$
$$(3) \quad S \cap S_1 \cap S_2$$
$$(4) \quad S \cap \bar{S}_1 \cap \bar{S}_2$$

All four sets have different significances for behavior; the first two contribute to one or the other response, and thus to a decision between them, but the second two do not help the subject decide.

Suppression of Aspects and the Resolution of Conflict

In most situations the subject will be in some conflict about his response. The only exception would be the case in which only the first, or only the second, set of aspects has any members. What does a person do in a conflict in which there is some reason for making response 1 and some reason for making response 2?

A simple mechanism, in this case, would be to suppress or disregard some aspect of the situation, trying to resolve the conflict. Perhaps, if the subject does not consider aspect a, he will find that the remainder of the aspects permit a clear decision. If this does not work he may suppress a second aspect, a', and if that does not work a third aspect, a'', may be suppressed. In this way the subject may eventually arrive at a reduced set of aspects all of which are in set $S \cap S_1 \cap \bar{S}_2$, or all of which are in set $S \cap \bar{S}_1 \cap S_2$. In the first case he chooses response 1; in the second case he chooses response 2. If it should

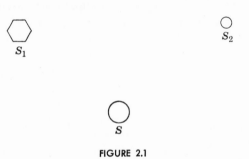

FIGURE 2.1

happen that the process of suppression ends with aspects in the set $S \cap S_1 \cap S_2$ or the set $S \cap \bar{S}_1 \cap \bar{S}_2$, no decision is reached. The subject either does not respond at all, or, if that is not permissible in the experimental situation, he may reinstate all the aspects and start over. The decision between response 1 and response 2 depends only on the sets $S \cap S_1 \cap \bar{S}_2$ and $S \cap \bar{S}_1 \cap S_2$.

It is presumed that the subject does not decide which aspect to suppress first in a conscious or systematic way, for if he did a theory of how he decides which aspect to suppress would be needed. If aspects are suppressed in an unsystematic fashion, the process can be represented as random sampling.

Imagine a subject faced with a decision from the method of triads of psychophysics. Two ideal stimuli are shown along with a test stimulus, and the subject's task is to judge whether the test stimulus is more like ideal S_1 or S_2. An example is shown in Fig. 2.1.

Approaching the psychology in an oversimplified and naïve way for the moment, suppose that the relevant aspects are size and shape. The test stimulus S agrees with S_1 with respect to size but not shape, and agrees with S_2 with respect to shape but not size. Hence, no simple conclusion can be drawn. The subject must take the position, "shape makes no difference," in which case he chooses response 1 on the basis of size; or the position, "size makes no difference," in which case he chooses response 2 on the basis of shape. By suppressing just one of the aspects he can make a choice.

In more complicated situations it may take many successive suppressions of aspects before a clear answer to the problem is reached. However, if aspects are suppressed at random, the probability of ending up at response 1 is simply the proportion of aspects in $S \cap S_1 \cap \bar{S}_2$ compared to $S \cap \bar{S}_1 \cap S_2$, and the probability of making response 2 is the proportion of aspects in $S \cap \bar{S}_1 \cap S_2$. For consider the nature of the process. The person begins with n_1 aspects in $S \cap S_1 \cap \bar{S}_2$ and n_2 aspects in $S \cap \bar{S}_1 \cap S_2$. He suppresses variables one at a time so that after i suppressions there are $n_1(i)$ and $n_2(i)$ aspects left. The process continues until either $n_1(i)$ or $n_2(i)$ is 0. The probability that $n_2(i)$ will reach 0 first is $n_1/(n_1 + n_2)$.

Proof: The actual decision is made when one or the other number reaches 0. However, the decision would not be changed if he continued further until there was only one aspect left. For suppose that $n_2(i)$ reaches 0 when $n_1(i)$ is, say, 5. Four more trials will leave only one aspect, and it will certainly be in set 1 and not set 2, for set 2 is already exhausted. If the process continues until just one aspect has survived, the one aspect could have been selected at random in the first place. The probability that an aspect of $S \cap S_1 \cap \bar{S}_2$ would be chosen, when there are n_1 such aspects and n_2 aspects in $S \cap \bar{S}_1 \cap S_2$, is $n_1/(n_1 + n_2)$.

The Probability of a Response

If all aspects are equivalent and there are a finite number of them, the measure of the sets $S \cap S_1 \cap \bar{S}_2$ and $S \cap \bar{S}_1 \cap S_2$ will be simply the number of elements in them. Then the above theory says that

$$P_1 = \frac{m(S \cap S_1 \cap \bar{S}_2)}{m(S \cap S_1 \cap \bar{S}_2) + m(S \cap \bar{S}_1 \cap S_2)} \tag{2.1}$$

It seems natural to use Eq. 2.1 even when one cannot assess the measure of the set simply as the number of aspects in it. If the aspects receive different weights, the weight of an aspect should be proportional to its probability of entering into the final decision. If so, the several aspects would have different probabilities of being suppressed, and the weight of any one aspect would be proportional to its probability of surviving the process. The argument above then goes through directly, and one obtains Eq. 2.1. If the sets of aspects are infinite, it would still be natural to think of the measure of a set as proportional to the probability that a single element taken at random would belong to it. Again, the argument given above leads to Eq. 2.1.

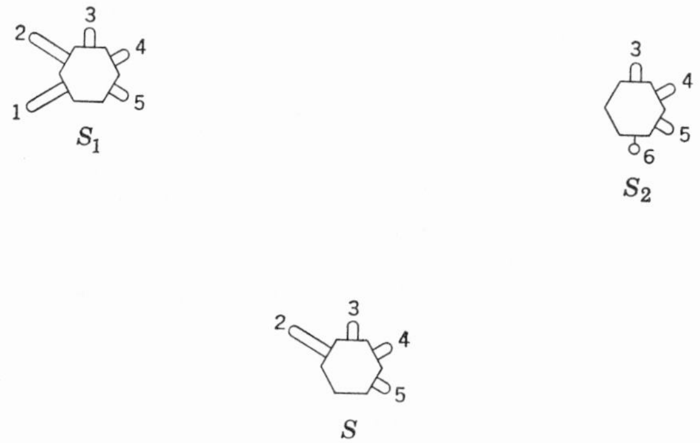

FIGURE 2.2

The empirical significance of using only the differential aspects in $S \cap S_1 \cap \bar{S}_2$ and $S \cap \bar{S}_1 \cap S_2$ may be illustrated by the following example. Consider a trial of the method of triads, with ideals S_1 and S_2 and a test stimulus S, as shown in Fig. 2.2. The subject is to decide whether S is more like S_1 or S_2. Consider that the aspects of the situation correspond to the various protuberances around the edge of the hexagon, for the sake of illustration.

The three small knobs are common to S_1, S_2, and S. The set $S \cap \bar{S}_1 \cap S_2$ contains the one long knob in the upper left-hand corner, and there are no elements in $S \cap \bar{S}_1 \cap S_2$. Hence the careful subject would always say that S is more like S_1, i.e., he will make response 1 with probability 1. This would occur despite the fact that S is similar to S_2 in several ways. If the knobs are named by the indicated numbers, we find

$$S_1 = \{1, 2, 3, 4, 5\}$$

$$S_2 = \{3, 4, 5, 6\}$$

and

$$S = \{2, 3, 4, 5\}$$

Now it is easy to compute that $S \cap S_1 \cap \bar{S}_2 = \{2\}$ and $S \cap \bar{S}_1 \cap S_2$ = $\emptyset$. Letting the number of elements be the measure of the set, we have

$$P_1 = \frac{1}{1+0} = 1$$

It should be emphasized that a stimulus figure cannot be analyzed in so rough and overconfident a way. It would be much preferable to determine, by experiment, whether the aspects of the situation can be reduced to the knobs and whether the various knobs are, in fact, independent and identifiable aspects. In any serious application of the theory these questions are to be answered by estimations from the data of a larger experiment.

Several Ideal Situations

If ideal situations arise from a training program there may be, not 2, but perhaps 100 ideal situations. Imagine that the subject has had 80 trials in which situation S_1 led to response 1, and only 20 trials in which situation S_2 led to response 2. The choice of a response would depend not only on the similarity of the test situation S to S_1 and S_2, but also on the sheer number of schemata leading to each response.

Suppose that S is just as like S_1 as S_2, so that if only the two ideal situations were present the probability of response 1 would be $P_1 = 1/2$. Now consider the condition in which there are 80 schemata containing S_1-R_1 and only 20 containing S_2-R_2. It seems natural to suppose that the subject has a much higher probability of selecting response 1 than response 2. In this case, since each ideal is as good a match to S as any other, the probability of choosing an S_1 ideal is just equal to the proportion of S_1 ideals in the training history, i.e., .80.

Compound Responses

The theoretical analysis of discrete choices covers a large part of experimental psychology, but there are important experiments in which the subject does more than simply choose, or in which the experimenter studies more than the frequencies of various choices. For example, the experimenter may measure the time it takes to make a choice or perform a response. Simple reaction time, in which the subject releases a key as soon as possible after the onset of a tone, cannot be handled by a simple choice model. The subject has no particular choice, and one is not interested in whether the key is released but when. The details or components of the response determine its speed. To approach such a problem the simple reaction is divided into stages or part-reactions, and the parts are recombined to give the total response.

Another example using the same approach is the reversal or restructuring of ambiguous figures. Perception sometimes undergoes an abrupt change when there is no objective shift in the stimulus, or when the objective change is very small. There are cases in which a gradual change in stimulus energies has no effect, at first, and then suddenly an abrupt and radical change takes place. The sudden restructuring will be described as the result of a sequence of part-changes, using the simple theory of compound responses.

A related problem arises in the psychophysical method of adjustment (average error). In one application, the subject faces a display with two screens side by side. The left screen is fixed by the experimenter at some standard brightness, and the subject adjusts the right screen until it matches the standard. In adjusting, the subject makes a sequence of comparative judgments, but instead of saying that the right screen is brighter he turns it down a little. The data reflect the end result of a process of adjusting back and forth, where the probabilities of movements up or down correspond to the probabilities of judging that the right screen is darker or lighter than the standard. The final "adjustment" is, therefore, to be analyzed into the stages or part-choices of which it is the result.

Subjects sometimes develop a whole system of judgments, as when they make numerical estimates or ratings of stimuli. It is a major problem of the last chapter of this book to relate such responses to the theory of simple choices.

These developments of the theory are merely mentioned here; in the second part of the book the theory will be developed and extended, in the course of applying it to a variety of experiments.

CHAPTER THREE

The Concepts of Order and Distance on Sets

One difficulty with a direct set-theoretic approach to psychological theory is the sheer number of sets which must sometimes be considered. Imagine, for example, that an experiment involves n situations. Each situation is coordinated with its set of aspects, $S_1, S_2, \cdots, S_n$. These sets, in turn, partition the universe of aspects into cells like

$$S_1 \cap S_2 \cap \cdots \cap S_n \quad \text{or} \quad S_1 \cap \bar{S}_2 \cap \cdots \cap \bar{S}_n$$

There are 2^n such cells. In many experiments the number n of situations is quite large, so that there are numerous cells. In practice it is almost never feasible to attempt to estimate the measures of all of these cells, but a definite and useful prediction can be made if the situations are arranged in some orderly way. The arrangement must reduce uncertainty about the various cells of the total partition—it may make a great many of those cells empty, or it may restrict the values of the cells. With two sets A and B, the partition of the universe contains four sets, $A \cap B$, $A \cap \bar{B}$, $\bar{A} \cap B$, and $\bar{A} \cap \bar{B}$, and these might have any four measures. With the assumption that A and B are independent and m is a probability measure, the four possible measures reduce to two values, $m(A)$ and $m(B)$. With independence, $m(A \cap B) = m(A)m(B)$. Then $m(A \cap \bar{B})$ is $m(A) - m(A \cap B) = m(A) - m(A)m(B)$, $m(\bar{A} \cap B) = m(B) - m(A)m(B)$, and $m(\bar{A} \cap \bar{B}) = 1 - m(A) - m(B) + m(A)m(B) = m(\bar{A})m(\bar{B})$. The measures of all four cells are given by knowing only two numbers. In fact, if one starts with n sets and assumes that they all are mutually independent, one can compute the measures of all 2^n cells simply from knowledge of the n measures of the sets. This is a great simplification, which may make the difference between a useful and a (for practical purposes) untestable theory of the experiment.

Another simplification used in psychological theory in general is the ordering or dimension. Physics uses a great many ordered variables: the three coordinates of space, along with time, mass, moments of movement, energy, etc. Psychologists have long used the same general approach to simplifying complex situations; for example, by studying the psychophysics of stimuli which vary along physical dimensions of intensity, frequency, or area; by measuring responses on physical dimensions such as location and strength; by factor-analyzing tests and sets of measurements; and by postulating systems of mental forces, response strengths, or physiological events on a hypothetical map of some kind.

The process of defining variables and treating them as the dimensions of a rigid space establishes a map on which observations can be located. Since the dimensions of the map are entirely imaginary and *ad hoc,* and the method of mapping is ambiguous, the solution is not without difficulties. However, taken at face value the set-theoretic approach offers no map at all. It is better to have an unreliable map than no map at all, and if set theory provides no map it cannot expect to become the major structure of psychological theory. Theories exist to satisfy needs of scientists, and a theory which fails to meet a major need, no matter how elegant and valid it may be, will be discarded.

It would be possible to use set-theoretic methods for some problems and the classical dimensional analysis for others. This is not a fundamentally clean solution to the issue, for the set-theoretic and dimensional models are logically incompatible and lead to entirely different approaches to theoretical problems. What is needed is a mapping system which is logically sound and fundamental and involves no postulated entities, but which does define a simple and intelligible structure with known properties. A first approximation can be given here, though it is realized that the properties of the maps produced are not adequately understood.* There are certain arrangements of n situations $s_1, s_2, \cdots, s_n$ which, if satisfied, lead to a simple structure, a kind of ordering, in which the situations can be

* A more concise and complete treatment of this material is given in Restle (1959a).

thought of as arranged along some dimension so that s_4 and s_5 are very similar, s_3 and s_6 less similar and more different, etc. An ordering of a set of situations greatly reduces the complexity of the structure and leads to a summary of the whole set of n situations by using only n numbers.

Assigning numbers to situations or other psychological entities, the process of psychological measurement, has been the subject of many investigations. Important progress has been made with the realization that there are general principles of measurement which serve as a trustworthy if incomplete guide to such enterprises. In particular, measurement amounts to mapping empirical observations onto some mathematical system in such a way that the formal structure of empirical operations and relationships corresponds exactly to the formal structure of operations and relationships within the mathematical system (Stevens, 1951, Chap. 1).

A standard example from physics will illustrate the measurement process. In measuring the length of objects certain operations and comparisons are well defined. The lengths of two objects are combined by setting the objects end to end. The lengths of two objects are compared by putting the objects side by side. The object made by putting objects A and B end to end is called $A \& B$. If any two objects C and D, when compared side by side, are equally long, C Eq. D.

Among a set of objects of various lengths with plenty of duplicates, relationships like the following are found by observation:

A Eq. B if and only if B Eq. A
$A \& B$ Eq. $B \& A$
$A \& (B \& C)$ Eq. $(A \& B) \& C$
If A Eq. B and B Eq. C, then A Eq. C

These relations turn out to be exactly like those governing the addition of positive numbers and the equality of numbers. For example, if a, b, and c are positive numbers,

$a = b$ if and only if $b = a$

$a + b = b + a$ (commutativity of $+$)

$a + (b + c) = (a + b) + c$ (associativity of $+$)

If $a = b$ and $b = c$, then $a = c$ (transitivity of $=$)

In other words, the operation $\&$ and the relation Eq. of objects obey just the formal rules of $+$ and $=$. (This is not actually quite true, for several reasons. Experimental errors produce difficulties —equivalence is not actually transitive in all cases—and the concept of length is extended to cases in which the fundamental operations cannot be carried out, as in astronomy. However, for many purposes the correspondence is quite close enough.) This means that all sorts of things about the combinations and equivalences of lengths can be deduced by applying theorems from ordinary algebra. No danger is involved so long as two conditions are met:

1. The formal relations of & and Eq. actually are the same as those of addition and equality of numbers, and

2. The theorems about numbers depend only on these formal properties of addition and equality.

There are only a few examples of fundamental measurement in physics; length and weight are the examples most frequently quoted. Most other measurements in physics are derived, and depend in an essential way on prior measurement of length and weight.

In psychology many attempts have been made to measure psychological variables by exactly the method used by physicists in the case of length or weight. These attempts have not been entirely satisfactory to date. Very likely the difficulty is the lack of a simple set of empirical relationships. Measurement is, after all, a case of the construction of a mathematical model or theory of a set of phenomena. Fundamental measurement requires a set of observations which satisfy some simple formal rules. These rules must be formally just like the rules of a mathematical system.

The difficulties of psychological measurement have been compounded by the usual requirement that the mathematical system must be ordinary algebra of numbers. For example, Stevens (1951, Chap. 1, p. 7) says, "in its broadest sense measurement is the assignment of numerals to objects or events according to rules." The restriction to *numerals* is a useful way of separating measurement from other, more general theoretical endeavors, for one might map objects or events onto sets, points in an abstract space, or even logical signs. These nonnumerical entities are mathematical, but they do not necessarily satisfy the rules which numerals satisfy. The rules of the algebra of sets, given in Chapter 1, are different in detail from the rules of the algebra of numbers. If it should happen that the empirical relations between objects or events differ in form from the relations between numerals, measurement is impossible. One way of avoiding such difficulties, in Stevens' view, is to consider that numerals may have different algebraic rules, and on this basis he considers ratio measurement, interval measurement, orderings, and mere arbitrary labeling.

Another and perhaps more enlightening approach is to think of the desired mathematical system as a theory of the phenomenon, recognizing that measuring is theorizing, and selecting as the formal rules of the mathematical system idealizations of observed (or theoretically expected) relationships in the data.

In the above discussion, psychological entities, such as situations, variables, stimulus elements, and responses, have been mapped onto a set-theoretic structure. In a sense, this could be called measurement. Instead, let us restrict the word *measurement* to cases dealing with numerals, and develop a measurement system theoretically. The proposal is to find the special cases of the set-theoretic system which lead to useful relationships between situations and numerals. In this chapter measurement is based, not directly on empirical observation, but instead on relationships within the set-theoretic theory. The aim is to construct a map of situations and decide what the distance between two places on the map will mean. Then, simple arrangements of places on the map can be specified.

An example of a simple arrangement is a set of points on a straight line. If all of a set of points are on a line, then each point can be assigned a number, and the distance between points a and b is simply $|a - b|$. If the points a, b, and c fall in that order, and if the distance from a to b is x and the distance from b to c is y, then the distance from a to c is $x + y$. It is useful to notice that in this case certain general relationships can be defined very nicely. Consider an infinite set of points $a_1, a_2, \cdots$ reading from left to right, where the distance between any two adjacent points, a_i and a_{i+1}, is x_i. Then the total distance between any pair of points a_i and a_j (where a_i is to the left of a_j) is simply $x_i + x_{i+1} + \cdots + x_{j-1}$.

This map, of a set of points on a straight line, corresponds to the psychophysical concept of a "dimension" like pitch, loudness, brightness, saturation, etc. The general idea of a dimension is also used, somewhat less exactly, outside of psychophysics. The "generalization gradient" in learning theory, the idea of a pure aptitude or personality attribute, the "utility" of an object, and the quality of "cohesiveness" of a group are examples of psychological concepts which are somewhat like dimensions. The set-theoretic position makes it possible to study these possible dimensions, see what their conceptual properties are, and thus analyze whether a certain proposed dimension is or is not capable of being represented by a line.

Distance Between Two Situations

First consider the degree of difference between two situations, s_1 and s_2. If the situations are the same, the distance between them should be 0. The difference between two situations is greater than 0 if they differ on some stimulus variable, i.e., if they have some different aspects. Suppose that the index of distance between s_1 and s_2 is some number d. Then if s_2 is replaced by s_3, which differs from s_1 on all variables in which s_2 differed from s_1 and some more besides, the distance between s_1 and s_3 will be greater than d.

A sharp mathematical concept of a "distance" is the notion of a metric. A metric is a function of pairs of points (or pairs of elements of some set) which satisfies the following axioms:

D1. $D_{XX} = 0$†
D2. $D_{XY} \geq 0$
D3. $D_{XY} = D_{YX}$
D4. $D_{XY} + D_{YZ} \geq D_{XZ}$

It has already been said that distance is related to the measure of differential aspects, and the relationship is monotonic. The more aspects there are which differentiate s_1 and s_2, the greater the distance between them. It seems reasonable, then, to interpret stimulus distance as being the measure of differential aspects.

DEFINITION: Let s_1 and s_2 be two situations, members of S^*. Let s_1 be the set of aspects characteristic of s_1 and s_2 be the set of aspects characteristic of s_2. Let m be a measure function defined over the set of aspects. Then we define the distance between s_1 and s_2, written d_{12}, to be

$$d_{12} = m[(S_1 \cap \bar{S}_2) \cup (\bar{S}_1 \cap S_2)] = m(S_1 \cap \bar{S}_2) + m(\bar{S}_1 \cap S_2)$$
$$= m[(S_1 - S_2) \cup (S_2 - S_1)] = m(S_1 - S_2) + m(S_2 - S_1)$$
$$= m[(S_1 \cup S_2) - (S_1 \cap S_2)] = m(S_1) + m(S_2) - 2m(S_1 \cap S_2)$$

† More exactly, $D_{XY} = 0$ if and only if $X = Y$. As written the axiom is not quite exact but is like that of a "pseudometric," which has the weaker axiom $D_{XY} = 0$ if $X = Y$, but permits the possibility that $D_{XY} = 0$ despite the fact that X is different from Y. In a pseudometric, two points may be distinct but so close together that the distance between them is 0. This can arise in a continuous space. In psychological applications, there might be two situations which are different but do not differ in any of the variables being used by the subject. If such insignificantly different situations were lumped together into an "equivalence class," then the metric of equivalence classes would be a true metric. This technical point will not happen to make any difference in the applications of the theory.

Here the notation $A - B$ is equivalent to $A \cap \bar{B}$, and is that part of set A which is not also in B. The various forms of the definition are easily shown to be equivalent by set algebra, and will be used interchangeably in further developments. The expressions on the left and right of each line are equal because the measure of the union of two mutually exclusive sets is the sum of their measures. One goes from the first to the second line by noting that $A \cap \bar{B} = A - B$. The third line requires a trifle more algebra. Note that the set

$$
\begin{aligned}
(S_1 \cup S_2) - (S_1 \cap S_2) &= (S_1 \cup S_2) \cap (\overline{S_1 \cap S_2}) \\
&= (S_1 \cup S_2) \cap (\bar{S}_1 \cup \bar{S}_2) \\
&= (S_1 \cap \bar{S}_1) \cup (S_1 \cap \bar{S}_2) \cup (S_2 \cap \bar{S}_1) \cup (S_2 \cap \bar{S}_2) \\
&= (S_1 \cap \bar{S}_2) \cup (\bar{S}_1 \cap S_2)
\end{aligned}
$$

Hence the measures in the first and third lines are equal. To get the right side of the third line note that $m(S_1 \cup S_2) = m(S_1) + m(S_2) - m(S_1 \cap S_2)$. In addition, since $S_1 \cap S_2$ is contained in $S_1 \cup S_2$, the measure of the set difference is the difference of the measures.

This concept of a distance is consistent with the axioms of a metric, D1–D4 given above. The result is stated as a theorem:

THEOREM 3.1: *The distance function d is a metric.*

Proof: The proof is quite easy, but is presented here as a further example of the algebra of sets and also because part of it leads to our next point. The sets of aspects are called X, Y, and Z for brevity of notation.

1. It is obvious that $d_{XX} = 0$. This is equivalent to $m(X \cap \bar{X}) + m(\bar{X} \cap X) = m(\emptyset) + m(\emptyset) = 0$.

2. $d_{XY} \geq 0$, since d_{XY} is the measure of a set, and from axiom M2 a measure is nonnegative.

3. $d_{XY} = d_{YX}$. This follows at once from the symmetry of the expressions defining d_{XY}.

4. $d_{XY} + d_{YZ} \geq d_{XZ}$. The "triangle inequality" can be proved most conveniently by constructing a partition of the universe on the basis of three arbitrary subsets X, Y, and Z. The eight cells of the partition are

$$
\begin{array}{ll}
Q_1 = X \cap Y \cap Z & Q_5 = \bar{X} \cap \bar{Y} \cap Z \\
Q_2 = \bar{X} \cap Y \cap Z & Q_6 = \bar{X} \cap Y \cap \bar{Z} \\
Q_3 = X \cap \bar{Y} \cap Z & Q_7 = X \cap \bar{Y} \cap \bar{Z} \\
Q_4 = X \cap Y \cap \bar{Z} & Q_8 = \bar{X} \cap \bar{Y} \cap \bar{Z}
\end{array}
$$

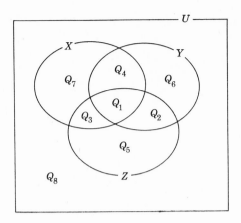

FIGURE 3.1

Figure 3.1 is a diagram of the sets and the elements of the partition. For simplicity, lower-case letters are used for the measures of sets, so that $q_1 = m(Q_1)$. The distance between X and Y is made up of the four cells Q_2, Q_3, Q_6, and Q_7. Hence,

$$d_{XY} = q_2 + q_3 + q_6 + q_7$$

Also,

$$d_{YZ} = q_3 + q_4 + q_5 + q_6$$

and

$$d_{XZ} = q_2 + q_4 + q_5 + q_7$$

Therefore

$$d_{XY} + d_{YZ} = q_2 + q_4 + q_5 + q_7 + 2q_3 + 2q_6$$
$$= d_{XZ} + 2q_3 + 2q_6$$

whence it is obvious that $d_{XY} + d_{YZ} \geq d_{XZ}$. This completes the proof that d is a distance function.

The last equation of the proof is now the source of further insight. The value of $d_{XY} + d_{YZ}$ is just equal to d_{XZ} in the event that q_3 and q_6 are 0. A diagram of three sets X, Y, and Z, in which the sets Q_3 and Q_6 are empty, is shown in Fig. 3.2.

Consideration of Fig. 3.2 shows that the sets X, Y, and Z are ordered in a particular and intuitively pleasing way. Y has a position between X and Z in two senses: First, any element which is in both X and Z, and is an element of their "closeness," is also an element of Y; formally, $X \cap \bar{Y} \cap Z$, or Q_3, is empty. Second, Y has no unique elements all its own, and is in no sense "outside" X and Z; formally, $\bar{X} \cap Y \cap \bar{Z}$, or Q_6, is empty.

A formula for this relationship of X, Y, and Z is simply that $X \cap \bar{Y} \cap Z = \bar{X} \cap Y \cap \bar{Z} = \emptyset$. Another formula, exactly equivalent, is that $X \cap Z \subset Y \subset X \cup Z$, which says that Y is contained in the union of X and Z, whereas the intersection of X and Z is contained in Y.

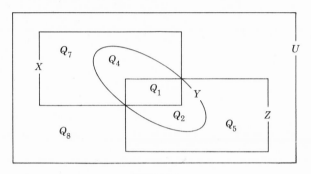

FIGURE 3.2

This is a very sensible and attractive intuitive idea of what it would mean for a set to be directly between two other sets. It applies, of course, to sets of elements which do not themselves have any locations, so that any idea of betweenness depends strictly on set theory. This suggestion for the ordering of three sets has been put forward by several writers (see Restle, 1959a), and is now given in a formal definition.

DEFINITION: If X, Y, and Z are three sets, then Y is between X and Z (written b_{XYZ}) if and only if $X \cap \bar{Y} \cap Z = \bar{X} \cap Y \cap \bar{Z} = \emptyset$, or, equivalently, if $X \cap Z \subset Y \subset X \cup Z$.

Now notice how the concepts of distance and betweenness agree, through the easy theorem,

THEOREM 3.2: If b_{XYZ}, then $d_{XY} + d_{YZ} = d_{XZ}$. If only the empty set has measure 0, the converse is true.

This has a straightforward relationship to the concept of a straight line in ordinary Euclidean space. Consider Fig. 3.3; $d_{XY} + d_{YZ} = d_{XZ}$ if and only if Y lies on the line from X to Z; a little trigonometry is sufficient to show that the cosines of the angles α and β must be 1, so that the angles are 0. Thus, distances are exactly additive only if the points lie on a straight line. This analogy suggests that sets X, Y, and Z lie on a straight line whenever b_{XYZ}. This notion leads to interesting consequences.

The first step is to generalize this idea beyond three sets, X, Y, Z, to longer arrays or lines of sets. That is, while it is pleasant to know that $d_{XY} + d_{YZ} = d_{XZ}$ if b_{XYZ}, it is much more important to show that if $X_1, X_2, \cdots, X_n$ are all in a row, $d_{12} + d_{23} + \cdots + d_{n-1,n} = d_{1n}$.

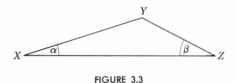

FIGURE 3.3

The analogy with Euclidean space suggests a simple extension of the idea of betweenness. If the points A, B, and C are on a straight line, and B, C, and D are on a straight line, then all four

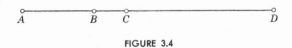

FIGURE 3.4

points, A, B, C, D must be on a straight line. This is intuitively evident from Fig. 3.4. This result has two consequences in Euclidean space (E-space), which may be called *interpolation* and *extrapolation*.

Interpolation

In E-space, if A, B, and D are on a line and B, C, and D are on a line, then A, C, and D are on a line. This example starts with three points A, B, and D, and interpolates a point between B and D. The new point C is also between A and D.

THEOREM 3.3: In a set-theoretic ordering if b_{ABD} and b_{BCD}, then b_{ACD}.

Proof: $A \cap D$ is a subset of C because $A \cap D$ is a subset of B, since b_{ABD}, hence is of course a subset of $B \cap D$. But since b_{BCD}, $B \cap D$ is a subset of C.

Similarly, C is a subset of $A \cup D$ because, in fact, C is a subset of $B \cup D$ (from b_{BCD}) and $B \cup D$ is a subset of $A \cup D$ from b_{ABD}.

Hence, the present system operates like points on a line in that one can interpolate new sets and find them on the same line.

Extrapolation

In E-space, if A, B, and C are on a line and B, C, and D are on a line, then A, B, and D are on a line. The contrary is the next theorem of the set-theoretic ordering.

THEOREM 3.4: It is not the case that b_{ABC} and b_{BCD} implies that b_{ABD}.

The theorem will be proved if there is a single case of four sets A, B, C, and D for which b_{ABC} and b_{BCD} hold, but b_{ABD} does not.

Two such examples will be shown, for together they give some hint as to the nature of the difference between this system and E-space. As examples, sets of numbers are used for the reason set forth earlier—there are plenty of numbers and they all have common names.

Counterexample 1. Let $A = \{1, 2\}$, $B = \{2, 3\}$, $C = \{3, 4\}$, and $D = \{4, 5\}$. Inspection shows that $A \cap C \subset B \subset A \cup C$ (since the empty set $\emptyset$ is a subset of any set) and $B \cap D \subset C \subset B \cup D$. Hence we have b_{ABC} and b_{BCD}. Also, $A \cap D \subset B$, for of course $A \cap D$ is the empty set. However, it is not the case that $B \subset A \cup D$, for $B = \{2, 3\}$ and $A \cup D = \{1, 2, 4, 5\}$. There is an element of B, namely 3, which is not an element of $A \cup D$. Hence there is at least one case in which b_{ABC} and b_{BCD} but not b_{ABD}, and the first two do not imply the third. Each adjacent triple of sets is in a straight line, but the betweenness relation does not hold because the middle set has elements shared only by its immediate neighbors, not by sets on either side but farther away. Notice that if the number of elements in a set is its measure, $d_{AB} = m(\{1, 3\}) = 2$, and $d_{BD} = m(\{2, 3, 4, 5\}) = 4$, but $d_{AD} = m(\{1, 2, 4, 5\}) = 4$. Thus the indirect distance, from A to D through B, is $2 + 4 = 6$, while the direct distance is just 4. The triangle inequality holds, but the distances are not additive, further showing that A, B, and D are not on a straight line in our sense.

Counterexample 2. Another example is constructed by using the sets

$$A = \{1, 2, 3\}$$

$$B = \{2, 3, 4\}$$

$$C = \{3, 4, 5\}$$

$$D = \{4, 5, 1\}$$

In this case B is between A and C, and C is between B and D, but B is not between A and D. The trouble is that the last set, D, has encroached back on set A—the row of sets is going in a kind of circle. Formally, the problem is that $A \cap D$ is not a subset of B, for $A \cap D = \{1\}$ and 1 is not an element of B. This case is of particular psychological interest because a sequence of gradual changes in a stimulus situation, continued long enough, may on occasion return to the situation with which it began. The color circle is an example, for each spectral color appears to be directly between its two neighbors, but the locus from red through orange to yellow to green to blue to purple eventually returns to red.

Theorem 3.4 makes it clear that it is invalid to extrapolate and connect together local relations of "betweenness." However, it is possible that there are *some* general conditions under which these difficulties do not arise. In particular, there may be a row of sets $A_1, A_2, \cdots, A_N$ over which the betweenness relation holds for any three sets. More exactly, a description is needed of a sequence of sets $A_1, \cdots, A_i, \cdots$ such that for any $i < j < k$ the relation $b_{A_i A_j A_k}$ (which may be written more conveniently as b_{ijk}) holds.

The most obvious case is a sequence of sets which are nested within one another. This is termed a monotone sequence of sets, and can be described as a sequence $A_1, \cdots, A_i, \cdots$ such that for any $i < j$, $A_i \subset A_j$.

THEOREM 3.5: If $A_1, \cdots, A_i, \cdots$ is a monotone sequence of sets, then for any $i < j < k$, b_{ijk}.

Proof: $A_i \cap A_k$ is a subset of A_i, and since $A_i \subset A_j$ it follows that $A_i \cap A_k \subset A_j$. Similarly, since $A_j \subset A_k$, it follows at once that $A_j \subset A_i \cup A_k$.

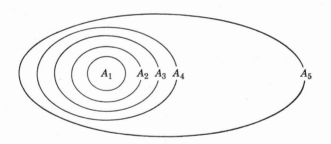

FIGURE 3.5

This theorem refers to "quantitative" or "prothetic" (S. S. Stevens, 1957) scales. The various situations differ only in that the ones with higher index numbers contain all the elements of lower-numbered sets plus some additional aspects. This implies two things: as one moves along the sequence of sets one picks up new aspects, and one never loses any of the old ones. Any such sequence of sets is ordered in a strict way, and distances are additive. Figure 3.5 gives an example of a small sequence of monotone sets. There is exactly one more way to make an array of sets all of which are in a straight line.

The Linear Array of Sets

Imagine two disjoint pools of aspects, A and B, and any fixed set C which has no overlap with A or B. Now make up a row of sets as follows. Start with the whole set A, to this unite C, and take no elements from B. The next set is made up by discarding some elements from A and adding some elements from B, retaining C. The third set is made up by discarding still more elements from A and adding still more elements from B, retaining C. Each step of the process involves discarding some elements from A and adding some new elements from B. Elements from A which have earlier been discarded are never reused, and elements from B which have been added are never discarded.

This is a substitutive or "metathetic" (S. S. Stevens, 1957) scale—each move along the scale involves substituting some elements from B for some of the elements of A.

Such a row of sets, which is here called a "linear array," preserves the betweenness relationship. That is, if X_i, X_j, and X_k are any three sets of the array which have been produced in that order, then b_{ijk}.

But for relaxing a few minor restrictions, this is the only kind of sequence of sets which preserves betweenness. It is possible, in moving along this sequence, not to discard any elements from A on a certain step, or not to add any elements from B. Also, if L^* is of any linear array of sets, then any array made up of part of L^* is also a linear array. It can be proved, with a little effort, that any sequence of sets on which the betweenness relationship holds everywhere, and consequently along which distances are strictly additive, can be dissected into a set A, a set B, and a common set C and then rebuilt by the substitutive processes described above (Restle, 1959a).

This development of a concept of a straight line or linear array of situations is introduced here because it has the effect of tying the notions of a scale down to more primitive concepts. Only the notion of a situation was taken as primitive. Stimulus variables were defined as partitions of the set S^* of situations, and aspects were defined as the cells of these partitions which differ from the background. It turned out that each situation could then be associated with a set of aspects. The distance between two situations was defined as the measure of the difference between them. This left the possibility of a complete tangle of distances, suggesting the need for some simple map or arrangement of situations. The most natural choice was the "straight line" of situations, in which distances would add directly. For the distances to add, the sets had to be in a special arrangement. This special arrangement can hold over a whole sequence of situations if and only if the situations are produced by substitution of one kind of elements for another.

The idea of a substitutive scale is certainly not new; it is basic to almost any notion of a scale arrangement of situations in terms of qualitative differences. What is new is that the idea has now been inserted within the theory in a very central place, and it is proved that a truly substitutive scale (exactly defined) is unique: it is the only scale which will permit direct addition of distances all along. In a sense the system is a house of cards: the uniqueness of substitutive scales depends upon the definition of distance, and the value of the measurement of distance is at least in part that it is directly additive in the case of substitutive scales. The two ideas support one another, and if one falls the other is severely weakened. However, the concept of distance is so direct and straightforward, and the notion of a substitutive scale is so well established in psychological thought, that the two together make a promising structure for analyzing concepts of scaling in psychology. It may be mentioned at this point, however, that the general set-theoretic development does not depend on this particular definition of distance and linear array.

Theory of Choice in Ordered Situations

The mechanism of choice described in Chapter 2 takes several interesting forms when the ideal situations S_1 and S_2 and the test situation S are all members of a linear array.

Imagine that the subject has two response alternatives available, 1 and 2, with an ideal situation for each, S_1 and S_2. In situation S, as was shown in Chapter 2, the probability of response 1 is

$$P_1 = \frac{m(S \cap S_1 \cap \bar{S}_2)}{m(S \cap S_1 \cap \bar{S}_2) + m(S \cap \bar{S}_1 \cap S_2)} \tag{3.1}$$

Consider first the case in which S, S_1, and S_2 all have the same measure and are part of a linear array, with the present situation S in the middle. In this case,

$$P_1 = \frac{d_{S,S_2}}{d_{S,S_2} + d_{S,S_1}} \tag{3.2}$$

Proof: Represent the three stimuli as points on a line (since they form a linear array). Since the numerical values of the end points are arbitrary, consider that S_1 lies at the origin and S_2 a unit distance away. Now, situation S lies somewhere in between, as in Fig. 3.6.

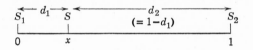

FIGURE 3.6

A linear array of sets can be thought of as three overlapping line segments. Let S_1, S, and S_2 be so represented, as in Fig. 3.7, and

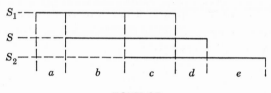

FIGURE 3.7

the lengths of the five subsets produced be called a, b, c, d, and e. Applying Eq. 3.1, $P_1 = b/(b + d)$. Furthermore, since the three situations have equal measures,

$$a + b + c = b + c + d = c + d + e$$

whence

$$a = d \quad \text{and} \quad b = e$$

by elementary algebra.

Considering the distances,

$$d_{S, S_1} = a + d = 2d \quad \text{and} \quad d_{S, S_2} = b + e = 2b$$

Hence the ratio of the distances, given in Eq. 3.2, is

$$b/(b + d) = 2b/(2b + 2d) = d_{S, S_2}/(d_{S, S_2} + d_{S, S_1})$$

which leads to Eq. 3.2.

An entirely formal proof is accomplished by merely defining the five subsets

$$a = m(S_1 \cap \bar{S} \cap \bar{S}_2)$$

$$b = m(S \cap S_1 \cap \bar{S}_2)$$

$$c = m(S \cap S_1 \cap S_2)$$
$$d = m(\bar{S}_1 \cap S \cap S_2)$$
$$e = m(\bar{S}_1 \cap \bar{S} \cap S_2)$$

The conditions of a linear array ensure that these exhaust S, S_1, and S_2.

This result can be generalized to any three sets in a linear array, even if they do not have the same measures. If the measures of the three sets and the two distances are known, the probability of

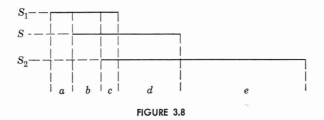

FIGURE 3.8

choosing response 1 can be computed. Begin with Fig. 3.8, again of three sets but now of arbitrary sizes, and the same definitions of a, b, c, d, and e. Now let $m_1 = m(S_1)$, $m = m(S)$, $m_2 = m(S_2)$, $\Delta_1 = d_{S_1,S}$, and $\Delta_2 = d_{S,S_2}$. The following list of equations arises directly from the definitions:

$$P_1 = b/(b + d)$$
$$m_1 = a + b + c$$
$$m = b + c + d$$
$$m_2 = c + d + e$$
$$\Delta_1 = a + d$$
$$\Delta_2 = b + e$$

Adding and subtracting the above identities to isolate variables leads to

$$c = \tfrac{1}{2}(m_1 + m_2 - \Delta_1 - \Delta_2)$$

whence, from the definition of m_2,

$$b + d = m - \tfrac{1}{2}(m_1 + m_2 - \Delta_1 - \Delta_2)$$

and

$$b = \tfrac{1}{2}(m - m_2 + \Delta_2)$$

so that

$$P_1 = \frac{b}{b + d} = \frac{m - m_2 + \Delta_2}{2m - m_1 - m_2 + \Delta_1 + \Delta_2} \tag{3.3}$$

Equation 3.3 is particularly useful when dealing with an array of sets which get larger. One might be dealing with an ordered array of stimuli which increase in complexity or in "strength," i.e., in contrast with the background. This would often seem to be the case when there are three stimuli ordered in size, brightness, loudness, or complexity (e.g., three drawn figures, each of which is produced from the preceding one by the addition of further detail). Such arrays of stimuli often do not act exactly like nested arrays, but show a con-

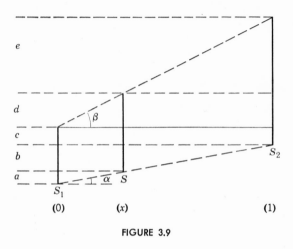

FIGURE 3.9

figuration rather like that in Fig. 3.8. One case which may be used as a simplified model has the characteristic that $b/a = e/d$. In effect, using Fig. 3.8, the lines shift to the right and increase in length at the same rate.

Figure 3.9 shows the same arrangement of sets as Fig. 3.8, but the lines representing sets are now upright, and the whole set of stimuli are indicated by the dashed guide line. Figure 3.9 shows a linear array in which the sets get larger in a regular way. Along the scale elements common with ideal S_1 are lost at rate α and elements common with S_2 are gained at rate β.

The probability of choosing response 1 can be expressed in terms of the two rates α and β and the location of the test stimulus x. Recall that, since a probability is a ratio of measures, the measures can be given an arbitrary scale of measurement. Let $a + b = 1$, since $a + b$ is a constant.

In these terms, $P_1 = b/b + d$. It is easily seen from the diagram that

$$b = 1 - \alpha x \quad \text{and} \quad d = \beta x$$

so that

$$P_1 = (1 - \alpha x)/(1 - \alpha x + \beta x)$$

However, to satisfy the diagram conditions, when $x = 1$ it is necessary that $b = 0$. Therefore, setting $x = 1$, we have

$$b_{(1)} = 0 = 1 - \alpha \cdot 1$$

whence, in these units of measurement, $\alpha = 1$. Thus, finally,

$$P_1 = (1 - x)/(1 - x + \beta x) \tag{3.4}$$

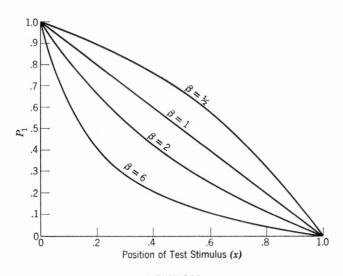

FIGURE 3.10

Here, β is a parameter indicating how rapidly the size of sets increases along the scale. $\beta = 1$ indicates constant sets, $\beta > 1$ means that the sets increase along the scale by a factor of β, and $\beta < 1$ indicates that the sets get smaller along the scale. Curves of P_1 as a function of scale position of the test stimulus x for a few representative values of β are shown in Fig. 3.10.

The effect deduced here is that the subject will tend to choose response 2 rather than response 1 when the ideal situation for response 2 is larger, i.e., has more aspects. The larger ideal has more control of behavior than the smaller.

The curves in Fig. 3.10 can be interpreted as "generalization gradients" or response gradients. Imagine that for some reason, perhaps previous training, the subject will certainly make response 1 at stimulus $x = 0$, and certainly will not make response 1 at $x = 1$. The probability of response to intermediate stimuli depends on whether the stimuli increase in measure ($\beta > 1$), in which case one has a concave-upward gradient, or the stimuli decrease in measure ($\beta < 1$), in which case one has a concave-downward gradient.

Ordinarily, this theory will be used with stimuli which are arranged on some physical variable like intensity of energy, size, etc. There is no assurance in advance that such situations form a linear array, and furthermore there is usually some question as to exactly how the physical variable is to be measured to give what is, in Fig. 3.10, the variable x. In the applications in later chapters, a structure like that in Figs. 3.9 and 3.10 will be put forward as a simplifying assumption or hypothesis. In practice, the assumption is no bolder than the assumptions usually involved in theoretical treatments of psychophysics.

PART II Applications

CHAPTER
FOUR

Choices and the Measurement of Utility

A knowledge of motivation is necessary to predict the behavior of another individual. Even if the person's motivation is known, errors may be made because his technique for satisfying his motives is not known or because his skill or vigor is wrongly estimated; but with a wrong assumption about motivation, predictions of behavior will usually be completely wrong.

This observation may lead to basic questions of human nature: What are the normal (and abnormal) human motivations? From what biological and social contexts do they arise? How intense, stable, and organized are they? These questions are difficult and no answer to them appears in this book, but they are related to a simple and more tractable problem which also requires an answer and which provides some theoretical interest. The question is: How do a person's motivations influence his behavior? By what logic can behavior be predicted on the basis of knowledge of motives?

The answer is very simple if the choice is merely between something the person likes and something he dislikes. Some doubt arises when the choice is more difficult, as when it is between two things which the individual likes and his preference is relatively slight. The question becomes difficult and interesting when the alternatives offered are complex, each involving some pleasant and some unpleasant aspects; or where the person chooses without being certain as to the outcome he will receive.

A large part of the relevant theory is found, not in psychology, but in mathematical economics, statistics, and decision theory. These disciplines seek to give good advice to a rational decision-maker by telling him how to choose in complex or risky situations. The aim of the advice is to get the chooser to be as successful, on the average, as is possible, so that he will obtain all he can of whatever it is he wants. Such advice can be given only in conjunction with knowledge of the person's desires, which must be measured. A basic issue in decision theory is the measurement of desires or, as the term is used in that field, the measurement of *utility*.

Any adequate theory of how motivations combine to produce choice behavior can be used to measure utility. The method is to have the person choose under a variety of conditions, and to record these choices. Then one can hypothesize a certain set of utilities and see whether those utilities, along with the theory of choice, lead to the choices actually made by the person.

The experiment has the appearance of circularity but is not circular. The person is given some restricted set of choices, and from those choices his utilities are estimated, using the theory. When the set of utilities is computed, the theory can be used to predict choices among combinations of alternatives which were not used in measurement. Thus the theory of choosing becomes testable.

The main theory of choice used in decision theory is based on the principle of maximum expected utility. Given a choice between two objects or situations, the subject selects the one with higher utility. In a situation involving risk, each alternative is a gamble. If a certain alternative A_1 is chosen, there are several outcomes $O_1, O_2, \cdots, O_N$ which might result. Suppose that these outcomes have utilities u_1, $u_2, \cdots, u_N$. Suppose further that the probability of O_1 is p_1, the probability of O_2 is p_2, etc. Then the expected utility of the alternative is

$$E(u; A_1) = p_1 u_1 + p_2 u_2 + \cdots + p_N u_N \qquad (4.1)$$

If the utilities are all finite there is some such expectation for each alternative A_1, A_2, etc. The person is presumed (or at any rate advised) to choose the alternative with the highest expected utility.

This principle will not be followed with perfect accuracy by all subjects in all possible situations. Some choices, like the choice of a life's work, involve so many complicated outcomes that most people would be at a loss to carry out the needed calculations. It is usually assumed that in fairly simple situations the person will choose according to the principle of maximum expected utility, and that such choices will be sufficient to enable us to measure the utilities of various outcomes for these people. Then in more complicated choices the measured utilities can be used to calculate what response the person should make to maximize his expected utility. This response is the rational choice, and the decision theorist can suggest this response as his advice.

The psychologist can use this same general strategy to ask the connection between motivation and behavior, though his interest will be more empirical than normative. The psychologist will more likely ask what choices people do make than what choices they should make. The present theory seeks to predict the probabilities of various choices given the situation and the known utilities of outcomes, and the same theory is used to measure the utilities.

If the person chooses the alternative with maximum expected utility he will (in many situations) choose a single alternative consistently. Even in cases where there is a unique best choice, however, people are somewhat inconsistent. Let us briefly survey the available explanations of inconsistent behavior, for inconsistency will be used later as an important characteristic of choice behavior.

One approach is to suppose that there is some margin of error within which people cannot choose consistently. If the expected utilities of two alternatives differ by more than a constant Δ (the margin of error) then the subject chooses consistently, but if the difference between expected utilities is less than Δ he chooses randomly. This model produces a certain proportion of inconsistent choices when the alternatives have very similar utilities.

Another approach is to suppose that the utilities of alternatives, or at least their "momentarily perceived" utilities, are subject to random perturbations. If someone is choosing between two alternatives which are quite close in utility, one of the utilities will usually be higher than the other, but their positions will sometimes be reversed. If the momentary utilities are normally distributed, it is possible to measure the difference between the mean utilities of two alternatives by considering the proportion of choices of each. In Fig. 4.1 are shown two hypothetical distributions of momentary utilities of two alternatives. On the average, alternative A is preferred to B. However, whenever B's utility happens to fluctuate to a relatively high value at the same time that A's utility happens to be low, B will be preferred to A. The third curve shows the distribution of $u(A) - u(B)$, which is usually positive but which is negative on a small proportion of the choices. The probability that B is chosen over A is indicated by the shaded portion of the third curve.

Both the threshold theory and the normal-curve theory state that inconsistent responses occur when the utilities of the alter-

natives are close together relative to the error of judgment (margin
of uncertainty Δ or standard deviation of the normal curve of perceived utility). This suggests that the error is contributed by the
subject in his judgments, and would be constant for all alternatives,
or that the error corresponds to intrinsic instability of the utility of
the alternative itself.

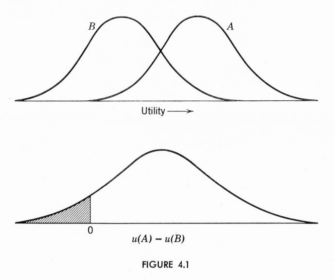

FIGURE 4.1

    However, consider this example. A person is asked to
choose between $1,000.00 and $1,000.01. A suitably penurious subject
would always choose the latter though the difference is only 1 part in
100,000. Now consider the same person trying to decide one winter
between a California and a Florida vacation. The difference in utility
between the two vacations will surely be more than 1 part in 100,000,
yet it seems likely that the choice will be relatively difficult and
uncertain. (The writer is thinking of vacations which would cost
about $1,000, so that the actual utilities of the vacations are com-
parable in amount to the utilities of the money choices.)

    Perhaps money is judged more accurately, or has more
stable utility, than vacations. This seems reasonable, but does not
fully solve the problem. For suppose that the momentary utility of
a vacation is highly unstable. Give our penurious subject the choice
between a California vacation and a California vacation plus 1 cent—
again we expect him to choose the latter consistently even though both
choices involve the (presumably unstable) utility of a vacation. The
point appears to be that the two vacations are relatively different

from one another in the detailed characteristics which make them desirable. When the person is forced to choose between very different things, there are a great many factors to consider. When he chooses between two very similar things, such as $1,000.00 and $1,000.01, the only difference is the odd penny and he actually can choose between $.00 and $.01. Similarly, when the penny is added to the California vacation, the two alternatives are precisely alike except for the odd penny and the choice is very easy.

This idea can be introduced into the normal-curve theory in which probabilities of choice depend upon the distribution of differences in utility of the two alternatives. If two alternatives are made up mainly of exactly the same outcomes, such as the California vacation and the same vacation plus 1 cent, then the momentary fluctuations of the two utilities will be very highly correlated. The standard deviation of a difference between two normally distributed variables such as u and v is calculated by the formula

$$\sigma^2_{(u-v)} = \sigma^2_u + \sigma^2_v - 2r\sigma_u\sigma_v$$

where r is the correlation between u and v. If the correlation r is very high (nearly 1) and σ_u is close to σ_v, then the variance of the difference is very small and a very small difference in utility would lead to quite consistent choices.

Used in this way, the normal-curve theory produces what seems a sensible mathematical representation of these judgments. There are some technical difficulties, however, which serve partly to vitiate what seems an elegant solution to the problem. To the writer at least, the assumption of normal distributions of utilities seems somewhat artificial unless it can be supported by a more fundamental argument. The mathematical problems of measuring utilities when the utilities of various outcomes have arbitrary correlations are formidable, so that attention has mainly centered on the cases of uncorrelated variables or sets of objects the utilities of which all have a constant and common intercorrelation. The most practical way of handling the sort of problem discussed above would be to estimate intercorrelations of the utilities of alternatives by considering the "common elements" entering into various alternatives. In the theory introduced below, the "common elements" approach is reduced to what is, in the author's opinion, its simplest mathematical form. An attempt will be made to carry through the necessary reasoning without normal distributions, without worrying about whether linear correlations (r) are sufficient to handle the problems of similar alternatives, and without supposing that the subject can make an accurate comparison of two randomly varying utilities so as to choose the alternative with the higher utility.

In the theory given in Chapter 2 it was pointed out that the only aspects entering into a differential choice are the differential aspects; one chooses between A and B on the basis of the sets $A \cap \bar{B}$ and $\bar{A} \cap B$. This gives an interpretation of probabilities of choice as they depend upon preference and similarity. Before the theory can be used, two preliminary steps must be completed. These are:

1. To define utility in terms of measures of sets of aspects.

2. To show how the resulting theory is related to actual measurements of utility in the laboratory.

The Probability of a Simple Preferential Choice

Consider an experiment in which a subject is given various choices and asked to state his preference in each trial. The subject is given full information about his choices and their consequences, and makes a careful and deliberate choice. Presumably, then, his choice will be governed only by the differences between the alternatives offered. If the alternatives are of similar total value but very different in their qualities, like the two vacations, then the subject will choose with a probability near 1/2, whereas if there is only a slight difference, all in favor of one choice, his probability will be near 1.

Consider the subject with two alternatives a and b, and| let the valued aspects of the two be A and B, where $m(A)$ is the total utility of alternative a. The aspects which lead to a choice of a are $A \cap \bar{B}$, and those which lead to a choice of b are $\bar{A} \cap B$. Other aspects do not lead to a decision and can be ignored. The probability that a is chosen over b is therefore

$$P(a, b) = \frac{m(A \cap \bar{B})}{m(A \cap \bar{B}) + m(\bar{A} \cap B)} \qquad (4.2)$$

Letting d_{ab} be the distance with respect to valued aspects (ignoring any properties the alternatives may have which have no bearing on utility or preference),

$$P(a, b) = m(A \cap \bar{B})/d_{ab} \qquad (4.3)$$

For the denominator of Eq. 4.2 is the distance between the sets A and B, as defined in Chapter 3.

A valued aspect may be defined as any aspect which enters into a preferential choice; but this does not advance understanding very far. Another approach is to notice that the subject may like or dislike a certain alternative, for various reasons. There are many things about a rotten tomato which are unpleasant, and many things about a pearl which are pleasant. Although they may be equally attractive, the valued characteristics of a Bach partita and a Shakespeare sonnet are quite different—but even here there may be some overlap. Some aspects of a situation, though perceivable, do not enter into preferential choices and simply are not valued. For example, the temperature of the cover of a book may be perceived but would have little to do with its purchase. The idea that there is a set of valued aspects, often heterogeneous, and that the utility of an alternative is the measure of that set, constitute the necessary theoretical assumption.

When the objects are very similar, e.g., money payments, a subject should discriminate nearly perfectly between pure alternatives no matter how small the differences in utility. When the objects are various and relatively incommensurable, incompatible and partly "random" choices appear.

Utility and Measures of Sets

The approach in Eq. 4.2 conflicts in many formal details with the typical concept of utility, and some further discussion is required to resolve the conflicts. In the present discussion the utility of a is represented by $m(A)$. However, m is a measure function, hence nonnegative. Utilities, as usually conceived, can be negative. In classical utility theory the utilities are unique only up to a linear transformation, and an arbitrary constant can be added or subtracted across the board. If a sufficiently large negative constant is added, some utilities will be negative, and the measure-function representation is inappropriate. Actually, what has happened is that the present theory implies stronger measurement (a system with a true zero, commonly called a ratio scale) than utility measurement (an interval scale). The stronger measurement comes in because the present system uses not only preferences but the probabilities of choices, whereas utility theory uses only the preferences. The present theory constructs probabilities as ratios of utilities and distances, whereas utility theory never forms such ratios and has no interpretation for an expression of the form U_1/U_2.

If, using the measure-theoretic approach, all objects are given positive utilities, further argument can arrive at anomalous results. Consider two objects, say a book and a record, of about equal attractiveness, and a third object, say, a ticking time bomb, which is in the ordinary sense of the word undesirable, i.e., has negative utility. In the set-theoretic system all three objects must receive positive utilities. Now offer book plus bomb as one alternative, and record as the other. If the utilities are additive or even nearly so in such a context, the book plus bomb will have higher total utility than the record, even though the bomb is not wanted at all. The book-plus-bomb bundle should usually be chosen, though this is of course entirely unreasonable on the face of it.

To avoid this possibility requires a broad view of the alternatives offered. Note that the book without the bomb is more valuable than the book with the bomb. Thus the choice is between book with bomb and record *without* bomb, and, since avoiding the bomb is more valuable than getting it, the second alternative should receive the higher utility. The universe of valued aspects must contain avoiding an unpleasant alternative as well as obtaining a pleasant one. Each object has both good and bad valued aspects, i.e., the value of obtaining and the value of avoiding it. The utility of a compound alternative consists not only of the value received when that choice is taken but also the value of avoiding objects not received. If all available alternatives avoid some object *b*, then the alternatives do not differ in this respect and elements from *b* do not enter into deciding the choice probabilities.

In no case is the subject in the usual experiment given an unpleasant electric shock for his choice; hence electric shock is not a source of valued aspects for any of the alternatives. Positive and negative qualities of all objects which are actually involved in the experiment must be considered, but not possibilities which do not really exist.

Still, some alternatives are so undesirable that they must certainly receive negative values—how about a sudden and horrible death? Avoiding this is so much better than receiving it that it must either receive a negative number or avoiding it must receive an infinitely large number. The latter choice would lead to infinite measures and defeat the attempted analysis.

This difficulty, like the previous one, depends upon an incomplete description of the experimental situation. A method of measuring utility will be incomplete unless the person will choose between all pairs of objects presented. If some parts of the experiment cannot be performed, then some utilities must remain unmeasured. The fact is, it would be very difficult to get a person to choose between (1) a sudden and horrible death and (2) a sudden and horrible death plus an apple. The sudden and horrible death cannot be used in the experiment.

If all choices between alternatives are to occur, the experimenter must hold something in reserve which is worse than the worst alternative in the measured set. The choices of interest are "voluntary" in that the person himself makes them, but in some cases they will be coerced in the sense that refusal to choose is made even more undesirable than any choice. Some reserve alternative, which is never actually measured, is present and establishes the floor of the utilities being measured. This goad or reserve alternative may be given a utility of zero, so that all measured utilities will be positive. When the goad is considered, the representation of utilities by the measures of sets is acceptable.

Actually, the present system operates quite like the standard utility notion in that preference depends largely on the differences between utilities. Let $m(A) = U(a)$, the utility of a. Then from Eq. 4.2

$$P(a, b) - P(b, a) = \frac{U(a) - U(b)}{d_{ab}} \qquad (4.4)$$

which in effect makes the difference between the probabilities of choice depend upon the difference in utilities. Recall that utilities are determined only up to a linear transformation, so that the unit can be multiplied by a positive constant or a constant, positive or negative, can be added without changing the significance of the set of numbers. In the present system the measure function m can be multiplied by a positive constant without changing any probabilities, since the probabilities are always the ratios of measures. The change of unit would cancel in any expression of a probability, hence the change could not be detected in behavior. An abstract interpretation of Eq. 4.4 would take the values of $U(a)$, $U(b)$, and d_{ab} as real numbers, detaching them from their intended interpretations as the measures of sets.

Now, consider the utility-theory notion that only the difference between two utilities, and not their absolute sizes, affects behavior, so that an additive constant makes no difference. Define a new set of numbers, abstract utilities, by the formula

$$U'(x) = U(x) + k$$

for any number k. This constant applies only to the utilities and not to the distances, which in any case have no significance in utility theory. Now,

$$P(a, b) - P(b, a) = \frac{U'(a) - U'(b)}{d_{ab}}$$

$$= \frac{[U(a) + k] - [U(b) + k]}{d_{ab}}$$

$$= \frac{U(a) - U(b)}{d_{ab}} \tag{4.5}$$

Thus, if the U' are thought of abstractly as numbers, they are subject to a linear transformation without changing the behavior of the system as a whole—negative utilities could be used, if k is chosen negative. It is essential to multiply d_{ab} by any factor which also multiplies the U's, but not to add or subtract constants from the distance d_{ab}. For the purpose of the present theory there is no reason for the abstract interpretation of utilities except as measures of sets, but it is perhaps useful to see that the present theory is compatible with an abstract utility function with the usual mathematical property of having an arbitrary origin. This mathematical restriction is the image of the intuitive idea that there is no neutral event except in contrast with other available alternatives.

Now notice that this system behaves suitably in the examples discussed above. The two vacations would presumably have a number of different valued aspects, so that the distance between them, d_{ab}, would be sizable. Hence even a nontrivial difference in utility would be insufficient to make $P(a, b) - P(b, a)$ equal to 1 (or -1), and choices would be uncertain. But the difference in valued aspects between $1,000.01 and $1,000.00 would be only the odd penny. Letting $1,000.01 be a and $1,000.00 be b, we should have

$$U(a) - U(b) = U(\text{the odd penny}) = m(\text{the odd penny})$$

and since d_{ab} would also be m(the odd penny),

$$P(a, b) - P(b, a) = m(\text{the odd penny})/m(\text{the odd penny}) = 1$$

whence $P(a, b) = 1$ and the larger sum is always chosen. The certainty of choice in such a case becomes a mathematical consequence, as desired.

In general, unpredictability of choice will be explained, in the present theory, as due to the degree to which the alternatives are different. The advantage of the formulation given here, over the normal-curve theory, is mainly that it is simpler. If it is agreed that dissimilarity between choices affects the inability to make a consistent choice, and if the argument that the present theory of choice (Chapter 2) is plausible is accepted, then there is no need for normal distributions. Uncertainty of choice is explained another way, by an analysis of the process of resolving a conflict.

Choices from More than Two Alternatives

The present system is formally similar to that of Luce (1959a). Luce bases his analysis upon an assumption about the choices of alternatives from various sets; hence he is especially concerned with choices from more than two alternatives. In effect, Luce takes the simplest law possible about such choices and then deduces a surprising variety of consequences. Luce's assumption is true of the present system if the various sets of valued aspects, $A, B, \cdots$, have no common elements, or if the only overlap between any pair is common to all the sets involved. Otherwise it is not entirely clear what the decision process will be, but it does not seem likely that it will be consistent with Luce's assumption.

Consider first the case in which the sets $A, B, \cdots$, are all discrete. In this case the probability of choosing a from some set, say $\{a, b, c\}$ of alternatives, is given by

$$P(a; \{a, b, c\}) = \frac{m(A)}{m(A) + m(B) + m(C)}$$
$$= \frac{U(a)}{U(a) + U(b) + U(c)}$$

In the case of disjoint sets, every element of every object enters into choice as a differential factor. The utilities $U(A)$ are equal to the measures of differential factors entering into choice, and Luce's theory applies directly. Luce's "v-scale" values would be proportional to $m(A), m(B), \cdots$, and could be interpreted directly as utilities.

If A, B, and C have a common set Z, then

$$P(a; \{a, b, c\}) = \frac{m(A \cap \bar{Z})}{m(A \cap \bar{Z}) + m(B \cap \bar{Z}) + m(C \cap \bar{Z})}$$
$$= \frac{U(a) - U(Z)}{U(a) + U(b) + U(c) - 3U(Z)} \tag{4.6}$$

The last equation follows from the assumption that Z is a subset of A, B, and C. In this case Luce's v-scale values correspond to the utility of the choice minus some constant: $v_a = U(a) - m(Z)$.

A more interesting possibility is that the subject chooses from three or more objects by partitioning them into subsets, choosing within the subsets and then between subsets. This will turn the choice into a process with more than one stage. In general, the partition used by the subject will make a difference in the probabilities of arriving at one or another choice.

There are several approaches the subject might take. For example, Luce suggests that,

To deal with complicated decisions, it is usual to subdivide them into two or more stages: the alternatives are grossly categorized in some fashion and a first decision is made among these categories; the one chosen is further categorized and a second decision is made; etc. (Luce, 1959a, p. 7.)

In this method the subject makes his first decision between categories and then chooses within the category. Such a procedure is difficult to analyze with the present model, unless the valued aspects possessed by a *category* of alternatives can be identified.

Another possibility also mentioned by Luce may apply to an attempt to rank three objects, x, y, and z. Luce says,

. . . suppose that $\{x, y, z\}$ [a set of three alternatives] is given and that in ranking it the subject selects a pair of alternatives at random (probability $1/3$), compares them, and decides which he ranks higher. Then he picks one of these at random (probability $1/2$) and compares it with the third. If this does not produce a ranking, then he compares the remaining two. (Luce, 1959a, p. 71.)

A third possibility will be considered here. Given three objects $\{a, b, c\}$ we suppose that the subject selects a pair of alternatives at random (or on some basis such as similarity) and chooses between them. The alternative chosen as superior is then compared with the third alternative, and the better of these is the final choice. This procedure differs from Luce's first procedure mentioned above in that choices are first made inside the categories and then between the "champions" of the categories, in the present approach, whereas Luce spoke of a procedure starting with comparison of categories with one another. The procedure discussed here is very similar to Luce's suggestion about ranking* except that, in the present sug-

---

*It should be emphasized that Luce merely mentioned the ranking procedure as an example, proving a general point by showing that such a ranking procedure exists as a possibility. He nowhere indicates that he thinks this multiple-stage procedure is the one actually used by subjects. In somewhat the same spirit, the procedure discussed in this section is only fairly plausible, and the discussion is intended more to emphasize the problems involved in multi-stage decision processes, and to fill in one more possibility, than as a systematic theory of such processes.

gestion, the champion of a category, i.e., the object chosen within the category, will always be the one compared with a third object. Furthermore, the present discussion is devoted only to a choice of one object, not to a complete ranking.

Given three objects, a, b, and c, the subject begins his choice process by partitioning them. The possible partitions are

$$\{a\}, \{b, c\} \quad \text{Partition I}$$
$$\{a, b\}, \{c\} \quad \text{Partition II}$$
$$\{a, c\}, \{b\} \quad \text{Partition III}$$

If partition I is used, the subject decides between b and c. If he chooses b as superior he then decides between a and b. The choice there is final. The procedure is like an elimination tournament in tennis or chess.

There are three pairwise probabilities which enter into the decision: $P(a, b)$, the probability of choosing a over b when the pair is presented, $P(a, c)$, and $P(b, c)$. These probabilities are given briefer names for the algebra ahead. Let

$$P(a, b) = p, \quad \text{and} \quad P(b, a) = 1 - p$$
$$P(a, c) = q, \quad \text{and} \quad P(c, a) = 1 - q \tag{4.7}$$
$$P(b, c) = r, \quad \text{and} \quad P(c, b) = 1 - r$$

Consider the possibility that the final probability of choosing a, say $P(a)$, is independent of which partition is used. If partition I is used, the probability of ending up with a is easily calculated. If the subject chooses b over c (with probability r) and then a over b (probability p), he ends up with a. Alternatively, he may choose c over b (with probability $1 - r$) and then choose a over c (probability q).

$$P(a) = pr + q(1 - r) \quad \text{Using partition I} \tag{4.8}$$

If the subject uses partition II he must choose a over b first (probability p) and then choose a over c (probability q). This is the only way he can end up with a, so

$$P(a) = pq \quad \text{Using partition II} \tag{4.9}$$

If he uses partition III, the probability of ending up with a is also pq.

The probability of choosing a is independent of the partitionings if and only if

$$pr + q(1 - r) = pq \tag{4.10}$$

Interestingly enough, exactly the same equation results from investigation of the probability of choosing b or c. For with the three partitions, following the above reasoning,

$$P(b) = r(1 - p) \qquad\qquad \text{Using partition I}$$
$$P(b) = r(1 - p) \qquad\qquad \text{Using partition II} \qquad (4.11)$$
$$P(b) = q(1 - p) + r(1 - q) \qquad \text{Using partition III}$$

and, for the probability of choosing c,

$$P(c) = (1 - r)(1 - q) \qquad\qquad \text{Using partition I}$$
$$P(c) = p(1 - q) + (1 - p)(1 - r) \qquad \text{Using partition II} \qquad (4.12)$$
$$P(c) = (1 - r)(1 - q) \qquad\qquad \text{Using partition III}$$

Now if $P(b)$ is the same in all of Eqs. 4.11,

$$r(1 - p) = q(1 - p) + r(1 - q)$$
$$r - rp = q - qp + r - rq$$
$$pq = q + rp - rq = rp + q(1 - r)$$

which is the same as Eq. 4.10. Similarly, if the three values of $P(c)$ in Eqs. 4.12 are all alike, Eq. 4.10 results.

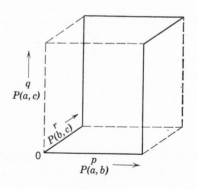

FIGURE 4.2

With the restriction that p, q, and r are all probabilities (i.e., that they are numbers between 0 and 1) Eq. 4.10 puts a surprising restriction on the probabilities p, q, and r. The possible points are shown as the solid line in Fig. 4.2. One characteristic of the locus shown in Fig. 4.2 is that two of the three probabilities must be at their extremes, 0 or 1, but having fixed two, the third probability is free to vary. Of the three pairwise decisions to be made, at least two must be certain if the partitioning is not to make any difference.

The difference between the edges allowed and those not allowed (there are six of each type in Fig. 4.2) is that the edges allowed indicate transitivity of choice and the edges not allowed are indications of intransitivity.

Consider, for example, one of the disallowed corners, in the front upper left, where $p = 0$, $q = 1$, $r = 0$. These three probabilities are, by definition,

$$P(a, b) = 0$$

$$P(a, c) = 1$$

$$P(b, c) = 0$$

which says that b is preferred to a, c is preferred to b, and yet a is preferred to c. This would be a clear case of intransitivity. In the back lower right we have another disallowed corner, $p = 1$, $q = 0$, $r = 1$, which says that a is preferred over b, and b over c, but c is preferred over a.

Thus, probabilities are independent of partitioning only when two of the three decisions are categorical (probabilities of 1 or 0). If the partition makes a difference, there is no unconditional probability for choosing a. A general solution to the partitioning problem would require prediction of the probabilities of partitions I, II, and III, after which three-choice probabilities as a function of the two-choice probabilities p, q, and r would be determined. Since virtually no experimental data are available on the comparison of pairwise and multiple-choice decisions, and on the partitionings (if any) subjects actually use, there seems to be little point in pursuing the matter further here.

It is perhaps useful to suggest that the probabilities of the partitionings may depend upon the similarities of the three alternatives a, b, and c. For example, if a and b are highly similar, so that $m(A \cap B)$ is relatively large, and if $m(A \cap C)$ and $m(B \cap C)$ are small, it would be natural for the subject to classify a and b together, using partition II. This approach yields at least the outline of a theory of multistage choosing.

Experimental Measurements of Utility

According to the theory suggested above, the relationship between utilities and probabilities of choice is complicated by the additional factor of the distance between the sets. To measure utility by this system it is necessary to know something about the distances between sets of valued aspects as well as the measures of the sets. There are a great variety of possible arrangements of sets. The discussion to follow considers three arrangements which give simple, or at least intelligible, results and which provide the first application of the theory of orderings of sets given in Chapter 3.

CASE 1. MUTUALLY DISJOINT SETS OF VALUED ASPECTS. If all the objects have mutually disjoint sets of valued aspects, then the probabilities of pairwise choices lead to utility values for each by the formula,

$$P(a, b) = \frac{m(A)}{m(A) + m(B)}$$

whence

$$m(A) = m(B) \frac{P(a, b)}{1 - P(a, b)} \tag{4.13}$$

The values of $P(a, b)$ for every pair of objects determine each utility as a multiple of the other. Once a unit of measurement is selected, all utilities are determined. Since with N objects there are only $N - 1$ values of utility to be determined and there are $N(N - 1)/2$ pairs, the utilities are considerably overdetermined. Luce's model and the appropriate statistical methods apply.

As mentioned above, the various objects may be thought to have some set Z of valued aspects in common. The data do not determine what measure to assign to Z, so that the final utilities determined may be adjusted by adding or subtracting a constant. This arbitrary constant is likely to be needed when the objects measured are compared with other objects not in the original experiment. In general, mutually disjoint sets of valued aspects will be rather difficult to find in practice, so that the case of mutually disjoint sets has limited application only to well-controlled experiments.

CASE 2. ORDERED SETS OF VALUED ASPECTS. By Eq. 4.4 the difference in utility between two objects, $U(a) - U(b)$, can be computed from the probability $P(a, b)$ that a is chosen over b, and d_{ab}, the qualitative difference between the objects. Equation 4.4 works for any arbitrary set of objects, and for that reason is relatively difficult to apply in any particular case. One example which is fairly convenient to analyze, however, is where the situations to be chosen form a linear array in the sense of Chapter 3. In that case the distances, d_{xy}, form a simple arrangement. If the utilities have a simple arrangement, it may be possible to deduce the structure of a large set of results.

Imagine an array of political statements ranging from extreme left to extreme right, which by some miracle of test construction have aspects which form a linear array. A subject is requested to choose between pairs of such statements, selecting always the one more attractive to him. It would be natural to suppose that the subject has some "ideal" political statement, and that each item on the questionnaire will be evaluated according to how similar it is to the subject's ideal. Then the distance between two statements will be measured from left to right, but the utility of a statement will be measured as a displacement from some ideal point which may be near the middle of the scale. Both difference in utility and qualitative distances can be measured on the same linear array, hence probabilities of choice can be predicted in a convenient fashion.

The big difficulty with this approach is in finding a set of statements which form a linear array. In politics or other live social problems, there is such complexity of opinion in society and in the subject that even simple statements will have a great many aspects, different for different subjects. A linear array might be achieved for a few people, but not for all. To circumvent this difficulty, Coombs (1958) devised an experimental analogue. He used 12 gray chips varying in arbitrary steps from almost white to almost black. The subjects were to compare these chips as to which was more preferred as a representative gray. * Each subject was free to select an ideal or representative gray. In the actual procedure Coombs had the subjects rank four stimuli at a time, presenting each of the 495 possible sets twice, and then computed the probability of choosing one stimulus over another by noting how frequently one stimulus was ranked higher than the other in those presentations which contained both.

Generally speaking, the subjects chose stimuli near the middle of the array as their ideals: Of the array of 12 stimuli, one subject chose as his most preferred stimulus 6, two chose 7, and the

---

*In this case the preferences are certainly mild, and in fact it is surprising that people have any stable preference for a particular gray. Not only the stimuli but also the principle of preference, i. e., the nature of the ideal, is artificial. However, this artificiality has purchased a set of stimuli which very likely form a strict linear array, greatly simplifying the theoretical problem. Experiments can be done on more interesting subject matter, now that the method is illustrated.

other chose 10. From the ideal stimulus out in the two directions (too bright and too dark) the results were consistent in the sense of showing transitivity. If gray 5 was chosen over 4 more than half the time, and 4 was chosen over 2, then 5 was chosen over 2 at least half the time. This is called *weak stochastic transitivity*. With this fact one can place the several stimuli in a rank order from most preferred to least preferred.

There now are two distinct orderings of the same set of 12 stimuli, from darkest to lightest, and also from most preferred to least preferred. Since the subjects were asked to state preferences with respect to brightness, and brightness was almost the only way the 12 stimuli differed, the two orderings should show a close connection. The connection, which was first noted and developed by Coombs, is called "unfolding." The stimuli are arranged according

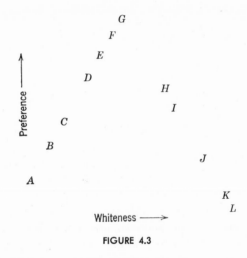

FIGURE 4.3

to brightness and labeled *ABCDEFGHIJKL*, with arbitrary spacings between the stimuli. Imagine "folding" this ordering at some point near the most-preferred stimulus. Then the most-preferred stimulus is on top, and the others are strung out below, with a mixed arrangement of stimuli on the left and on the right of the ideal stimulus.

Coombs' subject number 1 ranked the stimuli, in order of preference, in the order *GFEDHICBJAKL*. That this is a proper unfolding can be seen by examining Fig. 4.3, in which the unfolding is performed.

If the utility of the chips were to be measured using the classical Thurstone model, one might suppose that each stimulus would have a certain degree of desirability as a representative gray. The amount of confusion or inconsistency of judgment should depend upon how far apart the two stimuli are on the variable in question—in other words, one would use the top-to-bottom ranking of Fig. 4.3. To be consistent with the theory and its usual application, one cannot also use the left-to-right ordering of brightness when considering preference, though that ordering (and not the other) would be used if the subject were asked to judge which stimulus was brighter.

The probability of choosing G over any other stimulus should increase down the list. Similarly, starting with F (the second most preferred stimulus) and going down the list, the probabilities of preference should again increase in a monotone fashion, and similarly when comparing E with the remainder, etc. This is "strong stochastic transitivity": If a, b, and c are ordered in preference, $P(a, c)$ is greater than either $P(a, b)$ or $P(b, c)$. However, strong transitivity does not hold for the data. In Table 4.1 the proportions of preferential choice of one subject are shown, with the reversals of order in heavy type. For this subject, there are numerous reversals.

In Table 4.1, the underlined values are the probabilities when a stimulus on one side of the ideal in terms of brightness is compared with a stimulus on the other side; for example, when B is

TABLE 4.1

FREQUENCY WITH WHICH STIMULUS AT LEFT IS PREFERRED OVER
STIMULUS AT TOP

	G	F	E	D	H	I	C	B	J	A	K	L
G		52	67	72	**64**	76	91	**89**	99	100	100	100
F			83	83	**74**	80	98	99	100	100	100	100
E				50	67	64	92	97	97	100	100	100
D					61	63	90	100	91	100	100	100
H						68	**50**	72	100	99	100	100
I							54	66	97	99	100	100
C								92	94	100	100	100
B									83	100	94	100
J										83	99	100
A											62	97
K												100

compared with H, since B is brighter and H is darker than the ideal stimulus G. In the first row, none of the stimuli are underlined since they are being compared with G. Notice that every reversal in the rest of the table occurs when one of these cross-comparisons is made—every value in heavy type is also underlined. Of the 30 cross-comparisons, 6 are intransitivities, whereas of the 25 comparisons between stimuli on the same side of the ideal, none are intransitivities.

According to the present theory, the probability of choice depends upon the difference in utility between the two stimuli, divided by the qualitative difference between them in valued aspects, which here consist of brightness aspects. More exactly, for any two stimuli S_1 and S_2

$$P(1, 2) = \frac{m(S_1 \cap \bar{S}_2 \cap C)}{m(S_1 \cap \bar{S}_2 \cap C) + m(\bar{S}_1 \cap S_2 \cap C)}$$

$$1 - P(1, 2) = \frac{m(\bar{S}_1 \cap S_2 \cap C)}{m(S_1 \cap \bar{S}_2 \cap C) + m(\bar{S}_1 \cap S_2 \cap C)}$$

whence the difference between these two probabilities is

$$2P(1, 2) - 1 = \frac{m(S_1 \cap \bar{S}_2 \cap C) - m(\bar{S}_1 \cap S_2 \cap C)}{m(S_1 \cap \bar{S}_2 \cap C) + m(\bar{S}_1 \cap S_2 \cap C)} \quad (4.14)$$

The numerator of this fraction is the difference in preference level, i.e., the separation of the two stimuli on the up-down preference scale. The denominator of the fraction is the measure of the distance between the two stimuli in relevant aspects. If the subject ranks the objects in preference, then as one goes across a row of Table 4.1 the numerator of this fraction increases monotonically. However, whenever the subject is comparing two stimuli on the same side of the ideal stimulus, the distance between the two stimuli is small for they are very similar. When the comparison is across from one side of the ideal stimulus to the other, the distance between the stimuli is large because one is quite bright and the other quite dark.

Thus, though the numerator of the fraction increases monotonically, the denominator jumps from small values (when both stimuli are on the same side) to large values (when the two stimuli are on different sides of the ideal). When the numerator jumps up the whole fraction may be thereby reduced, and sometimes the effect will be sufficient to overcome the increase in the numerator. Thus one should expect the choice probabilities to run somewhat lower for cross-comparisons, and higher for comparisons of stimuli on the same side, and one also should expect reversals to occur most often at a switch from same-side to crossover comparisons. Inspection of Table 4.1 shows that five of the six reversals do, indeed, occur at switches from same-side to crossover comparisons. Thus, the failures of "strong stochastic transitivity" are rather well explained by the present formulation.

Coombs' analysis is more directly relevant to the idea of strong stochastic transitivity. Consider any triple of stimuli taken in the order of their preference; from Coombs' subject number 1, who had the preference ordering *GFEDHICBJAKL*, such triples include *FED, HBK, HIB*, etc. When all three stimuli in the triple are on the same side (in brightness) of the ideal, such as *EDC* or *HIJ*, this is called a "unilateral triple." There are also "bilateral" triples in which one element is from one side and the other two from the other side. There are two kinds of such triples: "split," where the odd stimulus is between the other two, as in *DHC*, or "adjacent," where the odd stimulus is first or last, as in the examples *FEH* and *BJK*.

In the case of unilateral triples, strong stochastic transitivity should hold. Consider Eq. 4.14. Suppose that S_1 is nearer the ideal, and S_2 is farther away in the same direction. If S_2 is moved still farther away, this will increase $m(S_1 \cap \bar{S}_2 \cap C)$ and decrease $m(\bar{S}_1 \cap S_2 \cap C)$. Both of these changes will increase the numerator of Eq. 4.14, and the first will increase and the second decrease the denominator. Consequently, the value of $2P - 1$ will show a net increase. If there are three stimuli 1, 2, and 3 in that order of preference, $P(1, 3)$ will therefore be larger than either $P(1, 2)$ or $P(2, 3)$. Of course, unreliability of the estimated probabilities will produce a fair number of slight intransitivities.

In the case of a bilateral split triple like *JAK*, transitivity is almost sure to hold. Because *J* is very unlike *A*, $P(J, A)$ will be near 1/2, having a large denominator in Eq. 4.14. Similarly, since *A* and *K* are very unlike, $P(A, K)$ will be near 1/2. However, *J* and *K* are very alike, and $P(J, K)$ should be relatively near 1. Hence, strong stochastic transitivity should hold almost all the time, since $P(1, 2)$ and $P(2, 3)$ are near 1/2, but $P(1, 3)$ is almost 1.

Bilateral adjacent triples are most interesting. In the case of a triple like *AKL*, the probability of choosing *K* over *L* should be nearly 1, since they are very similar, but the probability of choosing *A* over *L*, which by strong stochastic transitivity would be greater, should actually be near 1/2, since the two stimuli are very dissimilar. Hence, bilateral adjacent triples should produce a high proportion of intransitivities.

To summarize: Transitivity should almost always work for bilateral split triples; should usually work for unilateral triples; and should be most undependable for bilateral adjacent triples. This is exactly what happened in Coombs' experiment. Table 4.2, taken directly from Coombs' article, tells the story. What is called strong stochastic transitivity in the present book, Coombs calls "monotonicity." The numbers in Table 4.2 are not all independent, since

TABLE 4.2

NUMBER OF EACH KIND OF TRIPLE AND NUMBER VIOLATING MONOTONICITY

Subject No.	Bilaterals, Split		Unilaterals		Bilaterals, Adjacent	
	Total No.	No. Violating Monotonicity	Total No.	No. Violating Monotonicity	Total No.	No. Violating Monotonicity
1	34	0	20	1	66	18
2	24	0	56	2	40	24
3	38	0	20	2	62	29
4	38	0	20	10	62	48
Combined	134	0	116	15	230	119

the same pairs of stimuli may enter into more than one triple and thus may satisfy or violate strong transitivity (monotonicity) in more than one case. However, the results are completely convincing. When transitivity was "overdetermined" by putting the odd stimulus in the middle of the triple, not one single case of intransitivity occurred in the whole experiment. When the conditions for a possible violation of transitivity were met by putting the odd stimulus at the end of the triple, violations of monotonicity were slightly more frequent than satisfactions.

Coombs certainly understood the principle involved, for he did the experiment that clearly demonstrates the importance of similarity in the consistency of judgments. However, it is interesting that Coombs interprets his results in general accord with the Thurstone model of discriminal processes. His analysis of the data shows how the Thurstone theory, with distributions of momentary perceptions or "discriminal processes," may be applied.

Consider the case of a unidimensional latent attribute generating preferential choices. The stimuli are conceived as having a distribution of discriminal processes* on this attribute; and the individual whose preferences are being obtained is also conceived as having a distribution of *ideals* [see Fig. 4.4], an ideal being a point from which the individual evaluates the stimuli and states as his preference the stimulus which is nearer his ideal. Thus, for any judgment of preference, we consider that the individual has an ideal point,

"* Discriminal processes is Thurstone's term for what might synonymously be called *perceived magnitudes*."

each stimulus is represented by a point drawn from its distribution and the judgment reflects which stimulus point is nearer the ideal point. **

Let the term *unilateral pair* signify a pair of stimuli whose discriminal distributions are both on the same side of the scale relative to the distribution of ideals, and let the term *bilateral pair* signify a pair of stimuli whose discriminal distributions are on opposite sides of the distribution of ideals. There may be stimuli whose discriminal distributions overlap the distribution of ideals but these will be neglected in the following treatment.

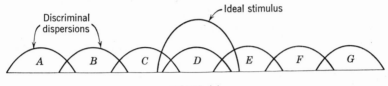

FIGURE 4.4

The inconsistencies of an individual's preferences between unilateral pairs as compared with bilateral pairs will be of a different order of magnitude according to this model. In the case of unilateral pairs, only the overlap of the discriminal distributions of the stimuli will generate inconsistency, whereas the inconsistency of judgments between bilateral pairs will be generated by the variance of the individual's distribution of ideals as well as by the discriminal dispersions.

This may be visualized more clearly if the individual is seen as folding this scale at his ideal point, and, as this folding point varies between successive judgments, the discriminal distributions of unilateral pairs will move nearer to or farther from him in unison, whereas those for bilateral pairs will move in opposite directions. (Coombs, 1958, p. 2.)

This theory handles the data nicely, and was the theory which led Coombs to the experiment. There are several fruitful comparisons between Coombs' theory and the one given here. First we note that Coombs' model, like all Thurstone-type models, represents stimuli as points on a line. Of course, such theories can be generalized to 2-, 3-, or even n-dimensional spaces, but the conceptual and computing difficulties increase rapidly. The theory simply is not defined for a set of stimuli which are not in an ordered or other very regular arrangement. The present theory deals originally with "general" stimuli, and defines specific orderings only as needed and justified by the experimental situation. In Coombs' experiment it is reasonable to believe that the 12 patches of gray formed nearly a linear array, but the point is that such an arrangement is not necessary

"** The concept of an *ideal* introduced here is not to be confused with the terms anchoring, frames of reference, or adaptation level as used in categorical rating studies. The ideal represents a hypothetical stimulus which S would prefer to all other stimuli and which are themselves preferred in order of their decreasing distance from the ideal."

for a set-theoretic analysis, though it is necessary for the normal-curve approach.

Second, Coombs' model introduces distributions of discriminal processes. The shape and parameters of such distributions are indeed difficult to determine, a problem which has led most writers to fortify the theory with normal distributions and equal variances.

The concept of an "ideal stimulus," which Coombs has introduced into scaling theory, is a powerful one. However, when he speaks of the "perceived magnitude" of a stimulus, in the first footnote, this concept of magnitude is not related to ideal stimuli. In Fig. 4.3, the ordering from top to bottom (preference) is defined relative to an ideal stimulus, but the ordering from left to right (from bright to dark) is defined without reference to an ideal. In the present theory, Coombs' idea of an ideal stimulus is used more systematically. Any choice, or any ordering of stimuli, must be based on the use of ideal situations. Thus, the present theory is somewhat more consistent and homogeneous.

However, the notion introduced in this chapter, that the probability of a choice of stimulus 1 over stimulus 2 depends on the difference in utility divided by their dissimilarity, finds a similar statement in Thurstone-type theory. The difference in utility in the discriminal-process theory is represented as the difference between the means of two distributions of discriminal processes, relative to their standard deviations. One then represents similarity and dissimilarity in terms of the correlation between the two distributions. If two stimuli are highly similar, one supposes that their distributions have a high positive correlation; if they are very dissimilar, they have a zero or perhaps even a negative correlation. With this approach, even small differences can be noticed consistently if the stimuli are similar, for the high positive correlation will reduce the variance of the difference. If the stimuli are very different perceptually, the correlation is small and the variance of the difference becomes larger again.

This is essentially the mechanism invoked by Coombs in the last paragraph of the quotation, for he points out that in unilateral pairs the variation of the "ideal" stimulus will have the same effect on both stimuli, hence will produce a positive correlation between their distributions; when the stimuli are on opposite sides of the ideal, variations of the ideal have opposite effects on the two stimuli, producing a negative correlation.

CASE 3. NESTED SETS OF VALUED ASPECTS. Suppose that the overlap of valued aspects between pairs of objects is so large that for any pair of objects a and b either $A \subset B$ or $B \subset A$. This is the sort of situation which arises when amounts of money are used for alternatives. There is nothing good about \$2 which is not also good about \$4. The term "money" encompasses any indicators or tokens of wealth which are without intrinsic (hence perhaps idiosyncratic) value. For purposes of discussion, consider small amounts of money which represent neither life and death nor great power. Suppose that money is finely divisible, and that different amounts of money can be discriminated perfectly by the subject. The possibility of too much money, which enters few lives and no experiments, will be disregarded for the present.

Under these conditions an algebraic (i.e., deterministic, non-probabilistic) theory of utility arises. Suppose that a and b are two amounts of money, a the larger. Then $B \subset A$, and the sets of elements leading to a choice are $A \cap \bar{B}$, which is not empty, and $\bar{A} \cap B$ which is empty. Hence, $p(a, b) = 1$. If a and a' are two equal amounts of money, the probability of choice is entirely indeterminate, being $0/(0 + 0)$. This may be set, by convention, at $1/2$, producing a strict relation of preference, saying that a is preferred to b if and only if $P(a, b) = 1$, and a is equivalent to b if and only if $P(a, b) = 1/2$. This is a strict ordering of utilities of money, but the probability-scaling technique of measuring differences in utility is not available; for if a is more money than b by any amount whatever, $P(a, b) = 1$ and the probability is no index of how much a is greater than b. We now need some method of measuring the amount of difference.

Two models of measurement can be used to obtain what is called cardinal utility of money. One is based on the assumption that the utility of the sum of two amounts of money, $a + b$, is $U(a) + U(b)$. In the case of money the assumption of additivity of utilities ensures that the utility of money will be linearly related to the monetary value.

Within the present theory, the situation in which one receives the amounts $a + b$ of money has, as its valued aspects, just those aspects held by either the situation where a is presented or the situation where b is presented. Let V_{a+b} be the set of valued aspects when $a + b$ is presented. Then the assumption of additivity is equivalent to

$$m(V_{a+b}) = m(V_a) + m(V_b)$$

This in no sense follows from the set-theoretic argument. Suppose, for example, that

$$V_{a+b} = V_a \cup V_b$$

i.e., that the presentation of $a + b$ gives all the valued aspects in either the presentation of a or the presentation of b. The additivity hypothesis would then follow if and only if

$$V_a \cap V_b = \emptyset$$

This is of course impossible, for if a is a greater sum of money than b, we have already asserted that $V_b \subset V_a$, whence

$$V_a \cap V_b = V_b \quad \text{and} \quad V_a \cup V_b = V_a$$

The additivity hypothesis actually means that once one has given the subject a, the value of b added to it is composed of elements disjoint from a. In this way (letting the value of b after a is given be written $V_{b|a}$) we may write

$$V_{a+b} = V_a \cup V_{b|a}$$

where

$$V_a \cap V_{b|a} = \emptyset$$

This last assertion makes sense because any benefits from the additional b units of money will presumably be separate from the benefits from the original a, unless the subject inadvertently pays for the same thing twice—a possibility which is unlikely to enter into his judgments.

However, the additivity hypothesis requires that $m(V_{b|a}) = m(V_b)$; i.e., the b dollars are just as valuable after receiving a as without the a dollars. This hypothesis does, as one would suppose, imply the linear relationship between utility and money, but it is the sort of statement one would rather verify than postulate.

In their experimental analysis of the additivity hypothesis, Adams and Fagot (1956) took a more plausible example. They imagined that objects might have either of two classes of properties. In their experiment they imagined prospective employees at various levels of intelligence and of "ability to handle people." Intelligence and ability to handle people are two stimulus variables, in our terms, and any one prospective employee is represented by two sets of aspects, one corresponding to his intelligence and the other to his ability to handle people. The utility of such an employee should be an increasing function of each stimulus variable taken separately, and the experimenters then asked if the results were in accord with an additive hypothesis. In this case, however, the objects were not money-like counters and as a result the data cannot be expected to be categorical—the choices should be probable and not certain.

Another approach to the measurement of utility of money arises from the original von Neumann and Morgenstern (1947) proposal. Let the subject choose between gambles and determine the utility of money by the gambles selected. The question, Is $2 twice as far from 0 as $1? is approached by offering a choice of two gambles—a 50:50 bet on $2 versus 0, or a sure thing for $1. If the subject chooses the 50:50 bet this suggests that $2 is more than twice 1, and if he chooses the sure thing, $1 is more than half 2. If the subject is indifferent, utility is linear in money at this point.

A difficulty encountered in this theory, and evident from the first test (Mosteller and Nogee, 1951) in the laboratory, is that subjects do not make certain choices between gambles though they may be perfectly accurate in their choices between "pure alternatives," i.e., between amounts of money offered with no gamble. To interpret these results and recover a useful theory requires a theoretical model of how a subject chooses between gambles.

A Theoretical Representation of Gambles

In a choice between two gambles, the stimulus situation arising is quite complicated from the point of view of the subject. Unfortunately, relatively little is known about the process of judging probabilities. Clearly, the "probabilities" of the gamble can be presented by the experimenter in several ways, and the method of presenting them will affect the behavior to be expected.

Perhaps the most natural interpretation, from a psychological point of view, is to let the subject become acquainted with the probabilities through experience. The experimenter could say "If this coin comes up heads you get a, and if it comes up tails you get b," and then toss the coin enough times for the subject to learn to guess the two possibilities from experience. The coin-tossing example is actually a mixture of two main types of presentation of probabilities: the subject has some a priori expectations about coins in the experimental context, and these are modified by his observations of the sequence of tosses. A priori probabilities can be studied by such devices as a spinning arrow, where the panel on which the arrow is set is marked off into wedges of various sizes. If the arrow is perfectly mounted, the probability of its stopping in any sector is just proportional to the width of that sector. The subject's judgment of the probability of any one sector is probably close to his judgment of angle—a question which presents some difficulties in its own right (see Chapter 9). If dice are used and the subject believes them to be evenly balanced, he may "compute" probabilities using whatever is his version of classical probability theory, through a combinatorial analysis. Anyone who has taught statistics knows that the naïve subject may arrive at any of a variety of conclusions in this way. The simplest form of presenting a priori probabilities is to give them directly to the subject in numerical values, as probabilities or as "odds."

The discussion to follow assumes that the probabilities in question are provided by some such a priori presentation, and are not "learned" by repeated observations of a random event. The extreme case of "learned" probabilities is where alternative events are shown the subject with no knowledge on his part as to how they are generated. For example, one shows two lights in irregular order with a certain average relative frequency, but the subject does not know whether these lights are generated by a random process or are controlled by a predictable program. Prediction of such events, as affected by past experience, is discussed in Chapter 6.

Imagine, then, that the subject is presented with a gamble of the form, "you get a if event E occurs and b if event $\bar{E}$ occurs," written aEb, where a and b are two alternatives which, alone, give rise to the sets A and B of valued aspects, the event E is some outcome of a gambling device, such as a coin coming up heads, a die showing an ace or deuce, etc., and $\bar{E}$ is the complement of E, the coin coming up tails, the die showing 3, 4, 5, or 6. Let the set of valued aspects of the gamble be G.

For a first analysis, suppose that the set of elements present with this gamble is composed of some elements of A and some of B. A little consideration shows that the elements in $A \cap B$ should all be present, along with some elements of $A \cap \bar{B}$ and some of $\bar{A} \cap B$. The subject, responding to the gamble, notes what values he is sure to receive and then, we may suppose, also adds in some of the aspects he *may* receive.

In the above gamble, suppose that $A \cap B$ is empty. The set of elements G corresponding to the gamble is therefore made up solely of elements in $A \cap \bar{B}$ and $\bar{A} \cap B$, or simply A and B. A "subjective probability" for E and $\bar{E}$ can be defined as follows. The measure of elements from A which appear in G corresponds to the subjective probability of E, and the measure of elements from B which appear in G corresponds to the subjective probability of $\bar{E}$. To put these in appropriate form, let the subjective probability of E be called e, defined as

$$e = \frac{m(G \cap A)}{m(A)}$$

Similarly, the subjective probability of $\bar{E}$ is $\bar{e}$, given by

$$\bar{e} = \frac{m(G \cap B)}{m(B)}$$

Note that these numbers need not add up to 1; although both are positive, they may add up to more or less than 1. This is an often-considered possibility for subjective probabilities. Whether the numbers e and $\bar{e}$ correspond to subjective probabilities in any useful sense depends upon whether they are independent of the particular objects a and b. A complete utility-measuring experiment uses more than two objects, and reuses the same chance event E. If one found that e and $\bar{e}$ take constant values no matter which objects are used in gambles, then e and $\bar{e}$ could be used as subjective probabilities in later calculations. If, as might happen, the values of e and $\bar{e}$ vary with different pairs of objects, there is no usable subjective probability for the chance events. In that case, the utility-theory approach, insofar as it involves subjectively expected utilities, would be difficult to apply.*

If e and $\bar{e}$ are independent of the objects presented in the gamble, then the above formulation can be shown to follow the "expected utility" formula. That is, by simple algebra, if G contains only elements in A and B,

$$m(G) = em(A) + \bar{e}m(B)$$

Letting the measures of valued aspects be called utilities (U) and the subjective probabilities be called probabilities (P'),

$$U(aEb) = P'(E)U(a) + P'(\bar{E})U(b)$$

which makes the utility of the gamble aEb equal to the expected utility of a and b—with the rather peculiar side effect that the "probability distribution" may not be a true probability at all, for it may not add up to 1. A possibility exists, of course, that the gamble may have its own unique valued aspects not present in either a or b. These would constitute the "specific utility of gambling," as it is called, and make life very difficult for a dedicated student of utility measurement. Clearly, if such elements exist at all they can be different for every gamble. In the event that A and B have common elements, and the above gamble is presented,

$$m(G) = m(A \cap B) + em(A \cap \bar{B}) + \bar{e}m(\bar{A} \cap B)$$

* The writer is indebted to R. Duncan Luce for pointing out the importance of the condition that e and $\bar{e}$ be independent of the alternatives involved in the gamble.

according to the hypothesis stated above. In the case of money gambles, where a is a larger amount than b, $\bar{A} \cap B$ is empty and the equation simplifies to

$$m(G) = m(B) + em(A \cap \bar{B})$$
$$= m(B) + e[m(A) - m(B)]$$

This shows why choices between gambles may be only probable, although choices between pure alternatives are certain. The gamble, when a is more money than b, consists of B plus some fraction of the aspects in $A \cap \bar{B}$, but it is not known which aspects of $A \cap \bar{B}$ are going to be present, for the subject does not perceive the gamble as being identical to the fixed amount of money, its expected value.

The picture may most simply be presented by using three arbitrary sets a, b, and c, consisting of amounts of money such that $a > b > c$. Hence we should have $C \subset B \subset A$. Consider three sets of numbers satisfying this relationship,

$$A = \{1, 2, 3, 4, 5, 6, 7, 8\}$$
$$B = \{1, 2, 3, 4, 5, 6\}$$
$$C = \{1, 2\}$$

and imagine the subject trying to choose between a gamble involving a and c versus certain presentation of b.

Let gamble g_1 be, "you get a if E occurs and c if $\bar{E}$ occurs," and the alternative g_2 be, "you get b for certain." The subject chooses between these gambles, where e (the subjective probability of event E) is set at $1/2$.

According to the hypotheses,

$$m(G_1) = m(C) + e[m(A) - m(C)]$$
$$= 2 + (1/2)(6) = 5$$

whereas

$$m(G_2) = m(B) = 6$$

The subject should prefer the sure thing, b. However, a sure choice is not going to occur. The set G_1 is not known; it contains the aspects in $A \cap C$, i.e., it contains the elements 1, 2, and it contains half of the remaining elements of A, three of the elements in set $\{3, 4, 5, 6, 7, 8\}$. There are 20 such subsets, and they lead to quite different probabilities of choice. Recall that

$$P(G_1, G_2) = \frac{m(G_1 \cap \bar{G}_2)}{m(G_1 \cap \bar{G}_2) + m(\bar{G}_1 \cap G_2)}$$

In every case, of course, $G_2 = B = \{1, 2, 3, 4, 5, 6\}$. Table 4.3 shows the possibilities and probabilities of choosing G_1 for each of the 20 subsets which might be chosen.

TABLE 4.3

POSSIBLE SETS G_1 AND PROBABILITIES OF CHOOSING G_1 OVER
G_2 IN EACH POSSIBLE CASE

G_1	$G_1 \cap \bar{G}_2$	$\bar{G}_1 \cap G_2$	$P(G_1, G_2)$
$\{1, 2, 3, 4, 5\}$	$\emptyset$	$\{6\}$	0
$\{1, 2, 3, 4, 6\}$	$\emptyset$	$\{5\}$	0
$\{1, 2, 3, 4, 7\}$	$\{7\}$	$\{5, 6\}$	1/3
$\{1, 2, 3, 4, 8\}$	$\{8\}$	$\{5, 6\}$	1/3
$\{1, 2, 3, 5, 6\}$	$\emptyset$	$\{4\}$	0
$\{1, 2, 3, 5, 7\}$	$\{7\}$	$\{4, 6\}$	1/3
$\{1, 2, 3, 5, 8\}$	$\{8\}$	$\{4, 6\}$	1/3
$\{1, 2, 3, 6, 7\}$	$\{7\}$	$\{4, 5\}$	1/3
$\{1, 2, 3, 6, 8\}$	$\{8\}$	$\{4, 5\}$	1/3
$\{1, 2, 3, 7, 8\}$	$\{7, 8\}$	$\{4, 5, 6\}$	2/5
$\{1, 2, 4, 5, 6\}$	$\emptyset$	$\{3\}$	0
$\{1, 2, 4, 5, 7\}$	$\{7\}$	$\{3, 6\}$	1/3
$\{1, 2, 4, 5, 8\}$	$\{8\}$	$\{3, 6\}$	1/3
$\{1, 2, 4, 6, 7\}$	$\{7\}$	$\{3, 5\}$	1/3
$\{1, 2, 4, 6, 8\}$	$\{8\}$	$\{3, 5\}$	1/3
$\{1, 2, 4, 7, 8\}$	$\{7,8\}$	$\{3, 5, 6\}$	2/5
$\{1, 2, 5, 6, 7\}$	$\{7\}$	$\{3, 4\}$	1/3
$\{1, 2, 5, 6, 8\}$	$\{8\}$	$\{3, 4\}$	1/3
$\{1, 2, 5, 7, 8\}$	$\{7, 8\}$	$\{3, 4, 6\}$	2/5
$\{1, 2, 6, 7, 8\}$	$\{7, 8\}$	$\{3, 4, 5\}$	2/5
Mean			.28

Although G_2 has definitely a higher mean utility than G_1, G_2 having a utility of 6 and G_1 a utility of 5, if the elements are sampled at random from $A \cap \bar{C}$ the probability of preferring G_1 is equal to .28. The gambles are not perfectly discriminated, although the pure alternatives are, of course, $P(a, b) = P(b, c) = P(a, c) = 1$.

Note that the value of .28 is fairly close to the value which could be predicted by noting that the mean value of $m(G_1 \cap \bar{G}_2)$ is 1 and the mean of $m(\bar{G}_1 \cap G_2)$ is 2, whence one might suppose that the mean $P(G_1, G_2)$ would equal $1/(1 + 2) = .33$. The discrepancy is of a type commonly found when one attempts to average ratios: The mean of x/y is not equal to the mean of x divided by the mean of y. However, for very large numbers of elements (as one might imagine exist in experiments of this general type) a good approximation is obtained by assuming that

$$P(G_1, G_2) \simeq \frac{\text{mean } m(G_1 \cap \bar{G}_2)}{\text{mean } m(G_1 \cap \bar{G}_2) + \text{mean } m(\bar{G}_1 \cap G_2)}$$

"Emergent" Aspects of a Gamble

The utility-theory approach to human choices seems much more powerful than it is. Imagine that a person has been given a great many gambles involving various amounts of money and various probabilities of winning, and has made all the required choices. According to the classical utility approach, the utilities of the amounts of money are not known, and the subjective probabilities of the events must be estimated from the data. This means that the data must be reduced by finding a great many parameters. These parameters combine in complicated ways, so that it is enormously difficult even to determine whether a utility function exists, and if it does exist one has great difficulty deciding what it will be. There are many configurations of choices which would make a utility function impossible, but there are also many different configurations all of which yield utility functions, but different ones. The question, What is the utility of money for this person? requires a large experiment and a great many computations.

In application, game theory and decision theory are likely to fall back on money itself in place of utility, hedging that the conclusions do not necessarily apply but are the best practical approximation. Even if the utility-theory approach is valid it is so inconvenient as to be of little use in real-world economics, and precise measurements of human preferences are not worth obtaining by such elaborate methods even for the psychological laboratory and clinic, where close study of an individual subject would more nearly be justified.

Coombs has recently reanalyzed the presentation of gambles in a fashion which throws doubt upon the whole concept of utility measurement and the analysis given above. Utility theory says, in effect, that the choice of a gamble depends on the subjectively *expected* utility. Now suppose that a person chooses

G_1: $1 with probability .9 versus $20 with probability .1 over another gamble

G_2: —$10 with probability .05 versus $4 with probability .95

Notice that the objectively expected value in money of the first gamble is $.9(1) + .1(20) = 2.9$, whereas the expected value of the second gamble is $.05(-10) + .95(4) = 3.1$. Therefore, the expected winning in the second bet is slightly higher. If the first bet is chosen, according to standard utility theory, the inference is either that the subjective probabilities are not like the objective ones, or the *utilities* of the four money outcomes, -10, 1, 4, and 20, are spaced in some way different from the money values.

However, say Coombs and Pruitt (1960), another possibility is simply that people prefer bets of large or small variance, and perhaps positive or negative skewness. In general, a bet of large variance is what one would think of as a "big" bet, and small variance means a small bet. Bets of a penny, $1, or $100 on the toss of a fair coin have a constant expected value of 0 but very different variances. Skewness can be thought of in this way: negative skewness is taking a small probability of a large loss along with a high probability of a small gain; positive skewness is taking a high probability of a small loss against a small probability of a large gain. The bets differ in the direction of the odds. Coombs and Pruitt (1960) have been able to show that the results of gambling experiments are closely consistent with the idea that gambles are evaluated on such properties.

Although Coombs and Pruitt use the Thurstone-type theory with Coombs' unfolding technique, their style of thinking is exactly what should be used in the present theory. First, notice that the total set of aspects arising from a gamble is different from the aspects arising from the pure outcomes—at least in the trivial sense that the subject knows whether he is offered a gamble or a pure outcome. The only remaining question is whether there are any *valued* aspects characteristic of the gamble which are not characteristic of the outcomes themselves. It seems that the nature of the gamble and forseeable consequences of taking a gamble should affect the choice. Uncertainty itself may attract or repel the subject, and he may consider the consequences of taking a ruinous risk to be particularly serious. This possibility does not enter in choices between pure outcomes unless strong coercion and very unfair offers are used.

To use Coombs' idea in a very general way, imagine that the person conceives of an "ideal bet" or, more likely, a rather varied set of acceptable bets. Among "fair" bets which have an objective expected value of 0, the ideal bet may be one with moderate variance (neither a very small nor a very large bet) and a certain skewness, say a positive skewness. A subject might have an ideal fair bet; a probability of 5/6 of a loss of $1 against a 1/6 probability of receiving $5. In general, two fair gambles will be compared on the basis of their similarity to this ideal gamble. One can determine the strength of "variance" or "size of bet" aspects as against "skewness" or "length of odds" by asking for a choice between, say,

G_1:   probability 5/6 of losing 1¢ versus 1/6 of gaining 5¢

and

G_2:   probability 1/2 of losing $2 against 1/2 of gaining $2

Here, G_1 is like the ideal bet in skewness or length of odds, but is a much smaller bet than the ideal. G_2 is of about the correct size of bet, but is a "shorter odds" bet than the ideal. Both of the above variables, size of bet and length of odds, can also be balanced against expected value; one might find that the person would prefer his ideal bet, which is only fair, against another bet which has an expected value in his favor. For example, the person might choose his preferred bet over one like

G_3:   probability .1 of losing $100 versus probability .9 of winning $12

Yet, in this case, G_3 has an expected value of $.1(-100) + .9(12) = .80$, or 80¢.

The apparent preferences for certain variances or skewnesses could arise from a nonlinear relationship between utility and money, or from distortions in subjective probability, or both. There is no overwhelming reason to believe that utility must be linear in money, and the form of subjective probability described earlier (if it exists) may be seriously distorted from reality. The advantage of the "ideal bet" approach is mainly that it is logically stronger. To apply the idea an experimenter need take only a relatively few measurements, identifying the subject's ideal gamble, finding out the importance of such aspects as variance and skewness, and gaining some idea of how the perceived similarity of two gambles depends upon particular money and probability values. From this information, quite strong predictions of performance can be computed, though it must be admitted that the theory is not yet developed to handle complex decisions. As Coombs and Pruitt have shown, relatively few combinations of choices are compatible with the concept of ideal bets, whereas those and a great many more combinations of choices are compatible with the utility-theory approach. Because of its greater strictness, the ideal bet theory should be relatively easy to disprove by laboratory tests if it is wrong. The more flexible utility theory is relatively difficult to disprove, and by the same token does not make equally sharp predictions from a small base of data.

Besides this logical advantage, it seems to the writer that the Coombs-Pruitt idea more adequately reflects the situation facing a subject in a gambling experiment, and suggests what seems a natural psychological process of choosing. Utility theory, being based on an abstract and mathematical notion of rationality, is not psychological.

CHAPTER
FIVE

Recognition and the Effects of Frequency

In Chapter 2 it was assumed that a subject chooses by matching his present situation S with two ideal situations S_1 and S_2. The tendency to make response 1 depends upon the measure of the set of aspects common to S and S_1 which are not also aspects of the other ideal situation S_2. In applying the theory to the measurement of utility it was assumed that a given choice will depend only on a certain class of aspects. In preferential choice, the relevant aspects were "valued aspects."

The present chapter extends these ideas in a different direction. Suppose that the person has a long history in which he has repeatedly observed that in situation S_1 response 1 is appropriate or correct, in situation S_2 response 2 is correct, etc. Each such experience has the formal structure of a schema, containing an ideal situation and information as to which response is correct. Each training trial leaves a schema, and the subject during training acquires a large number of schemata.

This assumption requires an idea of what access the subject has to his schemata. Chapters 2 and 4 dealt with just two or a few schemata, but when the subject has a long history, choices are based on a large number of schemata. The hypothesis to be considered in this chapter is that the subject chooses a schema at random from his available set, somewhat in the manner of a clerk reaching randomly into a file drawer. The present situation S is compared with the ideal situation of the randomly selected schema, and to the degree that the two situations are alike (have common aspects) they are likely to be matched. If situation S is matched with a schema in which response 1 is the response member, then the subject makes response 1. If the schema and the present situation do not match, the subject returns the schema to his file and then draws again at random, comparing S with this second schema, responding if they match, and resampling if they do not match. The hypothesis that schemata are chosen at random amounts to saying that the subject has random access to his memory bank (in the language of computers); this will be called the "random-access" hypothesis.

The probability of a match between the present situation S and some schema S' will be taken to depend upon the measure of $S \cap S'$. As in Chapters 2 and 4, it will be assumed that, in general, only aspects of S' which are differential have any effect in producing the response. However, in a learning experiment it is quite possible to have many trials in which essentially the same situation and response are repeated. It would be almost impossible for the subject to find differential elements unique to one such schema. This problem will not be discussed in detail in the present essay, for its solution requires a fuller analysis of learning than is intended here. Suffice it to say that during the learning process the subject separates out those differential aspects of situations which are useful in deciding among responses, and that after extended experience the differential aspects are the only ones available to the subject. Thus, after extended learning, a schema contains (in its ideal situation) only the differential aspects which will be used in choosing.

If a subject is trained until he readily makes suitable responses to each of several stimuli, and then is presented with some situation S and required to choose a response, the experiment is a study of what may be called "recognition," "generalization," or "equivalence of stimuli." There is a sizable experimental literature on such experiments, mainly involving manipulations of various stimulus dimensions. In much learning theory it is assumed that the effects of a test trial can be washed away by retraining the subject on the original problem. In the present theory it is supposed that each trial leaves its indelible trace, a schema, and that past test trials may have a large effect on responses to a present situation.

One experimental question, which can be investigated with the present theory, is the effect of the number of various schemata on the choice made. In its simplest form, the experiment in question is as follows: The subject has extensive experience with two kinds of trials, S_1-R_1 and S_2-R_2. The experimental variable is the relative frequency of the two kinds of trial, which may be equally frequent in a control group and which may have unequal frequencies in an experimental group that, for example, receives 75 trials with S_1-R_1 and only 25 trials with S_2-R_2. After training, the subject is presented with a situation S which is carefully designed to be just as much like S_1 as like S_2. The question is, How will the frequency of S_1-R_1 and S_2-R_2 affect the probability that the subject, in S, makes response 1?

The present theory gives a clear prediction. There are N_1 trials (75 in the example above) on which S_1-R_1 occurs, and thus N_1 such schemata in the memory bank. There are N_2 schemata, S_2-R_2. Suppose that the probability of matching S with S_1, assuming that an S_1-R_1 schema is sampled, is some number a. If the experimenter has constructed S according to specifications, then the probability of matching S to S_2, provided a S_2-R_2 schema is chosen, is also equal to a. It can be shown that the probability of making response 1 to situation S is equal to $N_1/(N_1 + N_2)$, and is independent of a; for the probability of choosing response 1 on the first sampling is $aN_1/(N_1 + N_2)$ and the probability of choosing response 2 on the first sampling is $aN_2/(N_1 + N_2)$. With the assumption of random sampling, in fact, these are the probabilities of choosing response 1 and response 2 on any sample, provided only that previous samples have failed to produce a match. Intuitively one can see that a particular sampling either produces a match and a response (with probability a) or fails to produce a match and requires another sample (with probability $1 - a$). If a match occurs, no matter when it occurs, the probability of response 1 is $N_1/(N_1 + N_2)$. To complete the proof that the probability of response 1 is $N_1/(N_1 + N_2)$, it is only necessary to show that a match will, in fact, be made. This, however, is not difficult to show. The probability that no match is made on any of the first n samples is $(1 - a)^n$. Provided that $a > 0$, i.e., that a match is possible, one sees that $(1 - a)^n$ goes to 0 as n increases. Thus if the subject is given sufficient time, the probability that he never makes a match approaches 0; hence the probability that he does make a match approaches 1. Thus, for example, if $N_1 = 75$ and $N_2 = 25$, the probability of response 1 to situation S is $75/(75 + 25) = .75$.

How would an experimenter make a situation S which is just as much like S_1 as S_2? Suppose that S_1 and S_2 are, for example, fairly complex line drawings which have several characteristics in common and which also have distinctive, separate markings. If situation S has exactly the marks common to S_1 and S_2, and none of the differential marks, then its aspects will correspond to the aspects common to S_1 and S_2, and $S = S_1 \cap S_2$. Then it is clear that

$$S \cap S_1 = S \cap S_2 = S_1 \cap S_2$$

This simple device produces a test situation S which is equally similar to S_1 and S_2. In such a situation, the probability of response 1 to situation S should be $N_1/(N_1 + N_2)$. This prediction is easy enough to test, for N_1 and N_2, being the frequencies of presentation of S_1-R_1 and S_2-R_2, are decided in advance by the experimenter and exactly known. One need only do the experiment to see if the proportion of subjects who make response 1 is equal to, or a reasonable sampling variation from, the theoretical prediction.

For this experiment, the same prediction is made by the Burke and Estes (1957) theory of learning by sampling of stimuli. Burke and Estes suppose that whenever an S_1-R_1 trial is presented, some proportion θ of the elements of S_1 become conditioned to R_1, and whenever an S_2-R_2 trial is present the same proportion, θ, of the elements of S_2 become conditioned to R_2. They show that the elements in $S_1 \cap S_2$, which appear on both kinds of trials, will become distributed between the two responses R_1 and R_2, and that after extensive training the proportion conditioned to R_1 will be approximately $N_1/(N_1 + N_2)$. Thus when the situation $S = S_1 \cap S_2$ is presented alone, a proportion $N_1/(N_1 + N_2)$ of the elements should be conditioned to R_1. Their rule for computing response probabilities is that the probability of a response is equal to the proportion of elements in the situation conditioned to that response. Hence, the probability of R_1 should be about $N_1/(N_1 + N_2)$.

There are those who are interested only in the crucial experiment which distinguishes between two theories. However, even though two quite different mathematical theories predict the same result in this experiment, it will be of interest to see if the results agree with these predictions. After all, it is entirely possible that two competing theories may both be wrong, and an experimental test of these predictions might disconfirm both theories and clear the way for new speculations.

In a recent monograph, Binder and Feldman (1960) report a series of experiments on the recognition of forms as a function of the frequency with which the forms have been shown to the subject in a training series.* The general technique of the experiments is straightforward. The subject first learns nonsense-syllable responses

* The author is grateful to Drs. Binder and Feldman for making available a prepublication draft of this monograph.

to each of a set of figures by the usual paired-associates or discrimination-learning technique. On each training trial one figure is shown, the subject guesses the correct response, and then the correct response is shown. After extensive training so that the problem is well learned, the subject is shown some ambiguous figure and is asked to choose the nonsense syllable which seems the best response to it.

A typical part of the experiment has two stimuli, like those shown in Fig. 5.1, as training stimuli. Notice that the two stimuli are alike except for particular distinctive parts, in this case a triangle or circle. The test stimulus is like the two training stimuli except that it has neither of the distinctive parts.

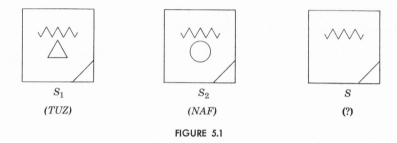

S_1 S_2 S

(*TUZ*)   (*NAF*)   (?)

FIGURE 5.1

The point of the experiment is that the stimulus with the triangle appears and is followed by *TUZ* more frequently than the stimulus with the circle appears with *NAF*. Suppose that the *TUZ* stimulus appears four times as frequently as the *NAF* stimulus, in a sequence of trials long enough to permit the subject to learn the responses accurately. This should result in the choice of response *TUZ* to the test stimulus four times as often as *NAF*.

In their first experiment, Binder and Feldman tested several cases of this hypothesis: two stimuli with relative frequencies of 80:20, two stimuli with relative frequencies of 67:33, and four stimuli with relative frequencies of about 50:17:17:17. The prediction was that the choices would distribute themselves in the same proportions as the frequencies of presentation during training, and this is essentially what was found. In the first experiment, the results were as shown in Table 5.1.

Note that the predicted and observed frequencies are extremely close together for all cases but one. The one deviation is in the 67:33 group, and is explained tentatively by a factor irrelevant to the present issue. Subjects in the experiment actually were learning a number of different discriminations all at once, and the evidence

TABLE 5.1

OBSERVED AND PREDICTED FREQUENCIES OF CHOICES OF RESPONSE TO
AMBIGUOUS STIMULI AS A FUNCTION OF FREQUENCY OF
EXPERIENCE: FIRST EXPERIMENT

Relative Frequencies in Training Series	Choice Frequencies	
	Observed	Predicted
50:50	15–15	15–15
50:50	15–13	14–14
25:25:25:25	8–7–7–11	$8\frac{1}{4}$–$8\frac{1}{4}$–$8\frac{1}{4}$–$8\frac{1}{4}$
67:33	20–3	15.3–7.7
80:20	20–6	20.8–5.2
50:17:17:17	13–15*	14.0–14.0*

* This number is the sum of frequencies of the three infrequent choices, which were not consistently distinguishable in the experiment.

indicates that the stimulus presented 33% of the time on this problem was confused with another stimulus which belongs to another comparison. Further study supported this interpretation. In a second experiment Binder and Feldman did not have the same subjects learn all comparisons, but separated the two which had caused confusion, giving one comparison to one group of subjects and the other comparison to other subjects. The results of this experiment are shown in Table 5.2. Here the 67:33 group is no longer out of line, and

TABLE 5.2

OBSERVED AND PREDICTED FREQUENCIES, WITH
PROBLEMS SEPARATED: SECOND EXPERIMENT

Relative Frequencies in Training Series	Choice Frequencies	
	Observed	Predicted
67:33	36–16	34.7–17.3
80:20	42–11	42.4–10.6
50:17:17:17	37–17*	27–27*

* Sum of frequencies of the three infrequent choices.

gives response frequencies very close to those theoretically expected. In this case, however, subjects on the 50:17:17:17 problem (which in this case was given alone to a separate group of subjects) tended to use the most frequent response too often. Binder and Feldman noted that during training the most frequent response was learned almost immediately, and the other three only very slowly. Apparently the subjects spent a great deal of time learning the specific differential characteristics of the three low-frequency stimuli, and when given an ambiguous stimulus would not see it as any of these low-frequency ones.

Binder and Feldman felt that if this interpretation was correct they would get better results if they made the frequencies of presentation of the four stimuli somewhat more alike, though distinctly different, so as to even up the rates of learning. Accordingly, they performed one more experiment using frequencies of presentation of 37:25:25:13, which did serve to equalize the learning rates and which had the outcome shown in Table 5.3.

TABLE 5.3

OBSERVED AND PREDICTED FREQUENCIES: THIRD EXPERIMENT

Relative Frequencies in Training	Choice Frequencies	
	Observed	Predicted
37:25:25:13	25–31*–9	24.4–32.5*–8.1

* Pooled frequency of two stimuli with frequency 25.

Although it may appear unwise to accept a major theoretical point on the basis of one experiment, the care and thoroughness of the Binder-Feldman study is unusual and the result seems unequivocal. The probability of choosing an ambiguous stimulus depends on the frequency of previous experience with the alternatives, and Binder and Feldman's version of the probability-matching hypothesis is well supported, for all the notable exceptions are explained away by further experimental demonstrations.

Fortunately, Binder and Feldman pursued this matter further and devised an experiment which seems crucial in distinguishing between the present schema theory and stimulus-sampling theory. The two training stimuli were half-moon faces of a familiar type which, when put together, form an ambiguous figure. The ambiguous figure itself was used as a test (see Fig. 5.2). Two different examples were used for each subject, the part stimuli being designated A_1 and A_2, the ambiguous figure A for one set, the other set being B_1, B_2, and B. A representative subject might have A_1 with frequency proportional to 4, A_2 with frequency 1, B_1 with frequency 2, and B_2 with

S_1 S_2 S

FIGURE 5.2

frequency 1. The frequencies of presentation of the part figures were counterbalanced, as was the order of tests, etc. In this experiment, as in the others, the frequency of occurrence of the training stimuli seems to control choices in the test.

The results reported in Table 5.4 are for the first test given

TABLE 5.4

OBSERVED AND PREDICTED FREQUENCIES: FOURTH EXPERIMENT
WITH FACES (FIRST TEST)

Relative Frequency in Training Series	Choice Frequencies	
	Observed	Predicted
4:1	22–7	23.2–5.8
2:1	17–8	16.7–8.3

each subject. Each subject was trained on all four training stimuli, $A_1, A_2, B_1,$ and B_2 with relative frequencies 4:1:2:1, and then received two tests, one on $A_1 + A_2$ and the other on $B_1 + B_2$. The first test for each subject gave the results shown in Table 5.4, but the second test on each subject gave quite different results in which the relative frequencies of training had little effect on choice frequencies. The writer does not know why this happened, and Binder and Feldman (1960, p. 25) are also unable to give a good explanation, though they noted that when several test trials are used in experiments of this type the responses are often nonindependent. The theoretical argument to follow hinges on the assumption that only the first test given each subject is valid—a point which is certainly controversial at the present time.

These results can now be interpreted theoretically, and we find an entirely new conclusion to be drawn. The outcome agrees with the schema theory, but not with the stimulus-element theory.

Consider stimulus-sampling theory. Assume that $m(S_1 \cap \bar{S}_2) \cong m(\bar{S}_1 \cap S_2)$. The elements in $S_1 \cap S_2$ are on a random reinforcement schedule, and the proportion π of them will, according to stimulus-sampling theory, be attached to the response which is reinforced π of the time. However, in this case the test stimulus contains all of the stimulus elements in S_1 and in S_2, or very nearly so. Hence the stimulus elements in the test situation are $S_1 \cup S_2$.

Because training was continued for quite a while, and the subjects were required to attain a rigorous criterion of correct response during training, a good approximation is that the elements of $S_1 \cap \bar{S}_2$ are almost all conditioned to response TUZ, the elements of $\bar{S}_1 \cap S_2$ are almost all conditioned to NAF, and about π of the elements of $S_1 \cap S_2$ are conditioned to TUZ and the rest to NAF. The probability of response TUZ in the presence of $S_1 \cup S_2$ should then be

$$P(TUZ \mid S_1 \cup S_2) \cong \frac{m(S_1 \cap \bar{S}_2) + \pi m(S_1 \cap S_2)}{m(S_1 \cup S_2)} \qquad (5.1)$$

Since the subjects respond quite accurately to the training stimuli S_1 and S_2 and rarely confuse them, one is tempted to assume that $S_1 \cap S_2$ is not very large relative to $S_1 \cap \bar{S}_2$. Let us introduce the numbers

$$d = m(S_1 \cap \bar{S}_2) \cong m(\bar{S}_1 \cap S_2)$$

and

$$c = m(S_1 \cap S_2)$$

where the letters d and c are chosen because they are the measures of differential and common stimulus elements. Then $m(S_1 \cup S_2) = 2d + c$, and Eq. 5.1 becomes

$$P(TUZ \mid S_1 \cup S_2) = \frac{d + \pi c}{2d + c} \qquad (5.2)$$

Now, if the differential elements have large measure relative to the common elements, this probability will be between π and $1/2$ but nearer $1/2$. In the data, the actual value observed is near π, which suggests the impossible conclusion that the common elements are relatively numerous. This cannot be, because the subjects have already learned to make consistent responses which must depend solely on the differential elements. If d and c are for example equal, the probability reduces to $(1 + \pi)/3$. In the group with frequencies of 80:20, this would be $1.80/3 = .60$, quite far from the observed value of about .75. In fact, to fit the data d must be only about one-tenth of c; the differential elements must be only a small fraction of the common elements in this situation. Such an assumption would be possible for the 80:20 group, but for the 67:33 group no such computation is possible, since the observations are slightly more extreme than the prediction. From these data it seems most reasonable to assume that $d = 0$, an entirely unreasonable conclusion since the subjects have shown the ability to discriminate clearly.

While the stimulus-sampling model is thus struggling with its difficulties, the schema-matching model finds these data exactly as expected. The probability of accepting a match of situation A with A_1 is equal to the probability of accepting a match of A with A_2, because of the symmetry of the figures and counterbalancing. Hence the probability of actually matching with A_1 should depend directly on the proportion of schemata from A_1, which will be π. It is this result more than any other which has led the writer to his interest in, and espousal of, the schema theory.

The schema theory can be extended to lead to further research. Binder and Feldman carefully counterbalanced and controlled to make the test stimulus as nearly as possible equally similar to the two training stimuli. If, however, the restriction is relaxed the schema theory still predicts choice probabilities. A control group is needed in which the two training stimuli are presented equally often, a 50:50 group, from the data of which the similarity of test stimulus S to the two training stimuli S_1 and S_2 is estimated.

Suppose that under this control condition the probability of response 1 to test stimulus S is some number

$$P(R_1 \mid S) = P_{1/2}$$

Another group has stimulus S_1 appearing on N_1 of the trials, and continues training to a rigorous criterion. The set of schemata now is composed of N_1 schemata of S_1, and N_2 schemata of S_2. Letting $N_1/(N_1 + N_2) = f_1$, the probability of response 1 should then be equal to

$$P_\pi = \frac{f_1 p_{1/2}}{f_1 p_{1/2} + (1 - f_1)(1 - p_{1/2})} \tag{5.3}$$

This gives a prediction for any stimulus bias $p_{1/2}$ and any bias due to the differential frequency π, and thus permits a fairly thorough exploration of this theory of recognition and frequency. The same formula should apply through two distinct ways of making up biased test stimuli—by reducing cues and leaving more from S_1 than from S_2, as in Fig. 5.3, or by putting together both sets of differential cues (of different amounts) as in Fig. 5.4. The generality of the hypothesis suggests that it will be interesting to test, though we shall no doubt gain new knowledge by overthrowing it.

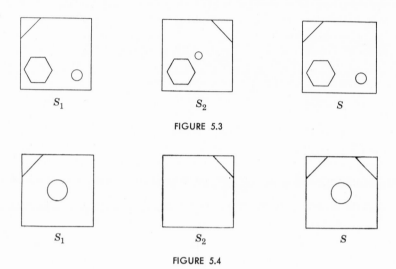

FIGURE 5.3

FIGURE 5.4

Implications of the Schema Theory

On the face of it the schema theory is implausible. It assumes that past experiences are laid down in the brain and remain there, essentially intact, until rearoused. The concept is rather like that proposed by John Locke (without the implication that the file is empty at birth) and thus seems outmoded. The most straightforward disproof is to point out that people cannot in fact remember everything that has happened in an experiment, hence the schemata are not there. This objection is not well taken, however, for the theory particularly emphasizes *access* to the schemata, pointing out that the individual has only random access and uses it only in matching some present situation with one in the past. The distinction between a schema and an association model is subtle. In the language of computers, one would say that the stimulus-response theory gives the subject only a small memory, for he knows only one response to each stimulus element and nothing of when or how the connection was made. This property, called the "independence of path" assumption, is crucial especially to the Markovian interpretations (Bush and Estes, 1959, Chap. 1). However, the subject has immediate access to stored information, provided he is given the appropriate stimulus—the response simply "pops out" when the stimulus is inserted. The schema theory, on the contrary, gives the subject a much larger storage capacity, presuming that the whole history of the problem is stored. By the same token, access is more difficult: the subject must scan the schemata by some random process, and generally selects just one item. The over-all effect, in terms of speed of learning and precision of response, can be about the same, for faults may be attributed either to lack of stored information or to inability to use information which is stored, according to the theory entertained.

Some common experiences suggest that a schema theory may be appropriate. People do, on occasion, remember specific past events, sometimes quite vividly, if the occasion arises. The idea that such memories are merely redintegrations or reconstructions from more general, associative information is possible, but it does not seem satisfying to most people except when needed theoretically. It is doubtful that many psychologists, no matter how devoted to stimulus-response theory, would actually distrust the validity of their own memories to the degree required by their theory.

There are certain conditions that seem to change the usual memory dynamics, and these can be thought of as theoretical leads. One is Penfield's observation of occasional flashes of vivid memory when a spot of the temporal cortex is stimulated during brain surgery (Penfield and Roberts, 1959). This finding suggests, though it does not prove, that the experiences were stored and are usually inaccessible, but are recovered or activated by the electric probe.

It might be objected that a complete record of a whole life experience is too bulky to be stored in the human brain, and thus that the schema theory is unrealistic. Although there is no ready answer to such an objection, a few comments may be in order. First, it is not at present clear whether the whole situation in its concrete details is recorded in a schema, or whether the schema is limited to those aspects to which the person paid attention at the time of experience. The results reported in this book do not permit one to decide how complete and detailed schemata usually are. Second, it is by no means certain that schemata are actually permanent—psychological experiments usually do not extend over enough time to permit such a decision. Overall (1960) has suggested a model, like the present one, which involves gradual random decay of schemata over time. If the decay is slow it would not be detectable with present experimental techniques but would relieve the brain of having to store very large volumes of information.

Actually, superficial assessment of the cerebral cortex gives very little indication of its information-storage capacity unless one knows the physiological details of storage. For example, imagine that a particular schema requires the use of 1000 neurons, and suppose that the total set of neurons numbers 2,000,000,000. If each combination of 1000 neurons can carry a schema, this would give the brain a capacity of 10^{5000} schemata. Allowing 10 schemata-producing experiences per second, a normal life span could hardly accumulate more than 10^{10} schemata, an infinitesimal fraction of the capacity computed above. Thus if schemata are combinations of neurons, there is no shortage of capacity. It is possible that a particular neuron, containing, as it does, large polymers which carry a remarkable amount of genetic information, might have other polymers which carry empirical information. Such a possibility explodes the already enormous number of items of information which might be stored. These are not serious physiological proposals, but merely cautions against too ready a dismissal of the schema theory without consideration of the numbers actually involved.

The possibility that an ordinary person has so vast a supply of stored information is, to the writer, both discouraging and stimulating—discouraging because of the complexity with which it invests every act, but stimulating for it suggests that human mental capacities are greater than human performance. If the schemata are there but cannot be reached, how powerful would be a tool which permits ready access!

CHAPTER SIX

Patterns of Events and Responses in Prediction Experiments

The world is in some measure unpredictable. People must act on conflicting evidence, predicting events even if they are random. Abstracting just this randomness as a characteristic of the environment, and concentrating on predictions of a simple random event, leads to an experiment which is elegant in its controls and yet of real significance. A typical form of this experiment has a subject guess, on each trial, whether a blue or a yellow stimulus will appear next, after which the stimulus appears, either confirming or refuting the guess. This experiment can continue for many trials, and the two events can be arranged according to any of a great variety of programs. The alternatives to be guessed may be blue or yellow lights, blue or yellow cards, the words "check" and "plus," or two lights on the left and right of the subject. The responses may be verbal or simple motor responses, including marking of a test answer sheet, pressing buttons, etc. No regular differences resulting from the characteristics of the events predicted or the form of the response have been found, so long as the two events are highly discriminable. To keep the notation simple this section deals with guesses of blue and yellow. The events will be called b and y, and the corresponding prediction responses will be called B and Y.

Many experiments have been designed to test consequences of mathematical models of learning, and other studies have been more empirical in aim. To understand the problem to be discussed here, it will first be useful to consider how the usual mathematical model of learning treats prediction experiments.

In the usual interpretation, a prediction experiment is a kind of learning experiment rather like the T-maze for rats. On each trial the subject makes one of two responses, B or Y, and receives one of the two "reinforcing events," b or y. Event b reinforces response B and event y reinforces response Y. There is some difficulty in reconciling these ideas with the usual theories of reinforcement, but it seems plausible that event b should strengthen the tendency to emit response B, hence that b is a reinforcer in the most general sense. If b occurs every trial the subject soon responds $BBBB\cdots$. This does not happen all at once but is the accumulated effect of smaller events—the individual events, b and y, must be having effects which cumulate to produce regular behavior, b events strengthening B and y events strengthening Y.

If this theory is correct, $P'(B)$, after a b event, will be greater than $P(B)$, before that b event. This idea is usually expressed by the linear difference equation that after a b event,

$$P'(B \mid b) = (1 - \theta)P(B) + \theta \qquad (6.1)$$

and after a y event, for reasons of symmetry,

$$P'(B \mid y) = (1 - \theta)P(B) \qquad (6.2)$$

These equations have several appeals: they are the only linear equations which are symmetrical in b and y and also permit perfect learning of the simple problem, $bbbbb\cdots$ or $yyyyyyy\cdots$. As Bush and Mosteller said (1951), linear equations are the natural place to start. Estes (1957), beginning with his idea of stimulus sampling, simply assumed that each element had the same probability of being sampled as any other, *ceteris paribus*, and derived these equations. In a sampling model, the uniform distribution is certainly the place to start.

Furthermore, these equations yield a remarkable theorem. For any of a very large range of problems (i.e., arrangements of b and y or randomized rules for generating them), it can be shown that as the number of trials, n, increases, the number of times the subject says $B, n(B)$, is controlled by the number of times b occurs, $n(b)$, with the following restriction:

$$\lim_{n \to \infty} \left(\frac{n(B)}{n(b)} \right) = 1 \qquad (6.3)$$

This is the "probability-matching" theorem (Estes and Suppes, 1959), which meets with approximate verification in a great many experiments.

However, the subjects' comments about their attempts to solve such problems suggest an entirely different picture. The subject is confused in a way which accords with the stimulus-sampling theory, but whatever ideas he can formulate consist mainly of "the events seemed to come in a sequence like *bbybyy*," or "I changed because there had been too many *b*'s in a row," or "I usually shift when I am wrong and stay when I am right," etc. The subject seems to think that he is responding to patterns. Such attempts are natural. The subject has no way of knowing that the events occur at random, and even if he is told that the sequence is random he does not understand this information clearly, nor is there any strong reason for him to believe it. Psychological experimenters do not have a reputation for veracity. If the sequence is random, and the subject knows it, he still cannot predict accurately, and consistent accuracy is the natural aim in a simple experiment like this. But if the subject can identify the *pattern*, he will solve the problem. It will not be easy to convince the subject that there is no pattern in the sequence, since he has a great many hypotheses and, with no facilities for keeping records, is quite unable to eliminate any but the simplest few decisively.

Given an alternating sequence of events *ybybybyb* the human subject will in a few trials figure it out, and respond with perfect precision *BYBYBYBY*. As soon as event *y* occurs the subject is sure to follow with response *B*, proving that event *y* does not simply strengthen the tendency to respond with prediction *Y*, but may have precisely the opposite effect. Rats are capable of learning such a problem in a T-maze or a Skinner box with two bars, and one would expect success from most higher animals under suitable conditions of experience. Certainly, then, the situation contains at least the previous event as part of the stimulus. In higher animals, especially adult humans, there is no great difficulty in teaching double alternation, using the sequence *yybbyybbyybbyybb* (Schoonard and Restle, 1961). Even more complicated patterns can no doubt be mastered by college students.

The stimulus-sampling theory can be used as a jumping-off place for understanding responses to sequences. Events earlier than the present one enter as "stimulus elements," which may be conditioned to one or the other response. Simple alternation can be explained by stimulus-sampling theory as follows: On the trial right after a *b* event, the stimulus situation contains stimulus elements from the preceding event b. Now event y occurs and the stimulus elements present, including those from preceding event b, are conditioned to response Y. The probability of Y following b, written $P(Y \mid b)$, is the proportion of elements conditioned to Y. The elements are partly from the recent event b and, of course, elements from other sources. Let the two sets of elements be B^* (those from having seen card b) and I^* (those from other sources). Let the set of elements conditioned to response Y be called Y. Then

$$P(Y \mid b) = \frac{m[(B^* \cap Y) \cup (I^* \cap Y)]}{m(B^* \cup I^*)} \tag{6.4}$$

In simple alternation, all of the elements of B^* will soon be conditioned to Y, hence $B^* \cap Y$ will come to equal B^*. However, other elements, those in I^*, are followed on alternate trials by b and by y, and should be conditioned now to one and now to the other in irregular pattern. After sufficient training,

$$P(Y \mid b) = \frac{m(B^*) + \frac{1}{2}m(I^*)}{m(B^*) + m(I^*)} \tag{6.5}$$

(Actually, the theoretical probability will be lower than this because the elements of I^* have just been conditioned to B and less than half of them should be conditioned to Y.) However, after a few trials, $P(Y \mid b) = 1$ or nearly so. It takes an alert college student only 5 or 10 trials to catch on to the alternating pattern and from then on he will make virtually no errors for 100 trials. The conclusions to be drawn from this are that virtually the only stimulus elements present are those from the previous event and, furthermore, that the sampling is very rapid—the data suggest that at least 0.3 or 0.4 of the elements must be sampled every trial. The sampling rate on this problem is considerably larger than that found in other learning situations.

Subjects can also learn a double-alternation problem, $bbyybbyybbyy$, in only a few more trials than a single-alternation problem. Learning double alternation requires that the individual pay attention not only to the previous trial but to at least two trials back. More detailed investigations of reaction to irregular sequences, discussed below, indicate that subjects actually are capable of responding differentially to events which are four or five trials back in the sequence (Anderson, 1960). This gives the stimulus-sampling theory two major theoretical difficulties. First, the speed and accuracy of adjustment to simple sequences implies that the person responds mainly to previous stimuli, which are highly distinctive to him. Second, since the subject remembers several trials back, there are a great many different "past experience" stimuli which the subject can and does discriminate quite well. This means that the analysis is very complicated. Sets of stimulus elements must be introduced for each of the previous patterns, and if the subject can remember five trials back there are 32 such sets of stimulus elements to introduce and keep track of in analysis. Furthermore, the subject has an extremely difficult task, for he must learn responses to all of these 32 patterns of events, a process which must take a long time simply because some of the patterns will very rarely occur. This stimulus-sampling theory is extremely difficult to apply, for it has a very large number of "free parameters," i.e., measures of sets of stimulus elements belonging to the many patterns of events, which must be estimated to permit accurate prediction.

A much simpler approach has been put forward by Jacqueline Goodnow (1955). (See also Nicks, 1959.) Goodnow notes that one way a subject can recognize the present situation is in terms of the length of runs of the events b and y. The various runs of b can be listed as yb, ybb, $ybbb$, $ybbbb$, etc., and the runs of y are by, byy, $byyy$, $byyyy$, etc. Perhaps the subject remembers the length of a homogeneous run of events, and nothing else about the experimental sequence.

This is a powerful simplifying assumption because it provides the subject with only a small number of differential stimuli, even if he has a long memory. Figure 6.1 shows the advantage of this theory, by plotting the number of possible patterns remembered as a function of length of memory in trials, for the theory which permits all patterns to be remembered, and the theory which permits only homogeneous runs to be remembered.

In prediction experiments, it has been observed several times (Jarvik, 1951; Bush and Horlock, 1959) that in a random sequence the subject does not seem to believe in long runs. Consider a random 50:50 sequence of b's and y's, arranged without any particular order so that it looks like a segment of a sequence of tosses of a fair coin. If anywhere in the sequence a run of five or six y's occurs, the subject shows (on the average) an increasing tendency to guess B. Since a run of y's has a negative effect on Y, Jarvik called this the "negative recency effect." It is the gambler's fallacy in behavior; an inflated expectation of alternation in a random sequence.

If the sequence of events is "arranged" so that there are, say, 10 b's in every 20 trials, this will restrict the lengths of runs, produce a slight tendency for a b to follow a string of y's, and thus serve as a stimulus in the experiment sufficient to cause the negative

recency effect.   However, restrictions of the sequence generally have
a very small effect on the distribution of runs.   With 10 *b*'s in every
20 trials there cannot be any runs of more than 20, and it is unlikely
that there will be runs longer than 10.   Such runs are so infrequent
anyway, however, that their absence would hardly be felt in a few
hundred trials.   The negative recency effect is noticeable in runs of

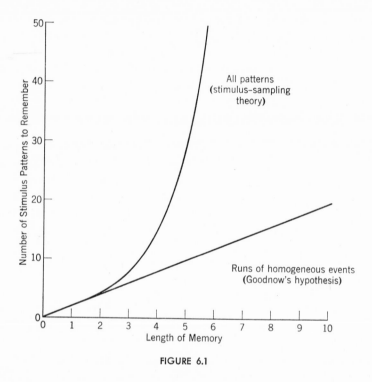

FIGURE 6.1

only three or four *y*'s, and in experiments where the discrepancy
between the actual and a purely random run structure is negligible.

In the discussion to follow, attention centers at first on
this negative recency effect, and then branches out to other characteristics of prediction data.

The standard approach would be to suppose that the subject enters the experiment with a belief that long runs of events will
not occur, and that the experimental program has too few long runs
to disabuse him of this opinion.   Hence, the tendency to alternate
after long runs is simply a holdover from pre-experimental experience
which is not generated by the experimental trials, but survives in
spite of them.   The difficulties with this hypothesis are evident.   First,
it appeals to uncontrolled and unknown experience, a doubtful pro-

cedure. Second, it is not at all certain that an ordinary person's experience would lead to the gambler's fallacy. There are plenty of sequences in the world in which the runs are quite long—even infinitely long, for there are consistencies in nature and in the nature of people. Finally, to suppose that a person's experience with chance situations, as with cards and dice, would lead to the gambler's fallacy requires that the theorist have hidden in his beliefs some faith in the fallacy —for unless this is really how the world operates, why should subjects enter the laboratory having learned this peculiar pattern?

Theoretically the assumption of pre-experimental learning is unsatisfactory for one more reason: different people should have the fallacy to different degrees, depending on their particular life histories, and thus the amount of fallacy is in principle unpredictable except in the sense of a survey of the population. Since the fallacy is not supposed to be caused by anything in the experiment, it is not evident how to control or modify it for study.

This last point suggests a final criticism of the theory, for the gambler's fallacy does not necessarily occur in experiments of this type. There is no clear evidence for it in experiments where consistent, 100% reinforcement is given, and what evidence there is suggests that the fallacy lasts only a few trials if it occurs at all. An experiment in which the negative recency effect failed to occur will be discussed later. Hence, it appears that the existence of negative recency or the gambler's fallacy behavior depends on something within the experiment, something that does not disappear with rather extended training.*

The possibility to be considered now is that the negative recency effect, and several related details of the patterning of guesses, actually arise from the experimental sequence and the way the subject responds to it. In approaching this problem, let us return briefly to the theoretical structure used in this book. As in any other choice, the subject attempts to match his present situation with some schema, and having made a match he responds with the choice appropriate to the schema. The probability of hitting a certain schema depends upon how similar the present situation is to the ideal situation.

Theory of Patterns in Guessing

Imagine a subject at some late point in a guessing experiment having just experienced k blue cards in a row, and deciding

---

* In a boring experiment all sequence effects may disappear after 1000 trials, according to data collected by Dr. Ward Edwards.

whether to respond B or Y. Suppose that he compares his present situation, say $ybbbb$ ($k = 4$), with previous runs. Any runs shorter than four, such as yby, $ybby$, and $ybbby$, are irrelevant to his present decision. A previous run of exactly four, $ybbbby$, indicates he should switch to response Y, having already used up the four b's. A previous run of length 5 or more ($ybbbbby$, $ybbbbbby$, $\cdots$) indicates that he should make response B, for there are more b's to come.

The probability that the situation is matched with schemata having run lengths of k, $k + 1$, $k + 2, \cdots$, leads to a formula for the probability of response y under these circumstances. In fact, after $ybbbb$, the probability of response Y is just the probability that the subject matches with a previous sequence $ybbbby$, and the probability of B is the probability that he matches with some longer sequence $ybbbbby$, $ybbbbbby, \cdots$, assuming that he does not match with any shorter runs, or with runs of y's.

The probability that the subject will match with a previous run of length k depends upon how frequently such runs have occurred and on how salient they are in his memory. Since one trial is very like another it seems reasonable to suppose that, other things being equal, longer runs are more salient than shorter ones. Since all trials are very much alike in guessing experiments, the natural assumption, made here, is that the probability of using a schema of length k is proportional to k.

These hypotheses yield the probability of response Y after the sequence of events $ybbbb$, as follows. Find the weighted sum of schemata of runs of length 4 by counting how many have occurred in the past, and multiplying this frequency by the length of the run, 4. Let this weighted sum of traces of length 4 be called W_4. Then do the same for all longer runs, obtaining $W_5, W_6, \cdots$. The probability of response Y after $ybbbb$ is

$$P(Y \mid ybbbb) = \frac{W_4}{W_4 + W_5 + \cdots}$$

$$P(B \mid ybbbb) = \frac{W_5 + W_6 + \cdots}{W_4 + W_5 + \cdots}$$

$$(6.6)$$

This computation can be generalized quite easily. The past history of the sequence of events determines $W_1, W_2, \cdots, W_n$ for the various run lengths. $P(B \mid k)$ is the general probability of response B after a run of k b's. The argument given above leads to the general expression

$$P(B \mid k) = \frac{\sum\limits_{j=k+1}^{\infty} W_j}{\sum\limits_{i=k}^{\infty} W_i} \qquad (6.7)$$

This system will show negative recency in the predictions of a purely random sequence of events. Consider a run of events in which y and b occur at random each with probability 1/2. The probability of a run of just one b is the probability that b occurs, times the probability that y occurs right after it. Since we are concerned right now with runs of b's, we may consider only cases in which a b occurs. Now the probability of a run of one b is $P(y) = \frac{1}{2}$. The probability of a run of two b's is $P(by)$, which is $\frac{1}{4}$. The probability of a run of exactly three b's is $P(bby)$, which requires three events in a row (bby) to occur in a specified order, and therefore has a probability $(\frac{1}{2})^3$. In general, a run of length k has probability $(\frac{1}{2})^k$.

TABLE 6.1

RUNS OF LENGTH k, THEIR FREQUENCIES, VALUES OF W_k AND
PROBABILITIES OF RESPONSES Y AND B

k	Frequency of k	W_k	$\sum\limits_{i=k}^{\infty} W_i$	$P(B)$
1	512	512	2036	.749
2	256	512	1524	.664
3	128	384	1012	.621
4	64	256	628	.592
5	32	160	372	.570
6	16	96	212	.547
7	8	56	116	.517
8	4	32	60	.467
9	2	18	28	.357
10	1	10	10	(.000)
11	0	0	0	——

In an experiment the actual distribution of runs may not fit the theoretical distribution exactly, owing to sampling fluctuations, but calculations will be based on nearly perfect distributions of runs. Imagine that the subject has had 1023 previous runs of b's, a total of 2036 trials, distributed as the theoretical run distribution of a

50:50 sequence. Table 6.1 shows the runs of event b of length from 1 to 11, the frequency with which each such run has occurred, the weighted sums for each, and the probability of response B after this many b events.

The important general fact about this table is that the probabilty of B *decreases* consistently as one takes longer and longer runs of event b, i.e., as k increases. Thus the system shows a negative recency effect. Furthermore, the negative recency effect is not caused by any peculiar experiences the subject may have had before the experiment, but follows directly from the experimental procedures themselves.

The results of Table 6.1 can be generalized to any probability of a b event, π, and the assumption of independent random events, in which case the probability of a run of k b's is $\pi^{k-1}(1 - \pi)$. In this case,

$$W_k = Nk\pi^{k-1}(1 - \pi) \tag{6.8}$$

where N is the total number of previous trials, assumed to be very large.

A little consideration shows that the probability of response B after k events b in a row is

$$P(B, k) = \frac{\sum\limits_{c=k+1}^{\infty} W_i}{\sum\limits_{i=k}^{\infty} W_i}$$

$$= \frac{N(1 - \pi) \sum\limits_{i=k+1}^{\infty} i\pi^{i-1}}{N(1 - \pi) \sum\limits_{j=k}^{\infty} j\pi^{j-1}}$$

It can be shown that

$$\sum_{i=k}^{\infty} i\pi^{i-1} = \frac{k\pi^{k-1}}{1 - \pi} + \frac{\pi^k}{(1 - \pi)^2} \tag{6.9}$$

and suitable substitutions yield

$$P(B, k) = \frac{N(1 - \pi)[(k + 1)\pi^k(1 - \pi) + \pi^{k+1}]}{N(1 - \pi)[k\pi^{k-1}(1 - \pi) + \pi^k]}$$

$$= \frac{k\pi(1 - \pi) + \pi}{k(1 - \pi) + \pi} \tag{6.10}$$

Equation 6.10, plotted for a given value of π and various values of k, gives a theoretical negative recency effect. It assumes that the events occur in random order with fixed probability of event b, and is of course suitable only after the subject has had sufficient experience. As k grows very large $P(B, k)$ approaches π, and otherwise $P(B, k)$ is larger than π.

Equation 6.10 and the preceding development depend not only on the assumption that the event sequence is random, but also on the assumption that the subject performs solely on the basis of runs of previous events. This is not the *only* kind of cue the subject can use in this sort of situation—other discriminable stimuli are present. Hence the theory is an oversimplification. However, it can be compared with data to see how bad it is and what kind of correction is indicated.

The first direct application of the theory is to analyze some negative recency effects in guessing data where random reinforcement schedules were used. In an unpublished note, Bush and Horlock (1959) made available the detailed data of an experiment conducted by Galanter and Derks using a 75:25 random reinforcement schedule. The experiment was quite long, though of course there were not too many long runs. It is possible to plot the probability of response B as a function of the number of consecutive b events preceding it. We shall deal with the more frequent event, which occurs 75% of the time. Predictions can be computed using Eq. 6.10 with $\pi = .75$, or by using the actual frequencies of events in the experimental sequence. Neither prediction is optimal, because the responses of the subjects are made before the sequence is entirely unfolded.

The results of the calculations and their comparison with data are shown in Table 6.2. Note that the predictions are quite good except for very short runs ($k = 1$) in which the predicted prob-

TABLE 6.2

PREDICTED AND OBSERVED NEGATIVE RECENCY CURVES, DATA FROM
AN EXPERIMENT BY GALANTER AND DERKS

Length of Run of b's (k)	Probability of B, $P(B \mid k)$		
	Obtained	Predicted from Actual Runs	Predicted from Eq. 6.10
1	.88	.93	.93
2	.92	.95	.89
3	.84	.82	.87
4	.76	.76	.85
5	.75	.85	.84
6	.74	(.86)	.83

abilities of B are too high, and for long runs (5 and 6) where the predictions are again too high. These discrepancies are not very large, but the theory can be corrected to take account of them. The suggestion which comes to mind is that with very short runs, or with very infrequent long runs, the subjects may fall back on cues other than sequence cues, and perhaps therefore tend to respond with probability matching.

Bush and Horlock in their report remark that the existence of a negative recency effect cannot be doubted seriously—the drop is statistically quite significant. Although the present formulation shows such a drop, it too is significantly in error for the longer runs, of lengths 5 and 6, where the subject drops back to probability matching.

A similar experiment by Goodnow, Rubenstein, and Lubin (1957) yielded data in better accord with the theory. They controlled the frequency of runs of various lengths, in a 75:25 sequence of events. Their data and the predictions from the theory are shown in Table 6.3. These data are in good agreement with theory,

TABLE 6.3

PREDICTED AND OBSERVED NEGATIVE RECENCY CURVES, DATA FROM
AN EXPERIMENT BY GOODNOW, RUBENSTEIN, AND LUBIN

Length of Run of b's (k)	Probability of B, $P(B \mid k)$	
	Obtained	Predicted from Actual Runs
1	.75	.91
2	.85	.86
3	.81	.80
4	.76	.76

except for runs of length 1. Again there is the suggestion that these very short runs do not fit the model, and subjects regress toward probability matching when responding to them.

If the general theory is correct, it should be possible to change response to run lengths by changing the distribution of run lengths in the sequence. Goodnow, Rubenstein, and Lubin (1957) ran three groups of subjects in a guessing experiment with short, medium, and long runs of events. The two events, b and y, were equally frequent, but in the short-run sequence the probability of b following b was only .25, in the second (random) sequence the probability of b following b was .50, and in the third (long runs) sequence it was .75.

Since Eq. 6.10 applies to the probability of b following b, it can be used directly to predict these data. The theoretical predictions and experimental results are shown in Fig. 6.2. Although the predictions are not accurate, they do reflect the general level and trend of the data fairly well. Certainly the differences between the three sets of data are of the same sort as the differences between the three curves. Precision cannot be expected here: the subjects had not had extensive experience with the sequences, and the curves computed are based only on an idealization of the run structure of the sequence.

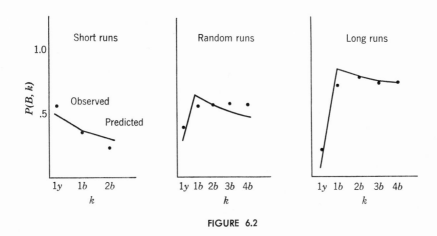

FIGURE 6.2

In the analyses given above the data were reported in just the correct fashion for the theory. An earlier experiment, the one in which negative recency was first demonstrated, provides another test of the theory. In this case the experimenter was a little less careful to segregate the various factors which entered into his results; consequently, his published findings are more difficult to interpret. However, it is an important value of a mathematical theory that it can often handle data which are available only in the form of complicated averages. In general, the method is to compute corresponding averages of theoretical quantities. In this way, although the data may not be the most exact test of the theory, they will serve as an indirect test of the flexibility and power of the theory.

Jarvik (1951) composed his sequences by balancing the relative frequencies of the two events b and y (he used the symbols "check" and "plus" for his study) within blocks of trials. The first task of analysis is to determine the frequencies of runs of various lengths in Jarvik's sequences. This can be worked out by considering information given in his Fig. 1 (p. 294 of the report) and in footnote 2 of the same paper. Though Jarvik did not at that early date use the exact run structure in his explanation, his insight was sufficient to lead him to include the necessary data.

The experiment involved three different groups, in which the over-all probabilities of event b were .60, .67, and .75. These groups also had different run structures, of course. In computing the negative recency effects, Jarvik presents the proportion of b responses following runs of b events of various lengths, including all subjects in each data point. This means that when he considers runs of two b's, the group with .60 b's is overrepresented, because the group had more short and fewer long runs than the other groups, and when he gets out to runs of five and six b's the group with .75 b's is over-represented because that group had more than its share of long runs. Thus most of the observations in one curve are the result of one run structure, and most of the observations in another curve are the result of a different run structure.

However, his procedure can be mirrored within the theory. The theoretical negative recency curves for the three groups give three different curves because the run structures of the three groups are somewhat different. The run structures given the three groups and the number of subjects in each determine exactly how many observations after yb come from group 1, how many from group 2, and how many from group 3. The calculation is repeated for condition ybb, $ybbb$, etc.

Predictions of Jarvik's data can be computed by taking the weighted average of the three theoretical negative recency curves and weighting each curve by the number of subjects from that group entering into the data point.

In reporting his results, Jarvik first considers runs of exactly two b's in the sequence. This is the basis for a short negative recency curve, for the probability of B may be higher after only one than after two b's. He then separately considers the runs of three b's, and gets a negative recency effect for the first, second, and third place in that run. This is continued up to runs of six. The data, and theoretical weighted curves, are shown in Fig. 6.3.

Again the theoretical fit is imperfect, though the relatively short training sequence (only about 90 trials) may explain the discrepancies. The data are averaged over the whole experimental run, but sequential effects could hardly have become very strong in the first, say, 50 trials. Generally speaking, the fit of experimental and data values is quite good, and suggests that the interpretation of negative recency effects given here is suitable for analyzing data even when some complications enter into the analysis.

The negative recency effect is small and difficult to establish sharply. In many of the experiments discussed above the sequence of b's and y's was randomized "with restrictions" which either fixed the run lengths, ensured that the desired relative frequencies were obtained in each block of 10 or 20 or 50 trials, or in some other way regularized the pattern of events. Furthermore, it has not been com-

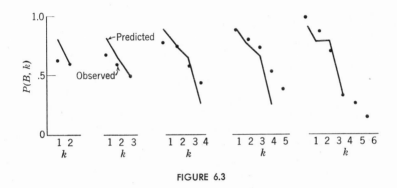

FIGURE 6.3

mon practice to make separate random sequences for each subject, though that would be sensible, and the experimental conditions have not been as rigorously controlled in the physical sense as one might wish.

During a visit to Indiana University in the spring of 1960, the writer learned that W. K. Estes and M. Friedman, with a new apparatus, had performed a quite elaborate experiment intended to repair all of the above faults. Each subject was trained extensively, with frequent rests and changes of sequence, under carefully controlled conditions. Furthermore, the events were randomized with a fixed probability and no other restriction, two independent sequences being constructed for the study. Under these conditions a slight but distinct *positive* recency effect was noted. Since the above calculations had been performed at the time, this intelligence was received with some dismay. However, further inquiries disclosed that the experimental design involved a factor which had not appeared in any earlier experiments; each subject was trained on a variety of different probabilities. The probabilities were $\pi = .5$, which served as a test situation used repeatedly, and also $\pi = .1, .2, .3, .4, .6, .7, .8,$ and .9. Each subject would have 48 trials on one of the unbalanced sequences, say, $\pi = .2$, then 48 trials on $\pi = .5$, then another 48 trials on, say, $\pi = .9$, then 48 more trials on $\pi = .5$, etc., for 16 sequences of 48 trials. Then a terminal run of trials at $\pi = .8$ was used. Of the 16 sequences, 8 were on $\pi = .5$ and the remainder were made up of one 48-trial sequence at each of the other 8 event probabilities. This experimental design is innocent of special effects if the subjects use, at most, a short memory. However, the theory under consideration in this chapter supposes that the entire training sequence is recorded in the subject's brain and that he has random access to all of his past experiences. With the present theory, the experience made up of a mixture of many different probabilities of the event may lead to behavior very different from what is found when only one probability is ever seen by the subject.

The average behavior of a subject in Estes' experiment can be calculated because the various probabilities (other than .5) are given in different orders to different subjects. A fair picture of average behavior is obtained by computing the distribution of runs in the experiment as a whole, computing the mean W_k for this distribution with the use of Eq. 6.8, and then computing $P(B, k)$ by use of Eq. 6.7. The calculations used were idealized and, by their nature, quite inaccurate. One difficulty is that the very long runs which may occur with $\pi = .9$ have a very large weight in the calculations. Since the series was in fact only 50 trials long the subjects would not experience the very long runs which, though improbable, are probable enough to have a sizable effect on the calculations.

Despite the inherent inaccuracies it is interesting to see that the schema theory does not predict negative recency effects for the Estes-Friedman experiment as it does for other studies, but instead predicts a positive recency effect. The values of $P(B, k)$ for $k = 1, 2, 3,$ and 4 increase. Values of .775, .790, .826, and .849 arise from the infinite sum of Eq. 6.9, taking account of the various probabilities used with Estes and Friedman's subjects and the proportion of training given at each of the probabilities. Estes, analyzing the data, found obtained recency proportions of .528, .614, .617, and .684 for $k = 1, 2, 3,$ and 4. All of his values are calculated from responses on the 50:50 segments of the experiment, which introduces a slight discrepancy from my calculations. I should increase the importance of the $\pi = .5$ series slightly.

It is a most unusual confirmation of the theory that this one experiment, in which positive instead of negative recency effects were found, happens to be one in which the theory also predicts a positive recency effect. On the other hand, the probabilities calculated are considerably higher than those obtained in the experiment. The discrepancy between calculation and observation may be due to the excessive effects of the $\pi = .9$ sequence in the calculations. If the probabilities are recalculated without the effects of the $\pi = .9$ sequence, the resulting values are .642, .632, .674, and .700, closer to the obtained frequencies and still with a generally positive recency effect.

Asymptotic Response Frequencies—Two- and Three-Choice Experiments

At the beginning of this chapter the "probability-matching law" was introduced, saying in effect that the subject's response probability $P(B)$ would approach the probability of the event, $P(b)$ or π. There are several versions of this theorem of statistical learning theory, differing mainly in the variety of sequences comprehended. In a simple situation with fixed probabilities of the individual events, the theorem follows from a great many of the stimulus-sampling and linear models available. It can be shown to follow from a Thurstone-type model or an urn-model (Audley and Jonckheere, 1956) adaptation of it, and from Overall's (1960) "Cognitive Probability" model, which is based on a trace theory very like the schema theory discussed in the last two chapters. Logically speaking, the probability-matching law is a very provable theorem. The question is, Is it true? Does response probability come to match event probability?

The question receives different answers depending on the alternatives one is willing to consider. Imagine that the subject tries to maximize the frequency of successes, guessing a random sequence with fixed probabilities. He will maximize his success by consistently choosing the most frequent event as his guess. This is a theory alternative to the probability-matching law, and on the basis of the available data one can conclude with confidence that the probability-matching law is the better theory. However, when subjects are given enough trials (say, 300 or 500), there seems to be a slight but consistent tendency for them to overshoot the event probabilities by a small margin. To a 70:30 sequence the subject may give responses distributed 73:27; to an 80:20 sequence, his responses may distribute 84:16 or so. The discrepancy is not large, it ordinarily is not statistically significant in any one experiment, and it will not appear if the subjects receive only a more modest number of trials. If anyone offers a theory which predicts such a small discrepancy, the matter will become of some importance. The present theory makes just such a prediction.

The computation of asymptotic response probability is, unfortunately, a trifle complicated. Predictions of negative recency curves gave a formula for $P(B, k)$, the probability of response B after a run of exactly k events of type b. This may be written in more explicit form as

$$P(B \mid \text{a run of } k \text{ } b\text{'s}) = \frac{k\pi(1 - \pi) + \pi}{k(1 - \pi) + \pi} \qquad (6.11)$$

from Eq. 6.10. The probability of response B given event b is

$$P(B \mid b) = \sum_{k=1}^{\infty} [P(B \mid \text{a run of } k \text{ } b\text{'s}) \cdot P(\text{a run of } k \text{ } b\text{'s} \mid b)]$$

where the second probability is the proportion of b's which are found at the end of a run of length k. In the random sequences which are of immediate concern,

$$P(\text{a run of } k \text{ } b\text{'s} \mid b) = \pi^{k-1}(1 - \pi)$$

whence, by substitution,

$$P(B \mid b) = \sum_{k=1}^{\infty} \left[\left(\frac{k\pi(1 - \pi) + \pi}{k(1 - \pi) + \pi} \right) \pi^{k-1}(1 - \pi) \right] \qquad (6.12)$$

Unfortunately, this sum is intractable. However, if π is not very near 1, the term π^{k-1} diminishes rapidly so that the sum converges quickly, and can be computed by hand with a little patience, a log-log slide rule, and a desk calculator.

In this calculation, $P(B \mid b)$ determines $P(Y \mid b) = 1 - P(B \mid b)$. Similarly, $P(Y \mid y)$ and $P(B \mid y)$ can be obtained. The asymptotic probability of response B, averaged over a random sequence, is

$$P(B) = P(B \mid b)P(b) + P(B \mid y)P(y) \qquad (6.13)$$

which can be calculated from Eq. 6.12, which gives the conditional probabilities, and knowledge of the event sequence which gives $P(b)$ and $P(y)$, or π and $1 - \pi$ in the conventional notation. Figure 6.4 shows that these theoretically predicted response asymptotes do not quite correspond to the probability-matching theorem, but instead suggest a slight overshooting most noticeable for about $\pi = .9$ and $\pi = .1$. The writer is not convinced that the prediction from the present theory is more accurate than that from the probability-matching theorem, though he has an impression that some overshooting is commonly found in longer experiments.

Fortunately, a large separation between obtained findings and the probability-matching theories has been found experimentally. Gardner (1957) studied ordinary prediction in a three-choice problem as well as in the more familiar two-choice problem, and found that the asymptotic response probabilities were not even close to the probability-matching law. The experiment has been repeated sufficiently to show that it is not a sampling error, nor due to some

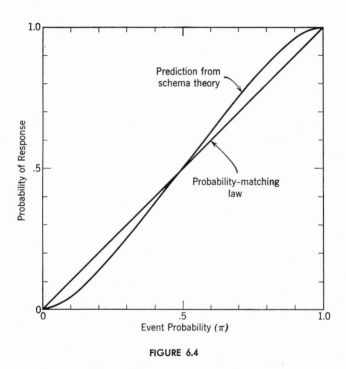

FIGURE 6.4

unknown flaw in the procedure. If the three events occur with probabilities such as 70:15:15, the subjects choose their responses with probabilities near 80:10:10, which is a discrepancy quite large enough to be detected by ordinary statistical tests.

The theory sketched in this chapter is not sufficient to handle a three-choice problem, but the way to generalize seems apparent. According to the model the subject notes the length of the current run of events, k, and then searches his memory bank for another run at least as long. If the run found is longer than k, the subject stays with the same response, and if the run found is of length exactly k, the subject switches. In the three-choice case this is an incomplete statement, for it does not specify the response to which the subject will switch. It seems natural to suppose that if the subject finds in his memory a run of k events of type 1 and the next event is of type 3, he will switch to response 3.

To maintain the present simple notation we continue with the example of the subject guessing colors: blue, yellow, and also green. Let the events be b, y, and g, the choices be B, Y, and G.

Equation 6.12 gives values for $P(B \mid b)$, $P(Y \mid y)$, and $P(G \mid g)$, but there are now six transition probabilities to consider: $P(Y \mid b)$, $P(G \mid b)$, $P(B \mid y)$, $P(G \mid y)$, $P(B \mid g)$, and $P(Y \mid g)$. Fortunately they are easily calculated. From the mere fact that they are probabilities,

$$P(Y \mid b) + P(G \mid b) = 1 - P(B \mid b)$$

and, in a random sequence, it is easily verified that the relative sizes of $P(Y \mid b)$ and $P(G \mid b)$ will be proportional to the probabilities of y and g in the previous sequences; for in a random sequence the probability that a y or g terminates a run of k b's will, in the limit, approach the probability of a y or g in the sequence as a whole. Hence,

$$P(Y \mid b)/P(G \mid b) = P(y)/P(g) \qquad (6.14)$$

Equation 6.12 gives $P(B \mid b)$, and Eqs. 6.13 and 6.14 determine $P(Y \mid b)$ and $P(G \mid b)$. The unconditional probability of response B over the whole sequence is

$$P(B) = P(B \mid b)P(b) + P(B \mid y)P(y) + P(B \mid g)P(g)$$

A similar computation, simply changing responses and events in the formulas, produces $P(Y)$ and $P(G)$.

These calculations were carried out for the event probabilities used by Gardner, which are a reasonable selection of the interesting cases. Gardner used both two- and three-choice problems and various distributions of the low-frequency events in his three-choice cases. One advantage of these data is that they were replicated by Cotton and Rechtschaffen (1958) with the same probabilities, similar apparatus and subjects, and comparable but independent sequences. The computations and data are shown in Table 6.4. Gardner also extended his results in a similar experiment with army recruits, using up to eight-choice problems (Gardner, 1958). The data of this "army" experiment are also included in Table 6.4 along with the predicted values.

The theoretical predictions cannot be called perfect, from the results of Table 6.4, but they seem to the writer to be very good. In every one of the 22 groups, the high-frequency event was predicted by subjects more often than it occurred. Thus, the probability-matching hypothesis is wrong on the low side every time. The present

TABLE 6.4

PREDICTED AND OBTAINED FREQUENCIES OF CHOICES IN TWO-, THREE-, AND
MULTIPLE-CHOICE GUESSING EXPERIMENTS

Obtained Frequencies of Choices

Frequencies of Events	Gardner (1957)	Cotton and Rechtschaffer (1958) (Highest Frequency Only)	Gardner (1958) (Army) (Highest Frequency Only)	Predicted Frequencies of Choices
70:30	.721–.279	.741	.728	.750, .250
70:15:15	.802–.099–.099	.802, .809, .785	.746	.774, .113, .113
70:20:10	.798–.129–.073	.801	—	.772, .158, .070
60:40	.618–.382	.641	.611	.627, .373
60:20:20	.676–.162–.162	.660	.608	.674, .163, .163
60:30:10	.684–.235–.081	.658	—	.654, .272, .074
70:10:10:10			.811	.784
70:5:5:5:5:5			.829	.794
60:8:8:8:8:8			.692	.687
60: (5.7): (5.7), etc.			.871	.692

model is also inaccurate, but it is on the low side 14 times and it is too high the other 8 times. It is usually closer to the obtained value than the probability-matching hypothesis. There exists a pattern of discrepancy—the schema theory predicts too high a probability of the frequent response in two-choice and the simple three-choice cases, and predicts too low in the multiple-choice cases. The one large discrepancy is in the eight-choice case, the last one in the table, where the subjects obviously chose the 60% event much more often than the theory would predict. It appears that with a large number of choices, most of which are of very low frequency, the subjects do not discriminate well among the low-frequency choices and instead tend to go mainly to the high-frequency choice. It is possible that in a problem with so many alternatives the subject is discouraged from attempting to deal with runs of events at all.

The results of these calculations are reported in some detail because, for one thing, they suggest that in multiple-choice guessing the subject does not stabilize at or even near the probability-matching asymptote, because instead he is attentive to runs of events. These three- and multiple-choice data have been a great embarrassment to statistical learning theory, but they have produced almost equal perplexity in the experimenters who have collected them. The subjects seem to hunt out quite definite asymptotes and stay at them for a long time, but the values obtained are difficult to rationalize. Gardner (1957) has tried his hand at a "balanced regret" idea, that the subject tries to make an equal number of misses of each event. In a 60:30:10 sequence this is impossible, and the closest approximation is never to choose the least-frequent event. That is not what the subjects do. The predictions from the schema theory, although imperfect, are the best and most reasonable available at this writing.

Conditional Probabilities in Guessing Data

Recall that Goodnow et al. constructed three different 50:50 sequences with short, random, and long runs. This sort of experiment has been pursued by other experimenters within the general framework of stimulus-sampling theory (or the Bush-Mosteller linear model, which for present purposes is about the same thing). One of the consequences of the linear reinforcement model, with no memory, is that any b event should raise the probability of response B, and any y event should lower the probability of B. Engler (1958) has reported a study which demolishes this simplistic theory. She made up sequences where b and y have the same relative frequency, 50:50, but with different conditional probabilities of b following b. When $P(b \mid b)$ is low, say, .10, the sequence of events alternates almost perfectly—a typical chain would be $bybybybyybybybybybybybbyby$, etc. Subjects soon notice this, and attempt to guess correctly by making response B after a y event, and response Y after a b event. This, of course, is the exact opposite required by the simple, memory-less model, for event b very sharply *decreases* the probability of response B immediately following. The results of the experiment were exactly as Engler expected, and her careful statistical analysis makes it clear that some sort of memory, or sensitivity to previous events, is required.

The next simplest model of the stimulus-sampling type is one which assumes that the just-previous event serves as a cue, or source of stimulus elements, for the response. If so, the stimulus traces from event b could become conditioned to response Y, because reinforcement y follows these traces immediately.

We may imagine two main sources of stimulus elements: the previous event and "other" elements. Since the chain of events is such that b follows b .10 of the time, it follows from the probability-matching hypothesis of statistical learning theory that elements from the trace of b will be conditioned mainly to response Y, but about .10 of them will be conditioned to response B. The "other" elements, if

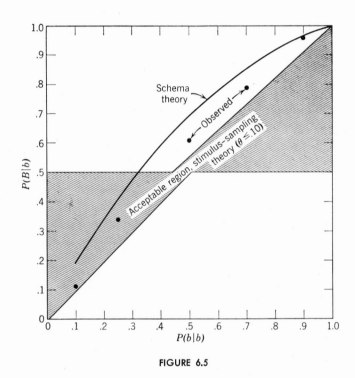

FIGURE 6.5

any, will be followed by b and y equally often, and will thus be distributed about 50:50 over the two responses. Right after a b event, though, there is a slight tendency for more of these elements to be conditioned to B than to Y.

In summary, the probability of B following event b according to a stimulus-sampling model should be somewhere between $P(b \mid b)$ and $P(b)$, for these are the probability-matching asymptotes for the two sorts of stimulus elements. In Fig. 6.5 are shown the conditional probabilities $P(B \mid b)$ found by Engler as a function of her controlled values of $P(b \mid b)$, and the region acceptable by stimulus-sampling theory is indicated.

The present theory predicts the response contingencies in a fairly simple way. Equation 6.11 gives the probability of response B following a run of k b's in a row. If Engler's event sequence was random (a condition she was careful to approximate), then the frequencies with which runs of length $k = 1, 2, 3, \cdots$ occurred are known except for sampling error. The over-all probability of response B after an event b is given by Eq. 6.12. The calculation was carried out and is shown in Fig. 6.5 as the solid line, "Schema theory," along with Engler's data. Very much the same results were obtained by Anderson (1960) in a related experiment.

Comparisons of data with theory indicates that the schema theory is fairly good at predicting conditional-probability data, though it is imperfect. The theory is that in solving this sort of problem the subject's main concern is with the run of events which has just preceded his present response. The writer believes the theory is in error when the sequence alternates or almost alternates. The schema theory as given above assumes that the subject remembers only homogeneous runs of the form $bbbb$ or $yyyy$. It seems likely that the subject also can remember alternation runs, $bybybyby$, quite well.

Anderson (1960) finds a specific effect of successive alternations; the sequence $bybyby$ seems to have a direct effect on performance other than as a string of runs of length 1. This is singled out by comparing the probability of B after $byby$ with the probability of B after $yyby$, for example. The run length is the same in both cases, but there are more B responses after $byby$ than after $yyby$, indicating that the subject may be responding directly to runs of alternation. In the final analysis, the hypothesis that predictions depend only on homogeneous runs must be wrong, and consideration of runs of alternation, and possibly runs of double alternation, may help solve the problems of analysis. If subjects did respond directly to alternation this would reduce the proportion of repetitions after homogeneous runs of length 1 (which are too high in all the theoretical curves) because runs of length 1 would fairly often be parts of alternation cycles.

Sequential Effects When Aspects Are not All from Runs

When the subject is at the end of a run of k events of type b, and seeks some previous experience which matches with his present situation, he may match not only on runs but also on the basis of other stimulus aspects. This tendency will presumably be most marked when it is not easy to observe runs, as when trials are widely spaced or other activities enter into the sequence to obscure previous events.

Suppose that these other aspects are fixed characteristics of the situation, and that the subject, when matching on the basis of these aspects, selects the response which was correct on the trial in question. If the subject, at trial 20, decides that the situation matches with that existing on trial 10 (on a basis not associated with runs), then he guesses B if event b occurred on trial 10 and Y if y occurred on trial 10.

In a standard guessing experiment the situation is held constant from trial to trial, except for the history of previous events. Hence it is natural to suppose that all previous trials have approximately equal probabilities of being matched with the present one, except that earlier trials may appear less similar on the basis of being "early" rather than "recent." In general, the probability that the schema drawn from memory is of a trial ending in b should be very close to the proportion of b events in the sequence. Hence such matches will lead to "probability-matching" behavior, by the present theory.

If the subject matches previous events on either of two bases—runs (of which the set of aspects may be called R) or stable characteristics of the environment (of which the set of aspects may be called S)—it is natural to suppose that the probabilities of the two kinds of matches will be proportional to the measures of R and S. After a run of k of type b, the actual response probability $P'(B, k)$ can be written

$$P'(B, k) = \frac{m(R)P(B, k) + m(S)\pi}{m(R) + m(S)} \qquad (6.15)$$

where the expression $P(B, k)$ has the significance it had earlier: it is the probability of response B after a run of k events of type b, when it is assumed that the subject responds only on the basis of runs. Since long runs are more perceivable than short ones, the measure or stimulus magnitude of a run is proportional to its length. Therefore in Eq. 6.15, $m(R)$ is proportional to the length of run, i.e., proportional to k. Then

$$m(R) = kC$$

and

$$P'(B, k) = \frac{kCP(B, k) + m(S)\pi}{kC + m(S)} \qquad (6.16)$$

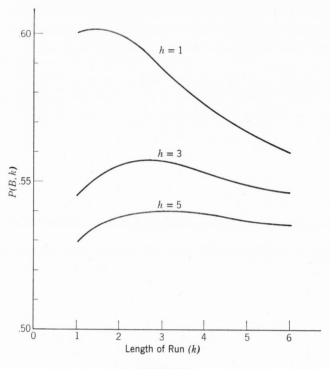

FIGURE 6.6

This may be made simpler in appearance by defining a constant

$$h = m(S)/C$$

whence Eq. 6.16 becomes

$$P'(B, k) = \frac{kP(B, k) + h\pi}{k + h} \qquad (6.17)$$

Equation 6.10 defines $P(B, k)$ in terms of k and π, and applies to a random sequence of events with probability π of event b. Inserting this definition into Eq. 6.17,

$$P'(B, k) = \frac{k \dfrac{k\pi(1 - \pi) + \pi}{k(1 - \pi) + \pi} + h\pi}{k + h}$$

$$= \pi + \frac{k\pi(1 - \pi)}{(k + h)(k - k\pi + \pi)} \qquad (6.18)$$

Since all the numbers in Eq. 6.18 are positive, $P'(B, k)$ will always be greater than π. However, as k becomes very large, $P'(B, k)$ approaches π, for the second term will then become proportional to $1/k$.

In Fig. 6.6 are shown some examples of negative recency functions, plots of Eq. 6.18, with $\pi = 1/2$ and various values of h. Notice that these curves rise and then fall, the maximum being displaced to higher values of k the larger h (the measure of nonsequential stimuli) is. Also, as h increases, the general level of the curve is reduced and it is flattened. It seems possible to estimate h from such curves but only on the basis of voluminous data from subjects with long and complete experience with the sequence.

Summary and Remarks

This chapter began with an introduction to stimulus-sampling theory which has been used to predict the results of guessing experiments, and then proceeded to a theory using the notion of schemata. The new theory proposed is that the subject records the result of each trial as a schema and chooses a response, on later trials, by attempting to match his present situation with a past situation. For simplicity in handling the data from the usual experiments, in which college students serve as subjects, it was assumed that the number of consecutive same events (k) is the main aspect of a given situation. This idea, as developed, leads to predictions of many of the sequential details of asymptotic performance in a guessing experiment, and a number of such predictions were computed and compared with relevant findings.

The predictions are, in detail, very different from those which would be made from stimulus-sampling (statistical) learning theory. In one important way the two sets of predictions are comparable: they can be made (in the main) without any reference to specific previous observations about the subject. The probability-matching hypothesis refers response probability to the probability of an event in the sequence, and needs no parameters about the subject. Similarly, many of the predictions of the present theory require knowledge only of the run structure of the sequence of events, and no parameters from the subject. In statistical learning theory, sequential effects in the data depend mainly on θ, the rate of learning. In the schema theory many such effects can be derived from the run structure alone, provided one is confident that the subjects are using runs as the main aspects of the situation. This assumption is fairly viable when college students are used as subjects, though some evidence of its imperfections has been collected.

It should be emphasized that the general idea of a schema theory does not require the further hypothesis that subjects respond on the basis of runs. It is perfectly possible (as in Chapter 5) to suppose that the subject pays no particular attention to runs but records each separate trial as a schema. If the two (or more) events are comparable as stimuli, and the subject always guesses or responds in a fixed situation, the schema theory would predict probability-matching. Such a theory has been developed by Overall (1960) as applying to infrahuman animals such as rats. Overall's development is very like the writer's and was developed quite independently, about one year before the present work. It should be remarked that such a theory, in which each event adds a unit trace to its corresponding response, behaves generally like the earlier Thurstone theory, and the recent English developments in the same direction (see Restle, 1959b). There are many ways to do an experiment in which the subjects will not respond primarily to runs of events: by using infrahuman animals, by spacing trials widely, by complicating the stimulus situation in which choices are made, etc. Such conditions should be investigated carefully by experiment, and a suitable theoretical analysis should be made. The "runs" hypothesis works as well as it does in the calculations of this chapter probably because the experiments use college students guessing a simple event with quite massed trials, in which sequential patterns are quite obvious, natural, and (apparently) promising as a way to solve the problem.

Another factor in guessing experiments, not discussed in this chapter, is the reward or satisfaction resulting from a correct guess, and the punishment, disappointment, or loss which may result from an error. When monetary or other such valuable rewards and punishments are involved, a suitable theoretical treatment must consider not only the purely cognitive factors studied in this chapter but also the utilities. Within the present approach one would invoke the ideas developed in Chapter 4. The integration will not be attempted in this volume, in part because the necessary body of data has not yet accumulated. It is hoped that some reader will find a useful stimulus, and perhaps a helpful suggestion, in these pages to further his research on the question, now but little understood, of the human being's attempts to deal with a risky and value-laden environment.

CHAPTER SEVEN

Detection and the Notion of Homogeneous Classes

Under optimal conditions the human eye can detect a few quanta of light, and the ear can detect a tone barely above the thermal noise level produced by random collisions of molecules of air. All of the human senses show remarkable sensitivity and resolving power when their accomplishments are measured physically, but there is some animal which outperforms the human on each sense. The detail vision of hawks, the night vision of cats and owls, and the auditory feats of the bat are well known, and the dog is far superior to humans in olfaction. Given the sensitivity and resolving power of a sense, physiologists and physicists can investigate how the sense organ and nervous system manage to perform as they do. Measuring sensitivity is, however, a psychological problem, and the methods devised by psychologists, called the psychophysical methods, constitute a basic problem in mathematical psychology.

Every sense, no matter how sensitive, is imperfect in that stimuli can be made too weak to be detected or too similar to be discriminated. There is always some "threshold" or limitation on the sense, and an important task for the psychologist is to locate these limits. The actual measurements may be made by a physicist, physiologist, ophthalmologist, otologist, or anyone else; but since such measurements usually involve judgments by human subjects, or indicative responses by animals, there is almost always a psychological

135

problem involved in interpreting behavioral indicators of the action of the receptor.

The judgments, in a measurement of threshold, depend in part upon the stimulus presented, in part upon the reaction of the receptor and the transmission system, and in part upon the method used by the subject in making his judgments. For the psychologist, study of the psychophysical methods makes it possible to obtain some understanding of methods of judgment, and thereby to further his study of behavior in general. The theory of how an individual responds when in conflict or uncertainty, put forward in the preceding chapters, will come under further investigation in this chapter in the context of studies of detection.

One limitation of this chapter is that it considers only psychophysical methods in which the subject makes a discrete response or choice. An especially sensitive psychophysical method permits the subject to vary one stimulus until he finds a point which is just detectable, or until he matches the variable stimulus with a standard. This "method of adjustment" is taken up as an example of compound responses in Chapter 8.

The Psychophysical Methods

Within the general field of psychophysics, several methods are used. The present chapter is limited to what may be called the discrimination methods, which give the subject a relatively simple problem, with only a few response alternatives, and provide full information about what is coming. In general, improvements in technique lead to better performance, and when further attempts at improvement fail to transcend what had been accomplished earlier it is assumed that the limits of the sense have been measured. In these studies the experimenter establishes extremely accurate control of physical sources, and takes elaborate precautions to screen out unwanted stimulation. The various methods used are closely related and amount to minor procedural variations, but it requires close attention to make the interpretations of results convincing and precise.

The Basic Methods: Constant Stimuli and Paired Comparisons

In the method of constant stimuli the subject is presented with a certain fixed standard stimulus and a second variable stimulus, and asked to judge whether the variable is, say, lighter or not, heavier or not, louder or not, bluer or not. The subject may be given three alternatives (heavier, equal, or lighter), or a forced two-choice problem (heavier or lighter), or an inclusive two-choice problem (heavier or not heavier). The variable stimuli, which usually range on both sides of the standard, are given in random and unpredictable order.

Paired comparison methods give the same sort of presentation and responses, but there is no fixed standard—the subject is simply given two stimuli and asked which is the heavier, etc.

Closely related to the method of constant stimuli is the usual procedure for detection studies. The subject is given various weak stimuli (including no stimulus on some trials) and required to report when he detects the stimulus. Again, stimuli of various strengths are presented in random order. This is precisely like the method of constant stimuli if the intertrial interval, when no stimulus at all is given, is thought of as a "standard."

These methods are basic mainly because of the simple randomizing control for disturbing effects and the fact that the response itself is simple and has a high degree of face validity. Failures of accurate discrimination must either represent limitations of the senses or the random interference of nonsensory factors in response, and cannot reasonably be attributed to an intellectual failure of the subject. Of course, when these methods are used with children or with lower animals it is not sure that they have the idea—but if this is a problem in the basic methods it is almost certain to be a more serious problem in the other methods.

Method of Limits

The method of limits is very like the basic methods except that the situations are presented not in random but in systematic order, and not all of the situations in a particular measurement are given. In assessing the absolute threshold, for example, the experimenter may take two measures, starting first with a very weak or with no stimulus and increasing it by steps until the subject detects it. The crossover point from failure to detection is then taken as an estimate of threshold. In the second measurement the experimenter starts with a strong stimulus which is always detected and reduces it step by step until it is no longer detected, obtaining another crossover point. These are the "ascending" and "descending" methods of limits. The two estimates may differ systematically because the subjects respond differently when in doubt. More complex distortions occur if the ascending and descending series are always started at the same point, for the subject can respond with perfect consistency merely by counting the number of steps. Actually subjects do not usually count, but they certainly have the feeling that they "should be seeing it by now" if the usual number of steps have been traversed. Some variation in the starting points is therefore introduced in most experiments, but it is not certain just how effective this is. Other biases are discussed later.

The method of limits is frequently used, despite these systematic biases, because it saves time, permits an easy computation of a threshold, and leads to measures which indicate great sensitivity. Recall that in standard psychophysics the "best" measure is that which gives the greatest sensitivity. Extreme sensitivity can be attained in the method of limits because the subject can "point" his attention for the critical trial, knows just about when it should arrive, and is not at all bothered by the recent presentation of stimuli of very high strength. Particularly in the descending series the subject receives continuous support for his schema or "ideal stimulus" during the series, and is trained very efficiently for an optimal response. Unfortunately, in the descending series any tendency to perseverate response, or any development of a tendency to say "yes" to parts of the situation other than the stimulus in question, will be confounded with discriminative performance. Hence sensitivity may be overestimated by this method, and "catch" trials are needed to measure the amount of overestimation. The optimal psychophysical method for detecting very weak stimuli is probably the descending method of limits with frequent catch trials inserted at just the critical stimuli. That is, the series is run from stronger to weaker but at threshold a stimulus of *zero* strength is frequently inserted. Positive response to a zero-strength stimulus is of course spurious. Correction for spurious responses ("false alarms") is discussed in the next section of this chapter.

On some occasions it is important that the subject *not* have a clear idea of the situation to be presented. An example is the study of perceptual defense, where the threshold for detecting a disturbing stimulus, such as a picture with sexual connotations or a word which has previously been accompanied by electric shock, may be higher than normal. Another possibility is that such stimuli will have lower-than-normal thresholds (vigilance). In such studies the stimulus must be a surprise to the subject, and yet the aim is to measure a threshold. For this purpose the ascending method of limits is useful: a very weak stimulus is presented and its strength is increased step by step until it is first detected or identified. By this method the threshold can be measured without contamination from superthreshold presentations of the stimulus. This procedure, however, leads to quite serious difficulties of interpretation, since it does not follow that a stimulus is ineffective psychologically just because a certain detection response has not been made, and there is no way to estimate and correct for the ordinary biases of the method of limits, let alone other effects introduced by using special stimuli.

Theory of Judgments in Psychophysical Experiments

"Absolute" and "differential" thresholds are not conceptually very different. It does not matter theoretically whether the experimenter shows a dim light and asks the subject whether he sees it, or shows two stimuli and asks which is brighter. In both cases detection is required, either of the stimulus itself or of a difference between two stimuli. In another approach, both are comparisons; the individual stimulus is compared with no stimulus or two stimuli are compared with one another.

According to the theory introduced in Chapter 2, a judgment always requires the subject to compare the present situation with ideal situations. The purpose of a discrimination experiment is to determine which ideal situations can be separated by the subject. Two or more ideal situations are set up, by instruction or training, and then test situations are presented to see if the subject can respond differentially. In the basic methods, the test situation is identical with one of the ideals. For example, the person may be shown a display with no light, and another display with a very dim light. Through training, an attempt is made to establish two contrasting ideal situations, without and with light. Responses "no" and "yes" are attached to these ideal situations to complete the schemata. On test trials, either no light or a weak light is shown, and the subject is required to respond yes or no. In principle his difficulties, if any, arise not because he cannot decide whether the test is more like the light or the no-light situation but because he cannot tell the difference between the two ideals in a reliable fashion.

Now consider any two ideals, S_1 and S_2, and a test situation S. Suppose that on this trial $S = S_1$; what is the probability of response 1? According to the theory of Chapter 2,

$$P_1 = \frac{m(S \cap S_1 \cap \bar{S}_2)}{m(S \cap S_1 \cap \bar{S}_2) + m(S \cap \bar{S}_1 \cap S_2)} \tag{7.1}$$

However, $S = S_1$, so the set $S \cap \bar{S}_1$ is empty, and so is its subset, $S \cap \bar{S}_1 \cap S_2$. Hence, if $m(S \cap S_1 \cap \bar{S}_2) = m(S_1 \cap \bar{S}_2)$ is not 0, $P_1 = 1$. But any difference between the ideals would ordinarily mean that $S_1 \cap \bar{S}_2$ is not empty, and therefore P_1 will almost always be 1.

There is no threshold, according to this approach, and the person always judges correctly.

Since this is not what happens, the theory is wrong. In fact, since the theory does not permit anything interesting to happen, it is entirely useless for analyzing discrimination data.

One possible revision is to say that S or S_1 and S_2 suffer from random perturbations. The trouble is that in Chapter 2 probability theory was developed in terms of the basic set of situations. To introduce another, extraneous source of randomness would be theoretically inelegant. Furthermore, the process of suppressing aspects is a random device, added earlier through necessity. Still another randomizer would severely damage the theoretical program. The point is not that there is no randomness in the system—there certainly is—but that we should find it within the theoretical resources already developed, and not merely add it. For the idea of random variation of the situation S requires some set of situations S^* which may be present when a certain target is displayed, and a probability distribution over this set S^*. But what is the set S^*, and what will be the form of the probability distribution? The writer cannot think of any good way of deciding such questions.

In any experiment there exist not only the physical targets but also other sources of stimulation impinging on the subject: proprioceptive impulses, visual and auditory activity (which may or may not be associated with external stimuli), and in fact all the consequences of the fact that the person is alive and functioning and his nervous system is in continuous, if somewhat undirected, activity. This random stimulation or "noise" might serve the purpose of reducing performance except for one thing. When the stimuli are sufficiently clear and distinctive, noise has no noticeable effect on behavior. A subject suppresses irrelevant stimulation under many conditions. If he cannot successfully suppress it, in the context of a psychophysical experiment, why not? The noise is minimized by controlling the environment, the subject is highly motivated to attend to stimuli, and the problem is clearly defined. There are several possible answers to this question, but here let us consider a possibility which seems interesting and which has implications beyond the narrow problem before us.

Homogeneous Aspects and the Notion of "Pure Quantity"

Against a black background, an intense light is more discernible than a dim one, and against silence a loud noise is more powerful than a soft one. In a set-theoretic treatment of aspects, the intense light has more aspects, or a greater measure of aspects, than the dim light. If the two lights had the same aspects but different measures, this would mean using at least two measure functions—in fact, since there are many levels of brightness, a great many measure functions; and this would lose all the benefits of using set theory.

However, although the bright light has more aspects than the dim one, the bright light seems to be an unanalyzed whole. There is no way of deciding which aspects of the bright light are the same as those arising from the dim light and which are new. Suppose that the set of aspects of the bright light is B and of the dim light is D, and $m(B) > m(D)$. If the bright light is just like the dim one in every quality except brightness, it seems natural to think that $D \subset B$. However, from set-theoretic algebra it follows that

$$m(B) - m(D) = m(B - D)$$

where $B - D$ is the set of aspects in B but not in D. Under the slightly idealized conditions that were stated above, it is impossible to define the set $B - D$. The aspects in the set D are exactly like those in $B - D$, and there is no actual situation which has aspects from $B - D$ and not from D.

The particular situation produces this difficulty. If a bright *square* were presented in a field of dim circles, it would have both "squareness" and "brightness" aspects. A dim square would have only "squareness" aspects in this surround. The difference between these two sets would consist of "brightness" apects, which could be presented by putting a bright circle in the field of dim circles. In this case, the larger set L, the smaller set S, and the difference $L - S$ would all be meaningful and associated with stimulus situations which can be produced. Technical difficulties might arise but at least it is apparent what is to be done in the laboratory.

In the case of bright and dim lights differing in no other way, the problem is conceptual. There is no way to produce a situation with aspects $B - D$, nor is there any conception of what the result should look like. It appears, intuitively, that such a situation if produced must be a light just like the bright and dim ones, but not so strong as the brighter of the originals. However, suppose that $m(B) = 2m(D)$. Then $m(D) = m(B - D)$. The dim light and the light representing $B - D$ would have exactly the same brightness, and they must look exactly alike in every other way—the lights corresponding to sets D and $B - D$ are indistinguishable. This means that any response which will be made to one will also be made to the other. Psychologically speaking, the sets D and $B - D$ are equivalent. The only natural representation is to write

$$D = B - D$$

which, since $D \subset B$, is false unless B and D are empty. Hence the set-theoretic assumptions lead to contradiction. There are several other forms of this same difficulty, and many ways of expressing it. However, it is essential to notice that the difficulties arise when the aspects of a situation are all alike.

To say that a bright and dim light are exactly alike except for their brightness is to claim that the difference is solely quantitative— the brighter light is merely "more of the same." In the ordinary use of set theory this is not an admissible concept, though it seems to be sensible in psychology.

Consider the set-theoretic status of the idea of "more of the same." Compared with a set, A, composed only of the number 1, i.e., $A = \{1\}$, a set B would consist of "more of the same" if it were, for example,

$$B = \{1, 1\}$$

Either B does not exist (the symbol on the right is written incorrectly) or $B = A$. Remember the rule that an element is written and counted no more than once in a given set—the rule which leads to the theorem that $m(X \cup Y) = m(X) + m(Y) - m(X \cap Y)$, in Chapter 1. Without this rule the algebra of sets and the notion of a measure function would change entirely.

Set theory cannot express "more of the same" where "same" means "identical." However, psychological theory needs a concept of equivalence or indistinguishability of elements within a class so as to say that a bright light is "more of the equivalent" elements.

Fortunately this need is not psychology's alone. Physicists dealing with subatomic particles have some of the same difficulties when they try to express the fact that all electrons are exactly alike, or all photons are indistinguishable. Having this problem, they have formulated answers of one kind or another. These answers are embedded in the particular mathematical framework appropriate to physics, but some of the abstract characteristics of their answer can be used to help clarify the present problem.

First, the physicist makes it clear that he is talking about individual elements which are indistinguishable *in principle*, not merely because of technical difficulties. When the physicist says that all of a beam of photons are the same, he means that he cannot single any one out and study it. The reason for this is complicated and physical, but it hinges on the idea that no conceivable technical advance would permit such analysis.

Another even more striking fact is that the gross outcome of physical experiments requires a concept that elements are not distinguishable. As Schrödinger (1950) describes it, there might be three instruments which will record the arrival of a particle, and a record of just two photons. Suppose further (as can be assumed with relative impunity in a large-scale experiment) that every possible outcome of the experiment is just as likely as any other. If the photons are numbered 1 and 2, and the three counters are A, B, and C, then the experiment can come out in the following nine ways:

Counter

A	B	C
1, 2		
1	2	
1		2
2	1	
	1, 2	
	1	2
2		1
	2	1
		1, 2

Now, of course, it is not technically possible to tell which photon is which but frequencies are recorded. The observable outcomes of the experiment, along with their frequencies of occurrence, are then as follows:

Counters Hit and Number of Hits	Frequency
A hit by 2 photons	1
A hit by 1, B hit by 1	2
A hit by 1, C hit by 1	2
B hit by 2	1
B hit by 1, C hit by 1	2
C hit by 2	1

It is twice as likely that the two hits are to separate counters as that both hits occur on a single counter. This is called "Boltzmann statistics." The deduction required that the two photons be given separate identities, assigned the numbers 1 and 2, so that A being hit by photon 1 and B by 2 and A being hit by photon 2 and B by 1 could be distinguished. But suppose the two photons are fundamentally indistinguishable. Then it is meaningless to distinguish the two cases—all that can be said is that A and B were both hit, once each.

This approach yields only six possible outcomes of the experiment:

Counter

A	B	C
xx		
x	x	
x		x
	xx	
	x	x
		xx

If each of *these* six outcomes has the same probability, it is just as likely that one counter is hit twice as that two different counters are hit. This is a very different conclusion from the one above. This case is called the "Boze-Einstein" statistics.

The difference in the experimental outcomes can be determined, though of course much more complicated cases, with more counters and more particles, will be used. Experiments with photons come out in accord with the Boze-Einstein rather than with the Boltzmann statistics.

Schrödinger explains what is going on in a very general way which applies to psychology quite as well as it does to physics. He points out that the common-sense idea is that any entity has an "identity," that it is unique and exists through time, as do gross physical objects. Consider this from the point of view of epistemology; how would one *know* an object exists through time? What are the observations?

An individual observes a sequence of situations, close together in time, and so far as the object in question is concerned these situations change only continuously. As he moves his hand in front of his face, the position of the hand never changes radically in any one instant, and the hand does not pop in and out of existence. With a vast accumulation of such cases, a person comes to expect continuous changes, so that if a book disappears he asks a reason consonant with the idea that it continued to exist—he looks for the trick. If a pencil is missing from a person's desk he assumes it fell off, or was carried away, or something; he never assumes that it has temporarily ceased to exist.

The criterion of identity of an object is that situations do not change abruptly and without cause, so far as that object is concerned. Subatomic particles, says Schrödinger, do not have identity in this sense—they change abruptly and radically from one state to another. Thus they do not actually have that property of continuity which would be necessary to give them fixed identity, and any attempt to "track" one of them would lead to hopeless confusion since the abrupt changes would leave the investigator in doubt. Suppose an experimenter is tracing two particles in states A and B, and then one particle changes to state C and another to D at the same time. The experimenter has no way of knowing whether the one in state C is the one which was in A or the one which was in B.

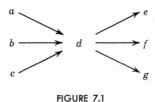

FIGURE 7.1

One reason the aspects making up a bright light might not have identities is the way they proceed through the optic tract. There is reason to think that the passage of a signal through a neural network is discontinuous, for effects coming in to a neuron leave whenever the neuron fires. In Fig. 7.1, impulses from neurons a, b, and c converge on neuron d, and d then fires, stimulating e, f, and g. The identity of the train of events is lost in the convergence. The three impulses from neurons e, f, and g, can in no way be paired up with the impulses coming from a, b, and c. Of course, exactly the same argument applies whether the effects of a, b, and c on d are direct synaptic stimulation or the build-up of electric potentials.

If a set of nerve impulses all move through the same relatively homogeneous mass of nerve tissue, there is no possibility of tracking any particular individual trail. If it is agreed that "stimulus aspects" correspond either to individual neural paths or to sets of such paths, it follows that in some cases the stimulus aspects are entirely and in principle indistinguishable.

This means that the only difference between the bright and the dim light is to be found in the frequency of action of the set of neurons involved, and not in which neurons fire. This explains why the set of aspects from the bright light, B, and the set from the dim light, D, can be defined, but not the set $B - D$.

The discussion above gives some idea of the mathematical properties of a class of indistinguishable elements. A more general summary statement will now be attempted.

Consider a class I of i indistinguishable elements. From this class, 2^i subclasses can be constructed. Since the elements of I are considered indistinguishable, they all must receive the same weight in computing the measure of any class, whence we let the measure of a class S be the number of elements in it, $N(S)$.

The point of saying that the elements are indistinguishable is that any two classes behave in the same way provided they have the identical number of elements in them. To say that two classes behave in the same manner amounts to saying that any function of one is equal to the same function of the other. Hence, all subclasses of I can be divided into $i + 1$ categories: those which have measures of $0, 1, 2, \cdots, i$. Any function of class S, which has n members, must have the same value as the same function of S' which also has n members. Hence the function can be written on n as well as on the classes.*

To define a class of indistinguishable elements, consider a family $\mathcal{F}$ of functions. In psychological applications, $\mathcal{F}$ is the set of functions which relate aspects to other things. For mathematical reasons it is helpful to specify that none of the functions has any of its range in I. Then

DEFINITION: I is a class of indistinguishable elements if, for every function F in $\mathcal{F}$, and for any subclass X of I, there exists a function f such that

$$F(X) = f[N(X)]$$

The reason the function F cannot range over I is this. Consider the function $F(X) = X$, a "class-valued" function. Let X and Y be two distinct classes such that $N(X) = N(Y)$. Then by the

---

* Here we are using the mathematical definition of a function, which is some assignment of elements of a set X onto elements of a set Y such that every element of X corresponds to exactly one element of Y. Then X is the domain of the function and Y is its range.

definition, $F(X) = f[N(X)] = f[N(Y)] = F(Y)$. But $F(X) = X$ and $F(Y) = Y$, whence $X = Y$. This contradicts the assumption that X and Y are distinct classes.

With this restriction, the idea that $F(X) = f[N(X)]$ amounts to saying that any psychological effect that X may have depends only on $N(X)$, the number of elements in X. This in turn makes X only a representative of its magnitude, and explicates pure quantity divorced from any qualitative variations.

This concept of homogeneous classes can be applied to the problem of false alarms and response biases, and leads to formulas similar to those put forward by Luce (1959a).

Detection of a Single Target

In detection, the subject's instructions are to say "yes" if he detects a certain target and "no" when no target is detected. If the target is sufficiently weak the subject will say no on some trials when the target is present, and will probably say yes on some trials when there is no target, giving "false alarm" responses.

In this case there are two ideal situations, one containing the target and leading to the yes response, the other having no target and leading to the no response. In such an experiment there will certainly be stimulus aspects other than those of the target, and we call all such aspects "noise." The subject can suppress most of these noise aspects, but suppose that there is some class I of noise aspects which is indistinguishable from the class T of aspects of the target. Let the other aspects, which are present whether the target is given or not, and which are distinguishable from the target, be named B, the background class.

Imagine that the subject is in situation S which contains the target. This situation has the aspects $T \cup I \cup B$ in common with ideal S_1, and the aspects $I \cup B$ in common with ideal S_2. If in the course of deciding the subject comes on an aspect in the class B, which is in $S_1 \cap S_2$, he will come to no decision and start over. However, if the subject comes on an aspect in $T \cup I$, he does not know whether to respond or not. Some of those elements are in $S_1 \cap \bar{S}_2$ and should lead to response yes, and some are in $S_1 \cap S_2$ and should be suppressed, but the subject cannot decide whether or not to suppress them because the differential and the common elements of $T \cup I$ are indistinguishable.

Imagine that certain aspects in $T \cup I$ are not suppressed, and the subject finally responds. These elements are in the class

$S \cap S_1$, of course, and they are also in $S \cap S_2$. The only difference is that there are more such elements in S_1 than in S_2, for S_1 contains $T \cup I$ and S_2 contains only I. Then,

$$P(\text{yes} \mid T) = \frac{m(S \cap S_1)}{m(S \cap S_1) + m(S \cap S_2)} \tag{7.2}$$

where S, S_1, and S_2 designate subclasses of the homogeneous class of aspects.

The subject is free to assign some of these aspects to the response yes and some to the response no, but the only way he can do this is by controlling the measures $m(S_1)$ and $m(S_2)$. Imagine that these indistinguishable aspects are divided so that some fraction y of them are in S_1, and $1 - y$ are in S_2; then y represents the tendency to say yes to the indistinguishable aspects. Now, when the target is present in S,

$$m(S \cap S_1) = ym(T \cup I) \quad \text{and} \quad m(S \cap S_2) = (1 - y)m(I)$$

so that

$$P(\text{yes} \mid T) = \frac{ym(T \cup I)}{ym(T \cup I) + (1 - y)m(I)} \tag{7.3}$$

The author is not sure how to prove it, but by analogy with the physical theories of indistinguishable particles he thinks that one should say that

$$m(T \cup I) = m(T) + m(I)$$

Making this assumption,

$$\begin{aligned} P(\text{yes} \mid T) &= \frac{ym(T) + ym(I)}{ym(T) + ym(I) + m(I) - ym(I)} \\ &= \frac{ym(T) + ym(I)}{ym(T) + m(I)} \end{aligned} \tag{7.4}$$

Now consider the response to a new situation in which there is no target, $\bar{T}$. Let the indistinguishable aspects of this situation be called S'. Clearly,

$$m(S' \cap S_1) = ym(I) \quad \text{and} \quad m(S' \cap S_2) = (1 - y)m(I)$$

Hence,

$$P(\text{yes} \mid \bar{T}) = \frac{ym(I)}{ym(I) + (1 - y)m(I)} = y \tag{7.5}$$

Equation 7.4 gives the probability of a correct detection as a function of $m(T)$, the strength of the target aspects, $m(I)$, the strength of indistinguishable noise elements, and y, which represents a certain bias or tendency to say yes when in doubt. Equation 7.5 gives the probability of a false alarm, a yes response when there is no target, which turns out to be y. These equations can be used to calculate the probabilities of yes responses, correct and false alarms, as a function of the size of the target. However, it is possible to use them another way, to study the effects of y, and this problem is particularly interesting.

It has been known for a long time that subjects make false alarms in detection studies, but the classical solution was to try to eliminate these false responses by instructing the subjects to be careful, by throwing out data which showed too many false alarms, etc. A second approach was to correct the data for guessing, by the formula.

$$P(\text{corrected}) = \frac{P(\text{yes} \mid T) - P(\text{yes} \mid \bar{T})}{1 - P(\text{yes} \mid \bar{T})} \qquad (7.6)$$

However, this formula commits one to an empirical regularity. If it is valid one should find $P(\text{corrected})$ a constant for constant target and viewing conditions, as $P(\text{yes} \mid T)$ and $P(\text{yes} \mid \bar{T})$ are varied. An experimenter can vary $P(\text{yes} \mid T)$ and $P(\text{yes} \mid \bar{T})$ by telling the subject to be more careful or to take more chances ("you are missing too many signals"). When this is done, Eq. 7.6 can be rearranged [letting $P(\text{corrected}) = k$] into the form

$$P(\text{yes} \mid T) = k + (1 - k)P(\text{yes} \mid \bar{T}) \qquad (7.7)$$

which says that $P(\text{yes} \mid T)$ should be a linear function of $P(\text{yes} \mid \bar{T})$. Some experiments on this problem by Tanner and Swets (1954), repeated since then, have made it clear that $P(\text{yes} \mid T)$ is *not* a linear function of $P(\text{yes} \mid \bar{T})$.

Using the discriminal-processes theory, and embedding the problem within the conceptual structure of statistical decision theory, Tanner and Swets put forward a possible explanation of their findings. Imagine that the situation without target produces an effect on the receptor which varies randomly—a discriminal dispersion. Suppose that the situation with target produces a similar dispersion, but with higher mean, and suppose that the two dispersions overlap. The subject cannot always be right. However, he can establish a criterion or cutting score, so that every stimulus above that value is called yes and every stimulus below that value is called no. In Fig. 7.2 are shown two discriminal dispersions, with and without target, and a criterion cutting line C. The hatched area represents $P(\text{yes} \mid T)$, the stippled area $P(\text{yes} \mid \bar{T})$. As the criterion C is moved back and forth, both

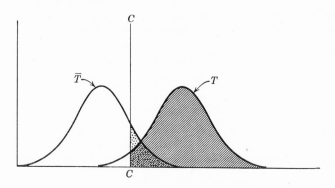

FIGURE 7.2

$P(\text{yes} \mid T)$ and $P(\text{yes} \mid \bar{T})$ change together, and the relationship between them is a curved line, called the Receiver Operating Characteristic function or just the ROC curve. Several representative curves are given in Fig. 7.3.

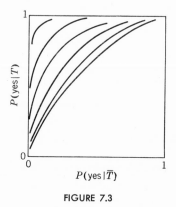

FIGURE 7.3

More recently, Luce (1959) reconsidered the ROC curve and derived, from his theoretical position, the formula

$$P(\text{yes} \mid T) = \frac{\alpha P(\text{yes} \mid \bar{T})}{(\alpha - 1)P(\text{yes} \mid \bar{T}) + 1} \qquad (7.8)$$

where α represents the strength of the target stimulus. This Eq. 7.8 is sufficiently close to the data to be acceptable, and is much more convenient to work with than the curves developed by Tanner and Swets (shown in Fig. 7.3).

Returning to the present theory, we can put Eqs. 7.4 and 7.5 together and obtain, by simple algebra,

$$P(\text{yes} \mid T) = \frac{[m(T) + m(I)]P(\text{yes} \mid \bar{T})}{m(T)P(\text{yes} \mid \bar{T}) + m(I)} \qquad (7.9)$$

This is identical with Luce's equation (Eq. 7.8). Notice that under the experimental conditions $m(T)$ and $m(I)$ are constants. Therefore, define the constant

$$\alpha = [m(T) + m(I)]/m(I)$$

Now, if every term of the right side of Eq. 7.9 is divided by $m(I)$, and the definition of α is introduced, Eq. 7.8 is obtained.

The curves in Fig. 7.3 and the functions, Eq. 7.8 and 7.9, tell us that for a particular weak target on a given background the subject will locate himself somewhere on a certain curve. We still must decide where on that line the person will be.

Tanner and Swets (1954) say that the person is at a point which maximizes his expected utility. They imagine that there exists an implicit or explicit table of utilities

	Target present	Target absent
Respond yes	u_{11}	u_{12}
Respond no	u_{21}	u_{22}

and an a priori probability π that the target will be present. Any choice of $P(\text{yes} \mid T)$ and $P(\text{yes} \mid \bar{T})$ (they must be chosen together, being functionally related) will yield an expected utility, for which an optimum can be found. The nature of the optimum itself will not concern us here.

A similar approach, using the maximum expected utility, was derived by Luce using Eq. 7.8, though Luce is doubtful about the accuracy of the expected utility hypothesis.

Both of these approaches give a way of determining the position the person should take on the curve, depending upon his payoffs and penalties and on the frequency with which the target is presented, but they do so by imposing on the subject a stringent criterion of rationality. In the present theory it is possible to locate the subject in a simpler way, without a rationality assumption, using the results of Chapters 4, 5, 6. Consider first the effect of π, the frequency with which the target is presented.

Suppose that through pretraining or a similar technique the subject realizes that on π of the trials the target is present and on $1 - \pi$ of the trials the target is absent. This will be represented, in the present theory, by proportional numbers of schemata of the two types. By the same principles which led to the analysis of Binder and Feldman's data on recognition (p. 96), this should mean that y, the probability of assigning homogeneous aspects to the response yes, should be proportional to π, the frequency of target presentations, other things being equal.

The "utilities" $u_{11}, \cdots$, are of doubtful meaning in the present theory according to the results of Chapter 4. However, if correct detection of the target is made valuable to the subject (has many valued aspects), this should have the effect of increasing the measure of each situation in which the response is yes, whereas penalties for false alarms should increase the measure of the situation in which the response is no. Each experience, then, will be weighted according to the payoffs, and the measures of these payoffs will combine with the probabilities π.

The detailed influence of π on $P(\text{yes} \mid T)$ and $P(\text{yes} \mid \bar{T})$ will be considered here, for this problem keeps clear of the awkward questions about utilities. According to the present model, if the effects of payoffs are constant, from Eq. 7.5, $P(\text{yes} \mid \bar{T}) = y$ should be proportional to π, the frequency of presentation of the target,

$$P(\text{yes} \mid \bar{T}) = k\pi \qquad (7.10)$$

Now consider a special case in which $m(T) = 3m(I)$, which by translation into Luce's formula means that $\alpha = 4$. Let the payoffs be such that when $\pi = .5$, $P(\text{yes} \mid T) = .5$, so that in Eq. 7.10 $k = 1$.

These special restrictions on the strength of stimuli and on the utilities make it possible to vary π and observe how the person will react. In the present theory, with $k = 1$,

$$P(\text{yes} \mid \bar{T}) = \pi \qquad (7.11)$$

from Eq. 7.10. Without developing Luce's optimization formula here (it is rather complicated in form), its consequences can be demonstrated in the same special case. In Fig. 7.4 is shown the "optimal" $P(\text{yes} \mid \bar{T})$ as a function of π calculated from Luce's optimization formula, along with the curve from Eq. 7.11. The optimization function generates negative values of $P(\text{yes} \mid \bar{T})$ when π is small, and values greater than

1 when π is large. It is assumed that values of 0 and 1 are the attainable optima when the calculation leaves the allowable range.

A careful experimental test of these conflicting hypotheses should be made, including also the even more complicated formulas required by the discriminal-process model of Tanner and Swets. Notice that the optimization formula used in Fig. 7.4 gives the impression that if the subject were shown a target on 90% of the trials

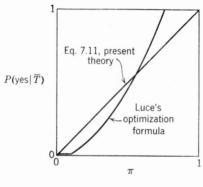

FIGURE 7.4

he would always say yes, producing 100% false alarms. This seems unlikely, even with the subthreshold stimuli dealt with in this experiment.

The main advantage claimed for the present model in this question of how the false alarm rate varies with the frequency of the target is that it does not depend upon an indirect argument that the subject "optimizes" in a rational way, but instead is directly related to experimental studies of how frequency affects choice probabilities.

Detection of Multiple Targets

When a soldier watches a radarscope, his instructions and the frequency of targets have established a value for the parameter y of Eq. 7.3, and the strength and clearness of images on the scope will determine $m(T)$ and $m(I)$, or, in more concise form (since only the ratio of the two is important), the discriminability parameter $\alpha = m(T \cup I)/m(I)$. Simplifying Eqs. 7.3 and 7.4,

$$p = P(\text{yes} \mid T) = y\alpha/[1 + y(\alpha - 1)] \qquad (7.12)$$

and

$$p' = P(\text{yes} \mid \bar{T}) = y \qquad (7.13)$$

Imagine that targets come not one but many at a time, and consider the probability that this soldier will detect k of a presentation of n targets. The complete calculations can be carried through even if the various targets have different discriminabilities, and with sufficient patience they can be completed for any (known) dependencies between the detections of the several targets. However, the theoretical question can be illustrated by the case in which the detections of the dots are independent random events, all of which have the same probability p of detection and p' of false alarm.

Without false alarms, Schlosberg's probability theory of multiple detection (Schlosberg, 1948; Casperson and Schlosberg, 1950) applies. Let p be the probability that any one target (dot) is detected, and $q = 1 - p$. Consider any particular subset of k of the n targets. The probability that all of those k targets will be detected (independently) is p^k, and the probability that all of the other $n - k$ targets will be missed is q^{n-k}. There are, however, $\binom{n}{k}$ distinct sets of k dots which might be detected. Hence the probability that k of n dots will be detected becomes

$$P(k;\ n) = \binom{n}{k} p^k q^{n-k} \qquad (7.14)$$

which is the binomial distribution. This leads to a variety of particular probabilities which may be interesting: The probability that at least one dot is detected is $1 - q^n$; the probability that all n dots are detected is p^n; the mean number of dots detected is pn, and the standard deviation of the number of dots detected is $\sqrt{npq}$.

However, there is also a possibility of false alarms, for the soldier may report a target when there is none. In order to deal with false alarms, consider that there are just N possible targets. These "possible" targets might be defined by laying a grid on the scope, fine enough so that there would not be two targets in the same place but coarse enough so that targets in adjacent places could be detected independently. There is probably no exact solution to this requirement experimentally, but the difference between using a fine grid and a low value of p', the false alarm probability for each place, or a coarser grid and a higher value of p', would have no large effect on the analysis of the data.

To derive the probability that the soldier will report k dots when there are n dots present, in a grid which could contain N dots, divide the k dots reported into r dots which are actually there and are reported, plus $k - r$ dots which are not there but which are falsely reported. The probability of reporting r of n dots is

$$\binom{n}{r} p^r q^{n-r}$$

Of the $N - n$ spaces which do not have any dots, the soldier reports $k - r$ of them as false alarms, each of which has probability p'. Let $q' = 1 - p'$. The probability of reporting $k - r$ dots falsely is

$$\binom{N-n}{k-r} p'^{k-r} q'^{N-n-(k-r)}$$

A report of k dots may be made up of any combination of r detections of dots which are there (from $r = 0$ to k) along with a false report of $k - r$ of the absent dots. If detections and false alarms of different dots are independent, the joint probability of reporting r dots correctly and $k - r$ dots falsely is the product of the separate probabilities. Since all of the combinations of r and $k - r$ are mutually exclusive, the probabilities for the various values of r are added to get the final probability,

$$P(k;\, n, N) = \sum_{r=0}^{k} \left[\binom{n}{r} p^r q^{n-r} \right]\left[\binom{N-n}{k-r} p'^{k-r} q'^{N-n-(k-r)} \right] \quad (7.15)$$

This distribution, the convolution of two binomial distributions (Feller, 1950) has a mean of $np + (N - n)p'$ and a variance of $npq + (N - n)p'q'$, and is all in all fairly manageable for experimental purposes. The theoretical point was illustrated in a recent experiment (Restle, Rae, and Kiesler, 1961) in which it was shown that four dots separated at the points top, right, bottom, and left are detected with reasonably independent probabilities. As was mentioned in that paper, one application might be to the question of detectability of a set of n targets, such as would result in case of a mass attack on defenses, or a breakdown of a machine the output of which is being controlled. The probability of detection of at least one target is given by the simple expression

$$P(1, \cdots, N;\, n, N) = 1 - q^n q'^{N-n} \quad (7.16)$$

TECHNICAL NOTE: In applications the number N of possible stimuli may be entirely indeterminate, except that it is large, and at the same time p', the probability of any particular false alarm, is very small. Given a record which makes it possible to estimate the total number of false alarms in a large number of trials, it would be natural to replace the second binomial distribution by a Poisson approximation, letting Np', which would correspond to the observed number of false alarms per trial, be a constant and letting N become very large. The theory and methods are given in Feller (1950, Chapter 11).

Differential Thresholds

If two stimuli are presented together and the subject is to say whether they are the same or different, some subjects will show a strong tendency to say yes, others no, and the results do not tell very much about the resolving power of the sense unless they are controlled by many "check" trials in which the stimuli are actually the same. With check trials the methods given above can be used, if one considers the difference between the two objects to be the target.

A more common and satisfactory technique is to present two targets which differ in, say, size, and ask the subject which is larger. This is a kind of forced-choice technique. The situation presented, S, involves two objects or sources of energy; the ideal situations S_1 and S_2 each contain two objects. In the ideals, S_1 has the larger object on, say, the left, and S_2 has the larger object on the right. The variable might be hue, loudness, weight, or any other difference between objects, and the two positions might be left and right, first or second in order, or any other arrangement which is convenient for experimental purposes. In a discrimination experiment, S is either identical with S_1 or with S_2. For discussion purposes, consider a trial in which $S = S_1$.

Following the argument given earlier for detection experiments, assume that the subject tries to match S with either S_1 or S_2. Performance would be perfect but for the indistinguishable elements in $S_1 \cap S_2$, which form a homogeneous class with $S_1 \cap \bar{S}_2$ and $\bar{S}_1 \cap S_2$. Restrict attention to this homogeneous class of aspects, interpreting S, S_1, and S_2 as all being classes of the homogeneous aspects.

The aspects in which S is like S_1 include all the difference $S_1 \cap \bar{S}_2$, which we may call T_1, along with some of the common aspects in $S_1 \cap S_2$. The rest of the common aspects make S like S_2 and lead to response 2. Consider that the common aspects are divided so that $v_1 m(S_1 \cap S_2)$ of them lead to response 1, and $(1 - v_1)m(S_1 \cap S_2)$ of them lead to response 2. Here, v_1 plays a role like that of y in the theory of detection—it might be called a response bias (Luce, 1959a). Then the probability of response 1, when $S = S_1$ (or target T_1 is presented), is

$$P(1;\ T_1) = \frac{m(T_1) + v_1 m(S_1 \cap S_2)}{m(T_1) + m(S_1 \cap S_2)} \qquad (7.17)$$

Similarly, the probability of response 1 when $S = S_2$, i.e., when the target $T_2 = \bar{S}_1 \cap S_2$ is presented, is

$$P(1; T_2) = \frac{v_1 m(S_1 \cap S_2)}{m(T_2) + m(S_1 \cap S_2)} \qquad (7.18)$$

The subject has the problem of distributing the aspects in $S_1 \cap S_2$ to the two responses. Suppose that the two ideals have occurred equally often, so that frequency is not a factor, but $m(T_1) > m(T_2)$, so that $m(S_1) > m(S_2)$. Since the aspects in $S_1 \cap S_2$ are not distinguishable from one another, the assignment can only be in terms of measures. The proportions of $S_1 \cap S_2$ assigned to the two ideals cannot be different from the proportions of differential elements, of $T_1 \cup T_2$, assigned to the ideals, for the common aspects are indistinguishable from the target aspects. It follows that v_1, the proportion of $m(S_1 \cap S_2)$ assigned to ideal S_1, must be

$$v_1 = m(T_1)/[m(T_1) + m(T_2)] \qquad (7.19)$$

To work out the algebra, a simplified notation for the measures of these classes of indistinguishable elements is used. Let:

$$t_1 = m(T_1)$$

$$t_2 = m(T_2)$$

$$c = m(S_1 \cap S_2)$$

Now,

$$v_1 = t_1/(t_1 + t_2)$$

Rewrite Eqs. 7.17 and 7.18 as

$$P(1; T_1) = P_{11} = (t_1 + v_1 c)/(t_1 + c) \qquad (7.17a)$$

and

$$P(1; T_2) = P_{12} = v_1 c/(t_2 + c) \qquad (7.17b)$$

These equations permit an explanation of the "time-order error" in the measurement of differential thresholds.

One clear-cut example of the time-order error is reported by Stevens (1957) in the measurement of loudness thresholds. Two tones were sounded, first a standard and then a variable tone, one after the other. The subject was to judge whether the variable was louder or softer than the standard. Results showing the time-order error are illustrated in Fig. 7.5; notice that when the variable is the same as the standard, it is judged louder almost 75% of the time.

There are many interpretations of this effect, which is quite generally observed. Since the second of two equal stimuli is judged greater than the first, a natural approach is in terms of "sinking traces." However, this interpretation does not hold up very well, especially since the effect can be obtained even when the two stimuli, standard and variable, are presented simultaneously. The peculiar thing about these results is that they hinge on which stimulus is the standard and which is the variable or comparison stimulus. Explanation for the effect cannot, therefore, be based on discussion of the sensory experiences themselves, but must depend upon the judgment and an asymmetry between standard and variable.

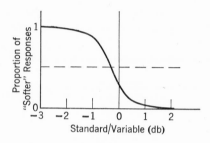

FIGURE 7.5

In the present model the difference between a standard and a softer variable is called T_1 and the difference between a standard and a louder variable is called T_2. Response 1 is, then, the response "softer," and T_1 is the situation when the variable is softer than the standard (the left side of Fig. 7.5), T_2 when the variable is louder than the standard (the right side of Fig. 7.5).

In the case of loudness (or any other variable of intensity or amount) the louder tone has a greater total measure of aspects. That is, $m(S_2) > m(S_1)$, hence $t_2 > t_1$, which means that $v_1 < 1/2$. The consequences may be seen by a numerical example. Let $c = 1$, taking the measure of common aspects as the unit of measurement. Let $t_1 = 2$ and $t_2 = 6$, so that $v_1 = 0.25$. For the softer stimulus, from Eq. 7.17a,

$$P_{11} = (2 + 0.25)/(2 + 1) = .750$$

whereas, with the louder stimulus, from Eq. 7.17b,

$$P_{12} = 0.25/(6 + 1) = .036$$

The larger stimulus on the right is judged accurately (.964 correct), whereas the smaller stimulus on the left has produced less accurate performance (.750 correct). Now consider what will happen when the variable stimulus is just like the standard, so that $t_0 = 0$. Inserting t_0 for t_1 in Eq. 7.17a or for t_2 in Eq. 7.17b,

$$P(1;\ T_0) = P_{10} = v_1 c/c = v_1$$

In the numerical example $v_1 = 0.25$, so the variable stimulus should be called softer only .25% of the time—this is the time-order effect!

Notice that the time-order effect is explained as a bias of the subject, produced even though the situations themselves, and their aspects, are in no way distorted. The person does not see things incorrectly, nor does he have a systematic distortion of memory (as in the falling-trace theory). The effect is solely due to the fact that the ideal situation for the judgment "louder" has a greater measure than the ideal situation for the judgment "softer." The remainder of the argument says that the "noise" aspects which are indistinguishable from the differences between the ideals are distributed to the two ideals in proportion to their measures. The validity of this argument hinges on the interpretation of the concept of "indistinguishable" aspects, which is a difficult point. The writer would conclude that the argument is coherent except that the concept of indistinguishable elements is not yet sufficiently developed and clarified. Certainly, though, the theory is controversial and should be criticized, for it does not fall under the heading of obvious or familiar psychological thinking.

Note that the time-order error will occur only if the ideals, S_1 and S_2, have different measures. In the case of tones which differ in frequency but not intensity, there is no reason to expect that the "lower" and "higher" ideals will have different measures. According to Stevens, the time-order error does not occur at all in judgments of frequency; it is consistently present in measurements of quantitative variables like loudness, brightness, size, and weight, and consistently absent in such qualitative variables as frequency and hue.

Biases in the Method of Limits

The method of limits gives the subject the same kind of choice he has in the basic methods, except that the stimuli are presented in a fixed order, increasing or decreasing. Consider the measurement of an absolute threshold by this method. Start with a strong stimulus to which the subject is almost certain to say yes, and decrease it step by step until he first says no. It is natural for the subject to consider each situation with respect to the previous one, so that in this case the common aspects will tend to have a high bias toward yes; the parameter y in Eq. 7.3 will be high. If we were to start with an extremely weak stimulus and increase it, the subject would start saying no and presumably the value of y would be low.   Let the value of y in the descending series be y_1, and in the ascending series be y_0, with the assumption that $y_1 > y_0$.   Imagine further that the stimuli are changed in equal steps.   In the ascending series, let $m(T)$ take the values $1, 2, 3, \cdots$ and in the descending series the values are $M, M-1, M-2, \cdots$.   Let $P_0(\text{yes} \mid t)$ be the probability of a yes response to a stimulus of strength t when in the ascending series, and $P_1(\text{yes} \mid t)$ be the probability of a yes response to the same stimulus in the descending series.   Then, letting $m(I)$ be a constant c,

$$P_0(\text{yes} \mid t) = \frac{y_0(t + c)}{y_0 t + c}$$

and

$$P_1(\text{yes} \mid t) = \frac{y_1(t + c)}{y_1 t + c}$$

There is a tendency to give more yes responses in the descending than the ascending series.   It would appear that the crossover point from yes to no would be low in the descending series, giving a low threshold, and the crossover point from no to yes in the ascending series would be higher, giving a higher threshold.   This is correct, except that there is a competing factor.   Experimenters sometimes mark the *first* crossover of response as the estimate of the threshold. This reverses the trend described above, for the subject's first yes response in the ascending series may be at a fairly low stimulus value, when the probability of yes is less than $1/2$.   This effect will lower the threshold in the ascending series, and *mutatis mutandis*, raise the threshold in the descending series, tending to counter-balance the biases mentioned above.

In order to see how this might work, the writer developed an example of the present model, using targets of size 0 to 9, $y_0 = 0.1$ and $y_1 = 0.2$, and $c = 1$.   The probability of a yes response for each stimulus, in an ascending-descending series, is shown in Table 7.1.

TABLE 7.1

PROBABILITY OF YES GIVEN TARGET OF SIZE t COMPUTING EXAMPLE OF THE
METHOD OF LIMITS

Size of t	0	1	2	3	4	5	6	7	8	9
Ascending	.100	.182	.250	.308	.357	.400	.437	.470	.500	.526
Descending	.200	.333	.428	.500	.556	.600	.636	.667	.693	.714

From Table 7.1 we see that the probability of a yes is higher in the descending than in the ascending series, and one might expect the threshold to be at about $t = 8$ in the ascending series, about $t = 3$ in the descending series.

However, suppose that the first yes response in the ascending series is called the threshold, and the first no response in the descending series is similarly called the threshold. The probability that the first yes in the ascending series is at $t = 0$ will be .100. The probability that the first yes is at $t = 1$ will be $(1 - .100)(.182) = .164$. The probability that the first yes is at $t = 2$ will be $(1 - .100 - .164)(.250) = .184$, etc. The same computation from the other end, working with probabilities of no responses, produces a distribution of "first-noes" for the descending series. The resulting distributions of "threshold measures" are shown in Fig. 7.6.

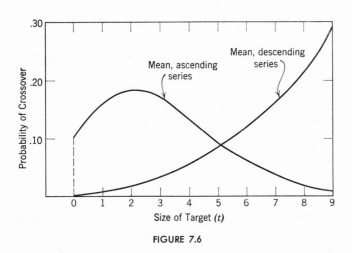

FIGURE 7.6

In Fig. 7.6 the threshold in the ascending series is at about 3, and the threshold for the descending series is about 7. This is the exact opposite of the expectation given above. The use of the *first* reversal as the indicator of threshold takes systematic advantage of chance. If the stimuli are closely packed together and the subjects try to make independent judgments at each trial, the result will be to raise the threshold in the descending series, and to lower it in the ascending series. There is a tendency for the first stimuli in the series to be "threshold indicators" simply because the later stimuli never have a chance if the first ones do show a reversal of response.

The two factors shown in Table 7.1 and Fig. 7.6 reveal that two systematic biases operate in the method of limits, in opposite directions. For practical purposes this means that the method of limits is not easy to interpret in an exact way. For theoretical purposes it would be interesting to determine the conditions under which ascending series give lower thresholds than descending series, and the reverse.

Some Unsolved Mathematical Problems

The idea of homogeneous aspects presents certain mathematical difficulties that have not been resolved above. The discussion makes it clear that we cannot use the algebra of sets or the usual notion of a measure function on classes of homogeneous elements. Strictly speaking, the set-theoretic connectives, ∩, ∪, and ⁻, are meaningless in the context of the present chapter. Since some such connectives were needed the author employed the set-theoretic symbols, but in the present chapter they are used only by an imperfect analogy.

Some of the difficulties found by the writer are listed here so as to give a lead to the reader who is inclined to logical or mathematical inquiries. The arguments given in this chapter are not correctly stated. The problem is to find either a system of connectives and rules of inference for classes of homogeneous elements which do what is needed for the psychological problems or a proof that no such system exists. The reader should feel free to change the approach in whatever way is necessary to obtain sensible results.

The difficulties center around the question, "How homogeneous are homogeneous elements?" The concept of homogeneity or indistinguishability arises because the subject cannot make infinitely fine discriminations, and it seems useful to say that he cannot find any experiential difference between some differential and some common aspects in a discrimination experiment. Management of these indistinguishable elements, in theoretical formulas, becomes difficult because ordinary set-theoretic algebra cannot be used safely. This difficulty led to the concept, "more of the same." Despite the importance of the concept of homogeneity, it became clear that homogeneous elements are not identical in the usual sense. Some of a class of homogeneous elements may come from a target and others from the background. The subject cannot tell them apart and the experimenter cannot present one subclass separate from the other, yet the two subclasses are different and "measures" or magnitudes are assigned to them separately in order to compute the probability of detection.

One unanswered question is whether the class of elements arising from the target and the class arising from the background can have any common elements. Similarly, what relationship holds between two subclasses and the whole class, particularly in magnitude? It has been assumed above that the sum of the magnitudes of two subclasses equals the magnitude of their "union" or combination. Although this seems natural, such a rule is difficult to state sensibly in general form. Imagine that a class C is divided into two subclasses A and B, so that the magnitudes of A and B, combined, equal the magnitude of C, using the formula $m(A) + m(B) = m(C)$. However, if C were combined with A to produce a new class, D, it would be necessary to say that this new class is larger than C. Following in this way, it would seem that any class could be combined with itself over and over, and eventually produce a class of infinite magnitude. In set theory if a set is combined with itself or with subsets of itself, no such increase is obtained.

In the psychological application, it appears that combining two homogeneous classes must involve the presentation of two sources of stimulation. The physical or external sources of energy are ordinarily easy to distinguish, even though the stimulus aspects received by the subject cannot be separated. Combination of classes of homogeneous aspects can be done, the author supposes, only by joint presentation of two sources of energy.

A class of homogeneous elements may arise partly from one source of energy (stimulus) and partly from another, and may have two different effects on behavior, one subclass leading to one response and the other subclass leading to the other response. The essence of "homogeneity" is, in a sense, that external divisions of the aspects according to source and internal divisions according to effect on responses are not correlated, so that the experimenter cannot bring about one pure effect by any manipulation of the environmental conditions.

These closing remarks do not, in the writer's opinion, constitute a definition of a homogeneous class of aspects. Being unable to frame an adequate definition he has written around the point in the hopes of communicating the idea intended and giving the reader sufficient background for him to be able to formulate the ideas clearly.

CHAPTER
EIGHT

Theory of Compound Responses

Thus far in this book, the response has been taken to be an unanalyzed whole which either happens or does not happen, and its probability of occurring has been studied. Measurements of reaction time or latency may also use the concept of probability of the response. However, greater theoretical flexibility is attained by supposing that the observed response is composed of parts all of which must be accomplished before the response is recorded.

It is always possible to analyze a given response into finer components, and the present theory, since it is not committed to any particular level of analysis, can be used at more than one level. Working at fine levels of analysis requires that the parts or components of the response be recorded separately, and this is sometimes beyond the technical capabilities of the experimenter. For example, auditory reaction time is studied later in this chapter by analyzing the simple response into a chain of internal physiological reactions within the subject. In principle there is no objection to inspecting this process by filling the subject with microelectrodes, but the technical difficulties are great. Applying the theory to the reversal of ambiguous figures, it is supposed that several partial changes must take place before the figure is seen to reverse. The partial changes are not directly observed. Similarly, though the solution of simple puzzles is described as involving several stages, it is difficult to record the subject's progress through the stages without disrupting the behavior.

In these examples the existence, number, and behavior of "parts" of a response are hypothetical. The method used is to find hypotheses leading to estimates of the number and behavior of the parts; then other properties of the data can be deduced from the estimates. It may happen that the parts can be isolated experimentally, but such experimental programs will be helped if indirect evidence has previously been collected and brought to bear on the problem, defining the size and kind of parts which should be expected and defining the properties they should display. In other fields of science it has sometimes happened that the existence and nature of small events are virtually established, entirely on the basis of indirect macroscopic evidence. This can be done only when the macroscopic evidence is so well formulated that detailed and elaborate deductions, usually mathematical, can be performed.

Sometimes the detailed behavior can be recorded by methods presently available, but is so complex that one wishes to deal only with the end result of behavior, not its intermediate steps. An example is the method of adjustment in psychophysics, in which the subject changes a variable stimulus so as to make it just like another stimulus or to bring it into some specified relationship with other stimuli. The actual process of adjustment involves a few sweeps back and forth, followed by an extended period of small adjustments this way and that before the subject is satisfied. It is easy to record the final settings, and they are the source of the main information desired. It is also feasible to track the entire course of adjustment, but this would soon collect such a mass of detailed tracings that analysis would be most forbidding. Yet to ignore the process of adjustment is dangerous, for the final setting certainly is the product of this complicated process. It is convenient to describe the process of adjustment by an abstract model and investigate the end products of that model, thereby making it possible to consider how the process determines its product without becoming lost in detailed data.

Elementary Theory of Waiting Times

Consider a series of occasions $i = 1, 2, \cdots$ on which a certain response might occur, and imagine that if it has not occurred by occasion k there is a certain fixed probability p, which is independent of i, that it will occur on occasion $k + 1$. In studying reaction time, we usually are interested in the *first* occurrence of the event. We now consider the probability $P(i; p)$ that the event first occurs on occasion i. The first trials are easily calculated:

$$P(1; \; p) = p$$

$$P(2; \; p) = p(1 - p)$$

for the event can occur at time 2 only if it does not occur at time 1 (which has probability $1 - p$) and then if it does occur at time 2, which has probability p. For the same reason,

$$P(3; \; p) = p(1 - p)(1 - p) = p(1 - p)^2$$

In general,

$$P(i; \; p) = p(1 - p)^{i-1}, \qquad \text{the } \textit{geometric distribution} \qquad (8.1)$$

Thus, if the event has a fixed probability p of occurring on each occasion and is a single unitary event, one can expect the distribution of reaction times or latencies to follow the geometric distribution. It may happen that one measures reaction time with a good clock and would prefer to deal with this distribution as a function of continuous time. Suppose that the various occasions are infinitely brief and numerous, in which case, of course, there is only a vanishing probability that the event will occur in any one occasion. However, let the probability of the event occurring in an interval of length h be $p(h)$ and the length of the interval $h \to 0$; under the conditions imposed for the geometric distribution $p(h)/h$ approaches a constant λ independent of time. Here λ is the "rate" or probability per unit time. By methods which are familiar from calculus, taking the limit the geometric distribution approaches a density function

$$f(t; \; \lambda) = \lambda e^{-\lambda t}, \qquad \text{the } \textit{exponential distribution} \qquad (8.2)$$

The geometric and the exponential distributions have about the same psychological meaning, except that the geometric distribution deals with discrete trials or opportunities, the exponential with continuous time. Both distributions express the waiting time for unitary events.

Some events can be thought of as the end result of a sequence of part-events, each of the parts being a unitary event. Suppose, for example, that five things must happen before a reaction appears, and that the reaction occurs just at the fifth event. Suppose, furthermore, that the five events must all occur on different occasions, but that otherwise each event (until it happens) has probability p of occurring.

Imagine that the fifth event occurs in trial n. This means that one of the components occurs on trial n and that there are exactly four other components scattered somehow over the first $n - 1$ trials, and $n - 5$ trials on which no component occurs.

On each trial there is probability p that a component occurs and probability $q = 1 - p$ that no component occurs. Thus, for any particular arrangement which puts the fifth event at trial n, the probability is $p^5 q^{n-5}$. However, there are a great many ways the four earlier components can be distributed over the $n - 1$ earlier trials, if n is large. The number of ways four events can be distributed over $n - 1$ trials is the binomial number $\binom{n-1}{4}$ and each of these arrangements has probability $p^5 q^{n-5}$. Hence the probability that the fifth event occurs at trial n is given by

$$P(n;\ p,\ 5) = \binom{n-1}{4} p^5 q^{n-5}$$

More generally, if the event requires the completion of r stages,

$$P(n;\ p,\ r) = \binom{n-1}{r-1} p^r (1-p)^{n-r},$$

the *negative binomial distribution*   (8.3)

(Feller, 1950, p. 218).

The negative binomial distribution corresponds to the geometric in that it deals with events which have a constant probability and which occur on discrete trials. It differs in that the final event which is observed at trial n is not a unitary event, but rather is the end of a chain of r components; in other words, the negative binomial distribution deals with *compound* responses.

Going from the negative binomial to continuous time, following the path from the geometric to the exponential distribution, leads to another distribution known as the gamma distribution. The result is stated without any attempt to prove it, because it requires mathematical methods not already introduced into the book; again a "rate" λ appears, r is the number of components in the response, and measurements are in continuous time t:

$$P(t;\ \lambda, r) = \lambda \frac{(\lambda t)^{r-1} e^{-\lambda t}}{(r-1)!},\quad \text{the } \textit{gamma distribution} \quad (8.4)$$

The negative binomial and gamma distributions are based on the assumption that all r parts of the response are alike in probability and are independent of one another so far as probability of occurrence is concerned. What compound response can be broken up into such equal components? Perhaps none. However, if a response is analyzed into parts and the occurrence of the various parts is not recorded, detailed differences between parts are not known. In empirical meaning the binomial and gamma distributions constitute a "model" of the response which may provide some idea of its inner complexity without being like the response in all ways.

Table 8.1 gives some of the properties of the four distributions.

TABLE 8.1

PROPERTIES OF FOUR DISTRIBUTIONS FOR REACTION TIME

Distribution	Time Scale	Mean	Variance	Nature of Event	Shape of Distribution
Geometric	discrete (n)	q/p	q/p^2	unitary event	extreme positive skew (J-shaped)
Negative binomial	discrete (n)	rq/p	rq/p^2	r component events	becomes more nearly symmetrical as r increases
Exponential	continuous (t)	$1/\lambda$	$1/\lambda^2$	unitary event	J-shaped
Gamma	continuous (t)	r/λ	r/λ^2	r components events	becomes more nearly symmetrical as r increases

Whether to employ discrete or continuous distributions depends on the nature of the experimental measurements. If a clock is used and the subject is always free to respond, the continuous models are suitable. If the situation is divided into discrete trials and the subject can only respond on those trials, the discrete models are picked.

The choice of a model of a unitary response or a compound response can often be made empirically. Study of the distributions will reveal that the negative binomial, with $r = 1$, is the geometric distribution: the gamma, with $r = 1$, is the exponential.

Application to Simple Reaction Time

In an elaborate and careful study, Chocholle (1940) measured the reaction times of several experienced subjects to pure tones of varying frequency and intensity. One characteristic of the data, remarked on but not used by Chocholle, is the following: The standard deviation of the reaction times was proportional to the mean reaction time over the whole range of data collected. Figure 8.1 plots the means and standard deviations for one set of data. Notice that over a range of reaction times from about 110 to over 300 milliseconds (ms) the standard deviation is almost exactly 10% of the mean.

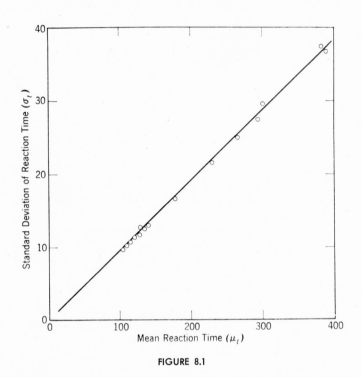

FIGURE 8.1

Since the measurements are in continuous time and there may be some number r of component events involved in a finger reaction to a tone, the gamma distribution is applied. From Table 8.1,

$$\sigma_t{}^2 = r/\lambda^2$$

and

$$\mu_t = r/\lambda$$

Therefore

$$\mu_t{}^2 = r^2/\lambda^2$$

and

$$\mu_t{}^2/\sigma_t{}^2 = r \qquad (8.5)$$

Since in our example $\sigma = 0.10\mu$,

$$\mu_t^2/\sigma_t^2 = 100 = r$$

This calculation indicates that over the whole range of tones the number of components in each response is approximately 100.

The idea that there are about 100 stages involved in a simple reaction to sound suggests that the stages represent individual synaptic connections or similar microneural events. The idea that a chain of about 100 cell actions is required to complete a simple reaction is not unreasonable in terms of the gross anatomy of the nervous system. With a maximal auditory stimulus, the mean reaction time is only about 105 ms, which suggests that at the best these stages can be passed at a rate of about 1 per ms—a number which agrees with the measurements of the afferent chain (Chocholle, 1940, p. 105).

Furthermore, Chocholle found that reaction time depends upon the loudness level of the tone: two tones of different frequency which would be matched for loudness yield the same reaction time. A further point noted about the Chocholle data (Chocholle, 1940; Woodworth and Schlosberg, 1954) is the relationship between mean reaction time and intensity of the stimulus. Assume that the effect of a stimulus of intensity I is some power of that intensity, I^a (Stevens, 1957; Luce, 1959b; Warren, 1958; and Chapter 9 below). According to the formulas developed earlier for the probability of a response, ignoring possible false alarms and other details,

$$p = \frac{m(T)}{m(T) + m(B)}$$

where B is some set of "background" aspects and T is the set of target aspects. However, $m(T)$ will depend upon intensity of the stimulus and $m(B)$ will be approximately a constant. Therefore, the probability of a response should be given by a formula like

$$p = \frac{I^a}{I^a + c}$$

where a and c are constants.

In the gamma function, the parameter λ is "probability of events per unit time." Therefore,

$$\lambda = b\,\frac{I^a}{I^a + c}$$

where b is a constant controlling the time scale. Recall that mean reaction time μ is r/λ. Therefore,

$$\mu_t = \frac{100}{\lambda} = \frac{100(I^a + c)}{bI^a}$$

$$= \frac{100}{b}(1 + cI^{-a})$$

By a rearrangement of terms,

$$\left(\mu_t - \frac{100}{b}\right) = \frac{100c}{b}I^{-a} \qquad \text{or} \qquad (\mu_t - \alpha) = \beta I^{-a}$$

whence

$$\log(\mu_t - \alpha) = \log \beta - a \log I$$

This long series of transformations has the final effect of saying that there exists some constant α which may be subtracted from the mean reaction times; and the net reaction time is a power function of intensity, so that a log-log plot will be linear. An example

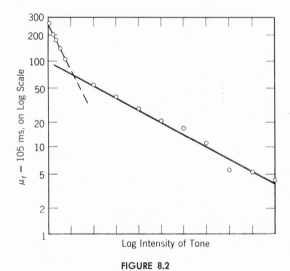

FIGURE 8.2

of such a fit is shown in Fig. 8.2, taken from Woodworth and Schlosberg (1954, p. 22). Although the formula is the same as that used by Woodworth and Schlosberg and by Chocholle, the argument given here is somewhat more complete and rigorous.

The fit of the function to the long reaction times, at very low intensities, is not good, and Woodworth and Schlosberg chose to put in a second line, shown dashed in Fig. 8.2. Actually, the difficulty is in part due to the fact that subjects respond only rather erratically to such weak stimuli, sometimes missing the stimulus completely and sometimes responding when there is no stimulus. They give false alarm responses here as in detection studies. The result is that Chocholle felt it expedient to throw away the extreme and peculiar observations, and the data cannot be taken too seriously (see Chocholle, 1940, p. 81).

Although this is by no means a treatise on reaction time, two relationships which make sense have been found: the constant ratio of standard deviation to mean, and the functional dependence of mean reaction time on intensity of the stimulus. With respect to the use of standard deviations, it should be remarked that Chocholle computed standard deviations for the performance of each subject over a series of well-controlled reactions. These are intended to be *minimum* standard deviations. If various subjects were mixed together or experimental control were loose, this might increase σ and not change the mean very much—producing quite distorted impressions of the number of components in the response.

Application to the Theory of Reversible Figures

There are several figures which yield two perceptions equally easily, so that the subject experiences a shift or reversal of

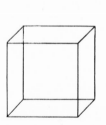

FIGURE 8.3   FIGURE 8.4

the figure. One type of reversal is that of perspective, e.g., the Necker cube shown in Fig. 8.3, and another is of figure and ground, as in the "Maltese cross" of Fig. 8.4. The cube may appear as a three-dimensional perspective drawing in either of two orientations, and commonly reverses between the two appearances on extended viewing. The cross may be seen as a white "X" on a black ground, or a black "+" on a white ground, and alternates between these appearances.

One of the first observations fitting the present approach was published by Bruner, Postman, and Mosteller (1950) regarding reversals of a reversible perspective drawing, the Schröder staircase. They noticed that the number of reversals per minute (which was the only form of data recorded) were approximately described by the Poisson distribution,

$$f(r, \lambda t) = e^{-\lambda t}(\lambda t)^r/r \tag{8.6}$$

However, as is mentioned by Feller (1950, Chap. 11), given a continuous sequence of events each with an exponential waiting time distribution, then the distribution of number of events per unit time will be Poisson. In other words, the observation by Bruner et al. of a Poisson distribution of number of reversals per minute would follow if the times between reversals are distributed exponentially. This, in turn, should mean that reversals are unitary random events. Actually, a small discrepancy from the Poisson distribution was found. Bruner et al. did not pursue this theoretical direction, but instead satisfied themselves by finding a transformation of scores which would yield relatively normal distributions with approximately equal variances. They then proceeded to employ analysis of variance techniques on their fairly complicated experiment.

The writer, seeing the possibilities of further exploitation of this theory, first performed a small experiment on himself. The Necker cube was viewed with a fixation point in the center for extended trials, and the time of reversals was recorded. The exponential distribution, by an elementary integration, yields the fact that the probability of a waiting time longer than t is given by

$$P(t) = e^{-\lambda t}$$

so that

$$\log_e [P(t)] = -\lambda t$$

with a large sample of N reversals the number of times longer than t, which we may call $N(t)$, will be approximately $N \cdot P(t)$, whence

$$\log_e [N(t)] = \log_e [N \cdot P(t)] = \log_e (N) - \lambda t$$

The data were plotted in terms of the $\log_e$ of the number of reversals which took more than t seconds, as a function of t. If the exponential distribution fits, the results should be a descending straight line. Figure 8.5 shows the results of the experiment.

These data seemed promising, so the problem was followed out more carefully by two students, R. Hoppe and L. Potter, at Michigan State University. The first experiment used a variation of the Maltese cross which had three white and three black segments.

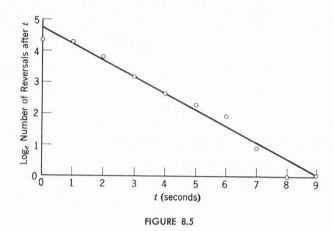

FIGURE 8.5

Close inspection of the distribution of reversal times led to the rejection of the exponential distribution in favor of the gamma with $r = 3$, i.e., with a three-stage or three-part response. The coincidence that a switch from seeing three white to seeing three black segments should

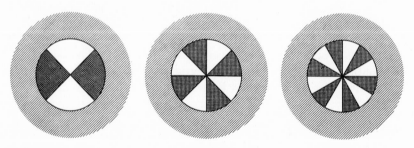

FIGURE 8.6

appear to have three parts led to a further study performed by Potter. Maltese crosses were made with two, four, and six black segments of white and black each on a mid-gray background, as shown in Fig. 8.6. Reversals were recorded on a moving tape so as to give essentially continuous measurements. The mean and variance of the holding times produced by each subject were computed, and using Eq. 8.5 it was predicted that the square of the mean divided by the variance would give us an estimate of r, the number of stages in a single reversal. The conjecture was that the three figures in Fig. 8.6 would give different values of r, in the neighborhood of 2, 4, and 6. However, the results were quite erratic and the gamma distribution did not fit the distributions very well. Five of nine subjects tested showed the expected trend in values of r, but not all of those yielded values in the neighborhood of 2, 4, and 6. The writer's conjecture, after extended observation, is that visual fatigue sets in within a minute or two and produces disorganization of the figure, so that the whole figure or at least parts of it desaturate and show no clear figure-ground organization at all. This effect is not easily avoided because it takes several minutes for the reversal pattern to stabilize. Hence, for the present it is not possible to report that this random model for reversals of perceived figures has any solid experimental support.

Solution of Eureka Problems by Individuals and Small Groups

In some problems the subject is given all the necessary information at the beginning but is required to come up with some particular idea which will lead to the answer. In such problems it is often a question whether the subject's solution involves only a single idea or a sequence of several ideas all of which must be invented and integrated. Inspection of a problem gives some idea of the number of psychological stages involved in its solution, and study of detailed verbal protocols is also useful, but one would prefer some simple objective index of the number of stages involved. This requires a decision on the consequences of having several stages in the problem.

The waiting-time theory employed in the study of simple reaction time and figure-ground reversal earlier in this chapter can be applied to the case of simple problem-solving. The assumptions to be used are fairly extreme, so that a careful empirical test of the ideas is called for.

Imagine that solving a problem involves r steps, and that the time to complete each step has an exponential distribution $\lambda e^{-\lambda t}$. Suppose further that each step has the same rate of solution λ and that all subjects who solve the problem do so by completing the same r stages, all with the same probability (rate) λ. Then the distribution of solution times of the problem as a whole will have the gamma distribution, Eq. 8.4.

This theory has been developed by James H. Davis in his dissertation problem at Michigan State University. Davis' first finding was encouraging; the distributions of solution times of large numbers of undergraduate students were adequately fit by gamma distributions. What is more, Davis used three problems which a priori seemed to involve different numbers of stages. There is no adequate independent measure of the number of stages in a problem, but several staff members and graduate students agreed that the problems differed in number of stages in a certain order. Previously it had been found that large numbers of undergraduate students would also agree quite well to the number of stages in problems of this sort. Judgments of the number of stages in various problems varied from 1 to some number less than 10. When gamma distributions were fit to the distributions of solution times on the three problems, the estimates of r (the number of stages) varied in the predicted order, ranging from 1.3 to 5.0.

The above results, though interesting in their own right (for they verify a theoretical prediction of the form of the distribution of solution times, and even permit reasonable identification of the parameters of that distribution), were merely preliminary to Davis' main problem. His further developments lead the argument slightly astray from the main point of this chapter, but they clearly show how a problem is clarified and enriched by a suitable mathematical analysis and are included for that reason.

The general question, which has been investigated before, is whether subjects working in small discussion groups are helped, interfered with, or unaffected by the group. This question, which seems entirely empirical, actually requires some theory for its answer, since one must decide precisely what level of group performance corresponds to the statement that subjects are unaffected by being in the discussion group.

Davis began with the Lorge-Solomon (1955) model of group problem-solving. Lorge and Solomon supposed that groups solve Eureka problems with higher probability than individuals simply because of the pooling of abilities and the fact that the group will get credit for solving when any individual in the group solves. If one knows that a proportion P_I of individuals will solve a problem, and if groups are formed at random from that population, it is possible to calculate the probability P_G that the group will solve, using the binomial distribution. Lorge and Solomon generalized the discussion by saying that a problem might consist of several stages—the solution of each such stage might follow the model sketched above—and that in this case a group might solve it even though no one person in the group alone could master all stages.

However, once the distributions of individual solution times had been collected to obtain the estimates of r, the number of stages, it became apparent that the Lorge-Solomon model was not the one needed. The reason is that the "proportion of solvers" among individuals or groups is a function of time. There will be few solvers in 3 minutes of working time, and more in 12 minutes. At any cutting time, the observed (actually, estimated) P_I for that time leads to a prediction of P_G. This calculation can be made for any time, and leads from individuals to a predicted distribution of group solution times. The calculations were made and the predictions were far from the data. This approach, of course, conflicts with the Lorge-Solomon assumption that the population is divided into two classes of people, solvers and nonsolvers.

Another approach is to apply the waiting-time theory more directly to the problem of group performance. Suppose that an individual has probability p of solving a stage of the problem in a time interval of length h. Then four people would have probability $1 - (1 - p)^4$ of solving the problem in that interval, if their contributions are independent. As the interval is taken smaller and smaller, p also becomes smaller, and $1 - (1 - p)^4$ gets closer and closer to $4p$. At the limit as in the gamma distribution, the result is that λ for a group of size 4, which we may call λ_4, is related to the λ for individuals, λ_1, by the equation $\lambda_4 = 4\lambda_1$. Now imagine that the theory stated above is correct; that the problem involves r stages, the solution of each of which is a random process with rate λ_1 for individuals, so that the individuals form a distribution of solution times $g(t; \lambda_1, r)$. Applying the argument just given about groups, the solution times of groups should follow the gamma distribution $g(t; 4\lambda_1, r)$, on the reasonable assumption that the size of the group cannot affect the number of stages required for solution. The gamma distribution $g(t; 4\lambda_1, r)$ specifies the whole distribution of group performance in advance, for λ_1 and r can be estimated from the performance of individuals.

Actually, this theory is similar in spirit to that of Lorge and Solomon. It gives a more complete prediction, in a simpler way and with a much more convenient method of calculation. Unfortunately, this model did not fit the data very well, for it gave almost exactly the same predictions as the Lorge and Solomon model which had been rejected as not factually correct. The groups tested did not solve as quickly as the theory predicted. Note that the theory merely attempts to make clear the idea that the individuals work, in the group, about as efficiently as they do as individuals. If actual groups are slower or less effective, some idea of "interference" is suggested.

Fortunately, a natural source of possible interference was found almost at once. On two of the problems, almost half the individuals failed to arrive at a correct solution, but instead found some wrong answer to give which apparently satisfied them. Drawn from the same population, the group members were presumably also apt to arrive at wrong answers, though it is unlikely that a whole group would agree on a wrong answer. The relative slowness of groups might, then, be attributed to the presence of a number of people who would not themselves come up with the solution; and it was also reasonable to suppose that they would take up their share of the time of the group.

Davis' group discussions were not sufficiently revealing for him to determine which, or even how many, members of a given group were on the wrong track. However, the individual performances indicated quite accurately what proportion of the population was nonsolvers, and the binomial distribution could be used to tell the proportion of groups which would have $0, 1, 2, \cdots$ solvers. Depending on the number of solvers and nonsolvers in the group, one could calculate its "group" rate of solution, λ_G, and the resulting gamma distributions could be averaged over the binomial distribution of composition of groups. The result of all of this is a predicted distribution of group solution times, based on a complicated but entirely manageable equation. As it happened, this prediction made a very good fit to the group data on all of three rather different problems despite fairly striking differences between problems in the estimates of λ_1 and r. The theory and experiment are not presented in great detail here, since Davis and the writer plan a more complete report in the journals in the near future.*

Davis' work shows, in the writer's opinion, that a theory of the present sort need not be limited in its applications to processes of sensation, perception, or simple learning which seem intelligible to us in detail, but can also be applied, with less confidence but perhaps even greater profit, to matters as mysterious as problem-solving, and even problem-solving in the context of group discussion. It cannot

* The writer is indebted to James H. Davis for permission to use this material before he had completed his own report, which was submitted as a doctoral dissertation to the College of Science and Arts, Michigan State University, 1961.

safely be assumed that Davis' particular model (for which the writer also had some responsibility) will be uniformly successful in comprehending all of group problem-solving, nor can it be concluded that people in groups are precisely as effective as they would be working alone. However, instead of introducing mysterious forces of group facilitation or inhibition, which in a mathematical model would at once be recognized as finagle factors, this approach leads directly to inspection of the details of the available data to find the advantages and disadvantages of group work. The road to complete understanding is long and stony, but Davis' results suggest it may be worth traveling.

The Psychophysical Method of Adjustment as a Random Walk

One of the most flexible and precise psychophysical methods is that of adjustment or average error, which can be used whenever the stimuli can be varied along a physical dimension. This method can be employed for measuring the absolute threshold (v. Békésy, 1959), but it is mainly used to measure differential thresholds. A standard stimulus is displayed along with a variable which is under the subject's control. The subject's task is merely to set the variable at a value which seems to him the same as the standard. The data appear in the form of a distribution of such settings.

The distribution of settings yields two numerical factors: (1) the response bias or "point of subjective equality," depending on the mean of the settings; and (2) the differential threshold, calculated as the standard deviation or the probable error of the distribution. The interpretation of the method is, however, incomplete. In discriminal-processes theory (Torgerson, 1958), the distribution of settings is an estimate of the distribution of discriminal processes. From that theory the method of adjustment seems the most primitive, and the comparison methods as indirect measurements of the same discriminal distribution. In the previous chapters, comparative judgments are primary: hence it is desirable to develop a theoretical representation of the process of adjustment based on discrete judgments.

A setting in the method of adjustment is not a simple act but the end of a dynamic process in which each transient setting leads to a judgment of too high (in which case the setting is lowered) or too low (in which case the setting is raised) until finally the subject accepts a certain setting. Each judgment is not recorded, but is allowed to affect the next setting of the variable stimulus. Data consist of final settings. This is a clear-cut example of a compound response, with the problem of determining the size and interactions of the components. Waiting-time theory does not apply because of the way the components are arranged. In reaction time, it was assumed that all of the components lead, in one direction, to the final response. The components are all direct contributors, and do not cancel one another out. Similarly, the reversals of parts of a figure were thought of as component events which combine to produce the recorded reversal. The whole point of the method of adjustment is that the various part responses, turning the control this way and that, cancel one another out.

In the method of adjustment, the variable stimulus is changed back and forth on some linear array of situations. This is like the movement of a point on a line. The point may either move up, move down, or remain where it is as a final setting. A move up corresponds to a judgment that the variable is below the standard, and a move down corresponds to a judgment that the variable is above the standard. At any particular stage of adjustment there are two stimuli and a judgment between them. The theory of Chapter 7 determines the probabilities of these two judgments, hence of changes in the two directions during adjustment.

The behavior of a point which may move in either direction on a line, with certain probabilities of moving to the right or left, is called a random walk. The general methods for solving such problems are discussed by Feller (1950, Chap. 15), and only a sketch of the solution to the present problem will be given here.

First, the subject not only moves the setting back and forth, making differential judgments, but he also makes a final judgment of "equality." The random walk is therefore a complicated one—the point moves back and forth on a line for a while, during adjustments, and then at some time falls through at the termination point. A complete solution involves the differential judgments, which are taken up below, and then also another judgment or decision to stop adjusting. The problem is made more manageable by ignoring the process of stopping, and merely considering the movements back and forth.

The steps moved by the point are not equal, for the subject ordinarily has a continuous variable stimulus which he moves at will; furthermore, the successive steps are not independent, for the subject may tend to keep moving in a particular direction once he starts. The movements are not all indicative of judgments, either, for a subject often runs the variable back and forth to both sides of the standard before beginning his final, fine adjustment. However, the process is idealized by ignoring nonrandom preliminary movements and considering just the process of fine adjustment. Also, imagine a subject who works very carefully, making small adjustments one way or the other, and then considering the situation each time, approximating separate independent moves. A further assumption, that the movements are of some unit amount rather than continuous and variable in extent, permits the use of a simplified mathematical structure. It should be recognized that these simplifying assumptions may be removed, at a price in mathematical difficulty, and that they are used merely to give an indication of the theoretical approach. A detailed experimental program would no doubt involve working through the general model.

Consider a subject at some stage in the process of adjustment, where the value of the standard is at 0 and the variable happens to be at $+t$. A comparison is made between the two. According to Eq. 7.17a, the probability that the subject will judge the variable larger than the standard is

$$p(1;\ t) = (t + v_1 c)/(t + c) \tag{8.7}$$

where t refers to the magnitude of the difference between variable and standard, c is the measure of the set of irrelevant aspects the subject cannot distinguish from the target and v_1 corresponds to a response bias. For the present, disregard response bias and let $v_1 = \frac{1}{2}$. Now, a judgment that the variable is larger than the standard should lead to a move to the left; hence the above probability is the probability of moving the variable one step to the left, from t to $t - 1$. With $v_1 = \frac{1}{2}$,

$$p_{t,t-1} = [t + (c/2)]/(t + c) \tag{8.8}$$

Since the probability of stopping is not considered, the probability of moving from t to $t + 1$ is equal to $1 - p_{t,t-1}$, so that

$$p_{t,t+1} = (c/2)/(t + c) \tag{8.9}$$

With no response bias the system is symmetrical, movements toward and away from the standard on the right being exactly the same as movements toward and away from the standard on the left. It is convenient to use only the right side of the distribution, since the left side will be its mirror image.

The only problem discussed here is to compute the "asymptotic" distribution of settings. Imagine that the subject continues to move the variable back and forth according to the model given. After a long while his starting position will have no residual effect, and he will move the variable back and forth without any net change in its average location.* The probability that the setting happens to be at some value of t during the final phase of adjustment will be some number u_t. We now attempt to compute the u_t.

Since the variable is assumed to be moved every time, the only way it can be at point t is that it was moved from $t - 1$ with probability $p_{t-1,t}$, or that it was moved from $t + 1$ with probability $p_{t+1,t}$. But in order for the variable to have been moved from $t - 1$ it must have been there, and it was there with probability u_{t-1}. Thus

$$u_t = u_{t-1}p_{t-1,t} + u_{t+1}p_{t+1,t} \qquad (8.10)$$

Solution of the infinite sequence of equations for the u_t which results from Eq. 8.10 is somewhat difficult, but can in principle be accomplished using Eqs. 8.8 and 8.9. A slightly more convenient computation results from the observation that, since the u's represent an asymptotic distribution, transitions of the variable stimulus cannot have any net effect on the distribution of u's. † Consider any pair of adjacent points, t and $t + 1$. Divide the whole asymptotic distribution into two halves, that part to the left of and including t, and that part from $t + 1$ to the right. There is some probability U_L that the variable is in the left half, and $U_R = 1 - U_L$ that it is in the right half. U_L and U_R will remain constant after a transition, on the average.

The variable stimulus can move from the left half to the right half, with probability

$$u_t p_{t,t+1}$$

and can move from the right half to the left half with probability

$$u_{t+1} p_{t+1,t}$$

Since there is to be no net change in U_L and U_R, these two "leaks" must have equal probability. Therefore,

$$u_t p_{t,t+1} = u_{t+1}p_{t+1,t} \qquad (8.11)$$

Cross-multiplying,

$$u_{t+1}/u_t = p_{t,t+1}/p_{t+1,t} \qquad (8.12)$$

---

* This is provable in a simple way if there are a finite number of possible settings and the subject moves indefinitely often—for we then have a finite Markov process which is ergodic. More general conditions are suggested by Lamperti and Suppes (1959).

† The author is indebted to Dr. Herman Rubin for suggesting the approach discussed here.

Introducing for the p's their values according to Eqs. 8.7 and 8.8,

$$u_{t+1}/u_t = \frac{(c/2)/(t+c)}{[(t+1+(c/2)]/(t+1+c)}$$

$$= \frac{(c/2)(t+1+c)}{(t+c)[t+1+(c/2)]}$$

or, letting $b = c/2$, for convenience,

$$u_{t+1}/u_t = \frac{b(t+1+2b)}{(t+2b)(t+1+b)} \tag{8.13}$$

Let the expression on the right-hand side of Eq. 8.13 be designated by a_t. If u_0 is the probability of being at the standard,

$$u_1 = a_0 u_0$$

$$u_2 = a_1 u_1 = a_1 a_0 u_0$$

$$u_3 = a_2 u_2 = a_2 a_1 a_0 u_0$$

In general,

$$u_{t+1} = \frac{[b(t+1+2b)][b(t+2b)]\cdots[b(1+2b)]}{[(t+2b)(t+1+b)][(t-1+2b)(t+b)]\cdots[(2b)(1+b)]} u_0$$

$$= \frac{b^{t+1}(t+1+2b)!/(2b)!}{[(t+2b)!/(2b-1)!][(t+1+b)!/(b!)]} u_0$$

$$= \frac{b^{t+1}(t+1+2b)b!}{2b(t+1+b)!} u_0$$

and

$$u_t = \frac{b^t(t+2b)b!}{2b(t+b)!} u_0 \tag{8.14}$$

Notice that the unit of measurement in Eq. 8.14 is the change in the stimulus. Fixing the measure of the irrelevant elements, $c = 2b$, gives a particular distribution. An example, for $c = 6$ and thus $b = 3$, is shown in Fig. 8.7. Equation 8.14 and computations such as in Fig. 8.7 give the shape of the distribution, but they do not give the actual probabilities unless all the computed values are "normalized" to add to unity. This merely requires solving for u_0, but is a sufficiently difficult task that the writer has not been able to accomplish it.

The main finding about the method of adjustment requires some fairly complicated reasoning about limits, but is worth following through. The proposition to be proved says that the subject can produce almost perfect matches if the movements of the variable stimulus are small enough and he continues to make independent judgments at each move. In practice, this is not a very interesting theorem in one way, for the limit is hardly attainable—with sufficiently

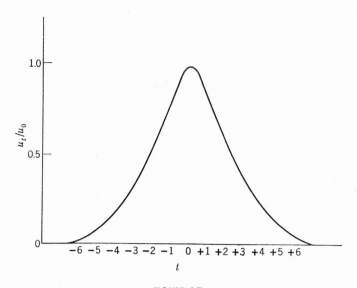

FIGURE 8.7

tiny movements the subject would take infinitely long to complete his adjustment. However, it indicates a trend. If movements of the variable are very fine and the subject is slowed down, the variability of the settings can be as small as may be wished.

As the unit of measurement is made smaller and smaller by making the steps of movement smaller and smaller, the numbers b and t in Eq. 8.14 both become larger. Imagine, therefore, that these numbers are to be increased by a factor of s, and s becomes infinitely large. Our theorem is the following:

Consider any point very near a perfect setting, so that $t/(t + b)$ is small but not 0. Then there is an s (corresponding to the fineness of the settings) so large that the probability of setting the variable stimulus as far away as $t/(t + b)$ approaches 0.

To prove this theorem, rewrite u_t as

$$u_{st} = \frac{(ts + 2bs)bs^{ts}(bs)!}{2bs(ts + bs)!} u_0$$

$$= \left(\frac{t + 2b}{2b}\right) \frac{bs^{ts}(bs)!}{(ts + bs)!} u_0 \tag{8.15}$$

When s becomes large, bs and $(ts + bs)$ will be large. The factorials of large numbers are very well approximated by Stirling's formula,

$$n! \cong \sqrt{2\pi}\, n^{n+\frac{1}{2}}e^{-n}$$

which becomes exact as s increases without bounds. Substituting this approximation for $(bs)!$ and $(ts + bs)!$ in Eq. 8.15,

$$u_{st} = \left(\frac{t + 2b}{2b}\right) \frac{bs^{ts}\sqrt{2\pi}\,(bs)^{(bs+\frac{1}{2})}e^{-bs}}{\sqrt{2\pi}\,(ts + bs)^{(ts+bs+\frac{1}{2})}e^{-(ts+bs)}} u_0$$

$$= \left(\frac{t + 2b}{2b}\right)\left(\frac{bs}{ts + bs}\right)^{\frac{1}{2}} \frac{bs^{ts}bs^{bs}e^{-bs}}{(ts + bs)^{ts+bs}e^{-(ts+bs)}} u_0$$

$$= \left(\frac{t + 2b}{2b}\right)\left(\frac{b}{b + t}\right)^{\frac{1}{2}}\left(\frac{b}{b + t}\right)^{(b+t)s} e^{ts} u_0$$

$$= \left(\frac{t + 2b}{2b}\right)\left(\frac{b}{b + t}\right)^{\frac{1}{2}}\left[\left(\frac{b}{b + t}\right)^{b+t} e^t\right]^s u_0$$

The relative size of the error of setting, relative to the indistinguishable elements b, is

$$T = t/b$$

Now,

$$u_{sbT} = \left(\frac{T + 2}{2}\right)\left(\frac{1}{1 + T}\right)^{\frac{1}{2}}\left[\left(\frac{1}{1 + T}\right)^{1+T} e^T\right]^{bs} u_0 \tag{8.16}$$

Notice that

$$e^T = 1 + T + \frac{T^2}{2!} + \frac{T^3}{3!} + \cdots$$

If T is very small, corresponding to a small error relative to b,

$$e^T \cong 1 + T$$

for the higher powers; T^2, T^3, $\cdots$, are negligible. Substituting this value in Eq. 8.16, and going to the limit in the constant terms which do not depend upon s, leads to

$$u_{sbT} = \left[\left(\frac{1}{1 + T} \right)^{(1+T)} (1 + T) \right]^{bs} u_0$$

$$= \left(\frac{1}{1 + T} \right)^{Tbs} u_0$$

which is the relative probability of making an error as large as T. Now notice that although the fraction $1/(1 + T)$ is very close to 1 it is always less than 1. If s increases without bound, the fraction on the right will approach 0. Hence

$$\lim_{s \to \infty} [u_T] = 0$$

for any T, however small, which is not 0.

The intuitive reason for this result is simple enough: the subject can make steps of only a fixed size, which in the limit are vanishingly small. Each step is made independently of any other. To obtain any significant error of setting, the subject would have to make a tremendous number of steps, a sizable proportion of which are in the wrong direction. With enough steps required in the very fine grain, the errors cancel out almost perfectly, and the process becomes almost determinate. Even a slight bias in probabilities—probability .51 of going in the correct direction and probability .49 of going in the wrong direction—will eventually pull the random walk to the true value.

The scatter of settings in the method of adjustment is, according to this analysis, not comparable with thresholds measured by the other psychophysical methods. The variability of adjustments depends partly on the smallness of steps and the independence of judgments, and thus will not be constant for given viewing conditions. In the method of adjustment the subject can use the location of the setting as an "integrator" which represents the sum of all his past individual judgments. The sum of the judgments is much more stable than individual judgments. From this argument the writer surmises that the variance of settings should be inversely proportional to the number of divisions in a given segment of the dimension, i.e., directly proportional to the fineness of grain of the settings. However, because of the difficulty of the distribution obtained, this idea remains a mere conjecture.

The above discussion can be extended to the method of adjustment with a bias v_1 not equal to $1/2$, using Eqs. 7.17 and 7.18.

The first observation is that very fine adjustments will hover around a position where transitions to the right and to the left are about equal. Consider the example of the time-order error from Chapter 7, especially the data provided on loudness in Fig. 7.5. The probability of a "softer" response corresponds to a tendency to increase the variable stimulus, i.e., to move to the right in our random walk, and the method of adjustment sets this near $1/2$. In this application, v_1 (=0.25) is the tendency to say "softer," i.e., to move the point to the right, and t_1 is the degree to which the variable is softer than the standard, i.e., it is the distance to the left of 0 on the random walk line.

The probability of a move to the right is given in Eq. 7.17a by

$$p = (t_1 + v_1 c)/(t_1 + c)$$

When this equals $1/2$,

$$t_0 = c(1 - 2v_1)$$

In the example, $v_1 = 0.25$, so that

$$t_0 = c/2$$

is the distance the variable will be set to the left, i.e., softer than the standard. This produces the usual negative time-order error, defined as the point of subjective equality t_0 minus the standard in physical measurements. The nonnormalized distribution of settings, under conditions of response bias, can be computed by the methods above.

The next chapter takes up some judgmental methods, such as bisection, fractionation, ratio production, etc., which partake of the characteristics of the method of adjustment. The subject varies a certain stimulus, not to match another but to appear "half" of another, halfway in between two others, twice another, etc. Complete analysis of such methods should take the dynamic process of adjustment into account, but the discussions will concentrate on the end result. One justification of this is the conclusion, discussed above, that methods of adjustment are precise or variable according to the care the subject takes and the fineness of the adjusting apparatus, as well as the difficulty of the discrimination. Hence, the variability itself is difficult to interpret without a great deal of supplementary information.

CHAPTER NINE

Complex Systems of Response—
Judgments and Estimations

Throughout this book it has been assumed that response depends on the perceived situation. In psychophysics, this relationship is used to uncover the experience of the subject from his responses. Chapter 7 and the last part of Chapter 8 discussed discrimination methods of psychophysics, in which the subject is given a simple but difficult choice. Chapter 9 extends these ideas to the methods of comparison, estimation, and judgment.

The sharp separation between these two kinds of psychophysical methods is theoretical rather than empirical. It is not always easy to decide whether a certain experiment belongs with discriminations or with judgments, for the laboratory procedures are similar. The theory of discrimination, in Chapter 7, depended mainly on the notion of indistinguishable classes of aspects. Since the differences between stimuli are usually large, the theory of estimation and judgment deals with ordinary sets of aspects.

In the method of triads, the subject is given two ideal stimuli, A and B, and a variable X, and is asked whether X is more like A or more like B. This method can be extended, in the event that A, X, and B are ordered on a dimension and X is continuously variable, to the method of bisection where X is adjusted to a point as much like A as like B. If A is always zero amount on a quantitative dimension, this becomes fractionation, and X is set at "half" of B.

X can sometimes be set outside the interval between A and B, and thus the methods of equal-appearing intervals and multiplication are obtained. Finally, the subject may be asked to make numerical judgments, either magnitude estimations (where any positive number is allowable as a response) or ratings (where a fixed range of numbers or adjectives is allowed).

These scaling procedures are the subject of a great debate in psychology, and it is not possible to begin the mathematical analysis without first considering very carefully what such judgments mean. Three main approaches have been tried: the sensationist or introspective, the cognitive, and the behaviorist. Each begins with a basic distinction between the physical world, within which stimulus objects, the intensities of energies, the sizes of figures, etc., are objectively measured, and an interior world of experience known only to the subject. The subject, in a judgmental or scaling experiment, is ordinarily asked to report regarding his experience rather than the physical world. Each of the three positions has its own interpretation of the basic distinction between the physical world and the world of experience. The way this distinction is drawn determines the interpretation given to judgments of similarity and amount in psychophysical experiments.

The sensationist or introspective position draws a line between the subjective (psychic) and the objective (physical) world. Physical variables are handled by the experimenter, who instructs his observer to attend directly to the psychic or mental experience. The "stimulus error" consists in erroneously responding to the physical rather than the mental events. If the subject can transcend the stimulus error (a skill which is admittedly rather difficult but not impossible), his judgments are presumed to reflect experience alone. In this interpretation, if the subject is permitted a direct and flexible means of judgment not subject to particular errors of estimation, his responses are presumed to reflect the qualities and amounts of various experiences. These amounts are the "psychical" parts of psychophysical equations or laws, which may be of immediate practical significance, which may be of theoretical value in understanding the sensory qualities of complex or novel stimuli, and which yield a direct reading of the transformation wrought on incoming physical energy by the receptors and nervous system.

The cognitive position argues that the fundamental event depends both on external events and the observer taken together as a whole or system. Physical theory amounts to an abstraction from such total situations, an abstraction which drops out all subjective factors and keeps only the intersubjective or *objective* aspects. Physical qualities and quantities are unaffected by whether they are observed or not (except when instrumentation of observations intervenes, in quantum physics—and there it does not matter whether anyone observes the measurement or not) for the simple reason that physics is concerned with objective phenomena. In psychophysical experiments the subject reports not only physical but also other aspects of the situation which depend on the fact of observation: illusions, appearances, hues, contours, etc., which are not physical because they depend on the observer. Appearances are not strictly subjective either, for they depend upon the objects and energies. In fact, the judgments the person makes are like physical measurements except that they involve more properties of the object-subject system. In this view the observer may take either a physical or a psychophysical attitude, but cannot respond to purely "mental" attributes, in isolation. The stimulus error is an abstract attitude in which the subject cancels out (as well as possible) just those subjective aspects of the situation which are of interest. When the stimulus error is transcended, response is allowed to depend upon the total interacting system of observer and object.

This position suggests an asymmetry between physical and psychical phenomena, which seems reasonable. One can abstract just the physical system, leaving out the observer, but one cannot construct a purely subjective theory. In terms of the laboratory, the point is this: the physical situation remains what it is whether the observer is there or not, and the events which occur can be explained by a psychophysical theory which simply cancels out all observer-effects. However, if a subject is given no physical situation, no prediction of his experience is possible from psychophysical theory. Thus, the cognitive position denies the existence of separate, independent "sensations" which can be measured separately.

The behaviorist position argues that only objective data are usable in natural science. One can define the stimulus situation and the response (the verbal or motor acts of the subject) in physical, objective terms. Only these terms can appear as essential in a genuinely scientific theory, and "experience," though it probably exists, must be excluded from serious consideration as being inaccessible. Any subjective experience becomes, at most, a hypothetical event the consequences of which may be tested by predicting what responses will be made in what physically defined situations. A behaviorist theory may predict the judgments made in a psychophysical experiment, but such judgments have no special status different from discrimination responses, turns of a rat in a maze, or eyeblinks.

If the introspective view is correct, judgments are measurements of sensations. If the cognitive view is correct, judgments are a function of the total situation, subject and object taken together, but they may be particularly useful for picking up the subjective or psychological aspects of the situation. If the behaviorist view is correct, judgments are merely responses like any other responses, which may be predicted if one wishes, and subjective events are mere hypotheses useful for such prediction.

Of these three views, the cognitive seems the most sophisticated, for it is the only one which gives an account of the physical analysis of a situation. In both the introspective and behaviorist positions the physical and mental are merely given as distinct—the introspectionist sets aside physical descriptions and directly investigates the mental, whereas the behaviorist sets aside the mental and stays within the physical descriptions. The cognitive view claims that mental and physical descriptions are both abstractions, and thus gives a framework within which both types of abstract descriptions can be interrelated.

The theoretical position developed in Chapter 2 of this book is cognitive, for it begins with "situations" which are not exhaustively described. Clearly, a physical description will not be exhaustive, so the situations must be interpreted as the observer-object systems of cognitive theory. Such situations have aspects that, since they are abstractions, on some occasions may be physical and on other occasions may be observer-object interactions. Since probabilities of response are correctly computed only when all suitable aspects are considered, it follows that responses will depend on the "situation-as-experienced," and all the physical and psychical aspects will enter into judgments. Not only the physical attributes of the immediate object, and the conscious experiences directly related to the object, but also instructions, expectations, the general arrangement of the room, etc., will be expected to enter into the judgments made by the subject. In this way one can make use of the special conditions of psychophysical judgment without committing oneself to the dangerous position that one has a direct view into the experience of one's subject. The sterility of behaviorism, and the introspectionist's commitment to a dualistic metaphysics, are both avoided.

Triads and the Concept of Similarity

In the method of triads the subject is shown two ideal stimuli, A and B, and a third stimulus X. He is asked whether X is more like A or more like B. It seems reasonable to suppose that choice depends upon the aspects of X which differentiate A and B. That is, the set of aspects leading to the choice of response a is

$$V_a = A \cap \bar{B} \cap X$$

and the set leading to choice of response b is

$$V_b = \bar{A} \cap B \cap X$$

If the subject is instructed to make his judgments with respect to some one kind of element, such as loudness, brightness, or area, then the above sets may all be restricted to subsets of the "criterion" set of loudness or brightness. However, the method of triads can be used without such restrictions, and therefore it is not limited to cases where experimenter and subject can agree on a certain defined variable.

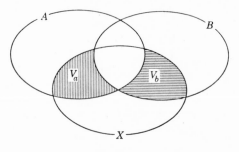

FIGURE 9.1

Figure 9.1 shows the sets involved in a judgment of the method of triads. Notice that most of the aspects present do not enter into the judgment, and that all elements in V_a and V_b are subsets of X. The mutual similarities of the sets A, B, and X are not determined by just the above judgment. The complete method of triads (Torgerson, 1958), in which each of the three stimuli serves as a test stimulus with the other two used as ideals, should be employed. Take, for example, three stimulus sets A, B, and C. When A is the test stimulus the two sets which lead to responses b and c are $A \cap B \cap \bar{C}$ and $A \cap \bar{B} \cap C$. When B is the comparison stimulus the two sets are $A \cap B \cap \bar{C}$ and $\bar{A} \cap B \cap C$, for responses a and c respectively. When C is the comparison stimulus the sets are $A \cap \bar{B} \cap C$ and $\bar{A} \cap B \cap C$ for responses a and b respectively.

Define $V_x(y)$ as the set of aspects which lead the subject to make response y when the comparison stimulus is object x. For example, when the comparison stimulus is A, the elements leading to response b would be $V_a(b)$. Then the above statements can be translated as

$$V_a(b) = V_1 = A \cap B \cap \bar{C}$$
$$V_a(c) = V_2 = A \cap \bar{B} \cap C$$
$$V_b(a) = V_1 = A \cap B \cap \bar{C}$$
$$V_b(c) = V_3 = \bar{A} \cap B \cap C$$
$$V_c(a) = V_2 = A \cap \bar{B} \cap C$$
$$V_c(b) = V_3 = \bar{A} \cap B \cap C$$

Thus, only three subsets enter into all the judgments. Figure 9.2 shows the three sets V_1, V_2, and V_3 for the three objects a, b, and c.

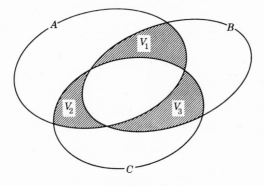

FIGURE 9.2

The complete method of triads yields three probabilities: the probability of b when a is the comparison stimulus, the probability of a when b is the comparison stimulus, and the probability of a when c is the comparison stimulus. The other three probabilities are just the complements of these three. Write $P_x(y)$ as the probability that alternative y is chosen when x is the comparison stimulus. Also, let $m(V) = v$, using lower-case letters for the measures of sets. Then

$$P_a(b) = v_1/(v_1 + v_2)$$
$$P_b(a) = v_1/(v_1 + v_3)$$

and

$$P_c(a) = v_2/(v_2 + v_3)$$

By cross-multiplying, this becomes a set of three homogeneous linear equations in the three unknowns v_1, v_2, and v_3:

$$v_1[P_a(b) - 1] + v_2 P_a(b) = 0$$

$$v_1[P_b(a) - 1] + v_3 P_b(a) = 0$$

$$v_2[P_c(a) - 1] + v_3 P_c(a) = 0$$

With arbitrary probabilities the three equations will be linearly independent of one another. In this case, however, there is no solution for v_1, v_2, and v_3.

The reader may recall from elementary algebra that the independence of the three equations is associated with what is called "nonsingularity," i.e., the determinant of the matrix of coefficients is not 0. Only if the determinant is 0 is there a solution to the set of equations, and values v_1, v_2, and v_3. The determinant in question is

$$\begin{vmatrix} P_a(b) - 1 & P_a(b) & 0 \\ P_b(a) - 1 & 0 & P_b(a) \\ 0 & P_c(a) - 1 & P_c(a) \end{vmatrix} = 0$$

A small amount of algebraic manipulation leads to the conclusion that

$$P_a(b) = \frac{P_b(a)[1 - P_c(a)]}{P_b(a)[1 - P_c(a)] + P_c(a)[1 - P_b(a)]}$$

If this condition holds, v_1, v_2, and v_3 are determined up to an arbitrary unit of measurement. It is at once apparent that this theory cannot agree with just any results; given the probabilities of two of the choices involved in the complete method of triads, the third is determined no matter what the three stimuli may be. The difficulties in putting this to the empirical test are, of course, the usual difficulties of obtaining suitable estimates of probabilities—successive choices by the individual are in general not independent.

Closely related to the method of triads, and of great value in studies with infrahuman subjects, is the method of generalization. Suppose that a subject is trained, by the usual methods of discrimination learning, to make one response in the presence of stimulus situation a and a different response in the presence of b. The subject is then presented with situation x, and his response is observed. Provided the subject uses only those elements of X which are common to A and B, the similarity of X to A will be $A \cap X$, the similarity of X to B will be $B \cap X$, and the sets of aspects leading to the two responses will be V_1 and V_2 as defined above. For the method of generalization to work with the present formulas it is essential that the subject not respond

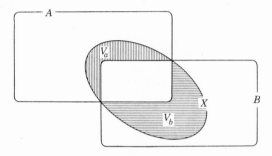

FIGURE 9.3

on the basis of elements in $\bar{A} \cap X \cap \bar{B}$, and there is difficulty in ensuring that no such aspects enter into choice.

Consider the method of triads when a, x, and b form a linear array in that order, so that $A \cap B \subset X \subset A \cup B$. The situation is diagramed in Fig. 9.3, along with the V sets which influence choice. If X is the middle set, the theoretical structure is not changed

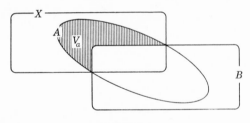

FIGURE 9.4

radically by having the sets ordered. However, for the "complete" method of triads, we should also consider what happens when the three sets are ordered X, A, B (the same structure is found with the ordering A, B, X); the result is shown in Fig. 9.4. V_b is empty, and the subject certainly says that X is more like A. Such results are to be expected unless sets are so nearly alike that indistinguishable elements play an important part, and the problem is one of discrimination.

Now consider the method of triads when it is used to measure the similarities of three stimuli which differ in a quantitative fashion, e.g., three tones of increasing loudness, or three weights of increasing number of grams. If the sets of aspects of the three objects will be nested inside one another, $A \subset X \subset B$, as in Fig. 9.5, then V_a is empty and the subject must always respond that X is more like B. This is

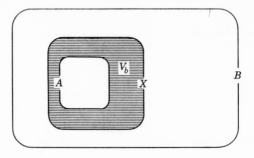

FIGURE 9.5

hardly likely to be the experimental result. Perhaps stimulus A has "smallness" aspects; if the three stimuli are weights of 50, 100, and 180 grams, the 50-gram weight may have the characteristic of "lightness" which differentiates it from the 180-gram weight. This will lead to a diagram of sets like Fig. 9.6.

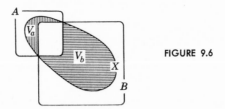

FIGURE 9.6

The natural experiment is to devise a sequence of stimuli which differ quantitatively, such as tones of increasing intensity, light patches of increasing brightness, or drawn figures of increasing complexity. Assume that the distances between stimuli or the nature of the changes is such that perfect discrimination can be maintained and thus that homogeneous classes of aspects need not be considered. Stimuli at the small end of the array have the property of "smallness" and stimuli at the large end have the property of "largeness." We first may ask whether the measure of the set of largeness aspects should be greater than the measure of the set of smallness aspects. If the judgment is purely comparative, the subject should see smallness and largeness as qualitative differences, and the largeness aspects of the largest stimulus might have the same measure as the smallness aspects of the smallest stimulus. However, if the subject also uses a "zero" stimulus as a base of comparison, there will be more largeness aspects, for the large stimulus differs more from the zero background than does the small stimulus. A structure like that in Fig. 9.6, with an increasing linear array of sets, should result when the stimuli increase in amount (difference from background or zero), and the subject compares various stimuli not only with each other but also with the common background. In a sense the subject is confounding relative largeness with absolute largeness.

The Method of Bisection

The method of bisection is a variation of the method of triads in which the three sets involved, A, X, and B, are members of a linear array, and the subject adjusts the middle stimulus X until he cannot decide whether it is nearer A or B.

Consider a linear array of sets $X_1, X_2, \cdots, X_i, \cdots, X_n$ stretching from A to B. The subject, having just produced some stimulus X_i, is in what is essentially a trial of the method of triads. If he decides that X_i is more like A than like B, he adjusts the comparison stimulus to X_{i+1}. If he decides the opposite, that X_i is more like B, then he moves from X_i to X_{i-1}.

If the subject is very patient, makes very small moves of the variable stimulus, and if each move represents a judgment independent of previous judgments, then the final distribution of settings will be narrow and will center closely about a point i where $P_{x_i}(a) = P_{x_i}(b)$.

Uniqueness

Is the assumption of a linear array sufficient to determine a unique bisection mid-point? This question has the following experimental meaning. Is it possible to construct a sequence of stimuli, which form a linear array from A to B, such that there are two stimuli X_i and X_j, which are neither identical nor adjacent, both of which can be accepted as bisection points while settings between them are not accepted? If not, the bisection point is unique.

It is easy to show that the bisection point is unique. Consider four sets, A, X_i, X_j, B, which are on a linear array in that order. By the definition of a linear array and the set-theoretic formula for betweenness, it follows that $A \cap X_j \subset A \cup X_i$, so that any aspects drawing the subject to the left from X_i are also going to draw him to the left from X_j. Similarly, $X_i \cap B \subset X_j \cap B$, so that aspects which will draw the subject to the right from X_j will also draw him to the right from X_i. Consequently, the probability of going left from X_i must be smaller than the probability of going left from X_j, and the probability of going to the right from X_i is greater than the probability of going to the right from X_j. If left- and right-going probabilities are equal at X_i, the subject will have a net left-going probability at X_j, unless X_i and X_j are the same set. Hence, the bisection point is unique.

Validity

There are two main cases to consider in investigating the validity of the method of bisection: (1) linear arrays in which all sets have the same measure, purely substitutive arrays; and (2) linear arrays in which the measure of the sets increases sytematically as one proceeds along the array; these might be called increasing arrays.

If the sets $A, X_1, \cdots, X_i, \cdots, X_n, B$ form a linear array and $m(A) = m(B)$, then the various sets can be located as points along a line as follows: Set A at the point 0 arbitrarily, and B at a point $d_{A,B} = m(\bar{A} \cap B) + m(A \cap \bar{B})$. Notice that the unit of measurement depends upon the measure function m and therefore is essentially arbitrary. We now prove the following validity theorem:

THEOREM: If $m(A) = m(B)$ and X_0 is the unique bisection point, then $d_{A,X_0} = d_{X_0,B} = \frac{1}{2}d_{A,B}$.

Proof: A purely formal proof is given here to strengthen the argument and as an exercise for the reader.

(1)	$d_{A,X_0} = m(A \cap \bar{X}_0) + m(\bar{A} \cap X_0)$ and $d_{X_0,B} = m(B \cap \bar{X}_0) + m(\bar{B} \cap X_0)$	(Definition of distance d, from Chapter 3)
(2)	$m(A \cap \bar{X}_0 \cap B) = m(\bar{A} \cap X_0 \cap \bar{B}) = 0$	(By hypothesis that A, X_0, B are on a linear array, hence X_0 is between A and B)
(3)	$m(A \cap X_0 \cap \bar{B}) = m(\bar{A} \cap X_0 \cap B)$	(By definition of the unique bisection point)
(4)	$m(A \cap X_0 \cap \bar{B}) = m(\bar{B} \cap X_0)$ $m(\bar{A} \cap X_0 \cap B) = m(\bar{A} \cap X_0)$	(From step 2)
(5)	$m(\bar{B} \cap X_0) = m(\bar{A} \cap X_0)$	(From steps 3 and 4)

(6) $\quad m(A) = m(A \cap X_0 \cap B)$ (By partitioning
$\qquad\qquad + m(A \cap X_0 \cap \bar{B})$ A into its sub-
$\qquad\qquad + m(A \cap \bar{X}_0 \cap \bar{B})$ sets and step 2)
$\quad\; m(B) = m(A \cap X_0 \cap B)$
$\qquad\qquad + m(\bar{A} \cap X_0 \cap B)$
$\qquad\qquad + m(\bar{A} \cap \bar{X}_0 \cap B)$

(7) $\quad m(A) = m(B)$ (Hypothesis
                                               about array)

(8) $\quad m(A \cap \bar{X}_0 \cap \bar{B}) = m(\bar{A} \cap \bar{X}_0 \cap B)$ (Steps 7, 6, and
                                               3)

(9) $\quad m(A \cap \bar{X}_0) = m(B \cap \bar{X}_0)$ (Steps 8 and 2)

(10) $\quad d_{A,X_0} = d_{X_0,B}$ (Inserting steps
                                               5 and 9 into 1)

(11) $\quad d_{A,X_0} + d_{X_0,B} = d_{A,B}$ (Since A, X_0, B
                                               are on a linear
                                             array, $b_{A,X_0,B}$.
                                               Then use Theo-
                                               rem 3.2)

(12) $\quad d_{A,X_0} = \tfrac{1}{2}d_{A,B}$ (Steps 10 and
                                               11)

Q.E.D.

The length of this proof is no index of its difficulty, for all of the steps are automatic. However, it may help the reader to recall the material in Chapter 3 on distances and linear arrays, as well as to make it clear that the main arguments on scaling used in this chapter are solidly based on the other material in the book.

Conceptually, the significance of this theorem is that the method of bisection is valid, under proper restrictions, provided that bisection should be measuring distances in the sense defined in Chapter 3, and the mechanism of choice discussed in this book is assumed. The theorem depends essentially on the assumption that $m(A) = m(B)$; under these conditions, the method of bisection does, in fact, find the halfway point. It should be noted that the method of triads itself has the same kind of theorem: if an X_0 can be found such that $P_{X_0}(A) = P_{X_0}(B) = 1/2$, then X_0 is halfway between A and B, if $m(A) = m(B)$ and the three sets are on a linear array.

It is not necessary that all the variable stimuli, the X's, have the same measure as A and B. It is never assumed in the proof of the theorem that $m(X_0) = m(A)$. However, in any complete scaling experiment all stimuli on the array should have equal measures, so that any pair of stimuli along the line can be bisected. The two members of the pair to be bisected must have equal measures, which eventually means that all the sets must have equal measures.

Now consider an array in which the measures of the sets increase. This occurs if the stimuli are quantitative (loudness, brightness, weight, size, etc.) and the subject compares them not only with each other but also with zero amount. Imagine that $m(A) < m(B)$, and $A \cap B = \emptyset$. The common aspects do not enter into judgments

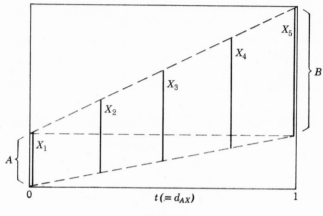

FIGURE 9.7

anyway, and they make the expressions appear quite complicated. Suppose that all the intermediate situations X_i can be represented as in Fig. 9.7, where each set is represented by a vertical line (see Fig. 3.9). Actually, of course, these are to be thought of as segments of a single vertical line, which are separated from one another only for ease of inspection. The dashed lines are straight, representing the regularity of transition, but it is not necessary that the various X_i be equally spaced. In bisection, the X_i are assumed to be nearly continuous. In this example, give A the scale value 0 and B the scale value 1, and locate intermediate scale values as numbers, t, between 0 and 1. The true scale score, t, is equal to $d_{A,X}$. In Fig. 9.7, the bisection point is a set which is half above and half below the central line, i.e., the set X such that $m(A \cap X) = m(B \cap X)$. Such a bisection point is nearer A than it is to B, displaced off to the left. Bisection, in this case, does not give the "central" location, but rather selects a set which has as many of the (relatively few) elements of A as it has of the (relatively many) elements of B.

If this linear array is thought of as a set of physical objects varying quantitatively on a simple dimension such as intensity, luminance, area, or weight, then the aspects of A are what might be called "smallness" aspects, and the aspects of B are "largeness" aspects. Bisection, in a sense, requires the subject to find a set which has as many smallness as largeness aspects. Under these circumstances the location of the bisection point is at* $m(A)/[m(A) + m(B)]$, hence closer to the left than the right. If the experimenter now chooses many different pairs of stimuli along the linear array and seeks the "bisection points," his bisection points will consistently be off to the left. Imagine, for example, that $m(A)$ is only half of $m(B)$. Then the bisection points are one-third of the way from A to B, no matter what A and B may be. On the erroneous assumption that bisection is valid, one can try to obtain a scale as follows. Lay off A and B on

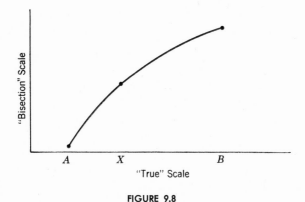

FIGURE 9.8

a scale, and place the bisecting X halfway between on a "bisection" scale. Note the physical values of each. Now bisect the intervals from A to X and from X to B, and follow the same procedure starting with other values along the continuum. In this case the "psychological" scale will be a negatively accelerated function of the "true" scale. For consider the three sets A, X, and B. On the true scale, X is only one-third of the way from A to B, but on the bisection scale it will be halfway. The resulting curve is shown in Fig. 9.8.

This procedure, interestingly enough, will not actually produce a scale if followed exactly. The simplest proof is graphical; imagine a true scale stretching from 0 to 6, and a bisection scale stretching from 0 to 4, as in Fig. 9.9. Start with stimuli A and E, which have true values of 0 and 6, and give them bisection-scale scores of 0 and 4, respectively. Then stimulus C, with a true value

* The reader may be interested in deriving this formula.

of 2, will bisect A and E and receive a bisection-scale score of 2. Now find a B which bisects the pair (A, C). B gets a bisection-scale score of 1, being halfway between 0 and 2 on the bisection scale, and its true value will be $\frac{2}{3}$. Similarly, bisect the interval (C, E), and find a D which is halfway, thereby receiving a bisection-scale score of 3. Its true score is $3\frac{1}{3}$, one-third of the way from 2 to 6.

But now consider the points B, C, and D. Their true scores are $\frac{2}{3}$, 2, and $3\frac{1}{3}$, so that they are evenly spaced and separated by $1\frac{1}{3}$ units on the true scale. Their bisection-scale values are

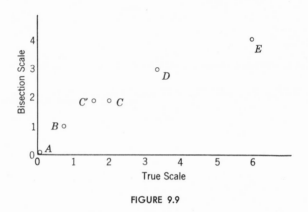

FIGURE 9.9

equally spaced at 1, 2, and 3, so that C should appear to be a bisection between B and D, but the bisection point will be one-third of the true interval from B to D, or one-third of the way from $\frac{2}{3}$ to $3\frac{1}{3}$. The interval is of length $2\frac{1}{3}$ and the proper location of the middle stimulus is therefore at $1\frac{5}{9}$. We may put a stimulus C', of true value $1\frac{5}{9}$, on the graph, but its bisection-scale score should be 2, for it bisects stimuli with values 1 and 3.

Now there are two different stimuli, one at a true score of 2 and the other at a true score of $1\frac{5}{9}$, both of which must have the bisection-scale score of 2. This inconsistency shows that a bisection scale does not exist for this array of increasing sets.

In an important paper on the theory of loudness scaling, Garner (1954a) took the position that bisection data were valid but that in fractionation the subject might set his half-loudness judgments, not at half, but at some other fraction, say, $\frac{2}{3}$. If this is true, though, it is equally possible that subjects do not set their bisection judgments at exactly halfway, but instead set them at some other fractional distance. If this happens, the subject cannot consistently form a bisection scale. Three overlapping bisections will conflict. In Garner's "equisection" experiment the subject first fixed tone C between A and E, then bisected the intervals (A, C) and (C, E), and finally adjusted the whole array as necessary. According to the present theory, if bisection was invalid, there is no exact solution for the subject and the order of listening to the five tones may make a difference. For example, the subject may try to get the last two bisections right and sacrifice the one heard first. The discrepancies between settings, depending on the order of listening, are shown in one typical set of

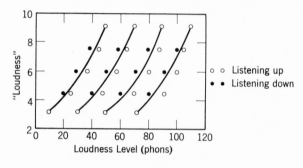

FIGURE 9.10

data from Garner's experiment in Fig. 9.10. The actual curvatures are against physical decibels, which are not the "true scores" of the present theory.

If Garner's scepticism about the face validity of half-loudness judgments is extended to bisection judgments, no loudness scale can be constructed by bisection methods. The difficulties subjects have, and the strong effects of the order of listening, can then be attributed to the impossibility of the task as a whole.

This theoretical result is helpful in experiments, for if the sets of aspects change in measure along the array, bisection is invalid (the subject does not select the midpoint of the stimuli as the bisection point) and it is impossible to construct a consistent scale from bisection data. Inconsistency in scaling then becomes an indication of invalidity of the scaling method.

Fractionation

In the case of purely quantitative dimensions, there is a clear-cut zero stimulus identifiable as "no stimulus." An inaudible tone has zero loudness, a dark patch zero brightness, "nothing" has zero weight, etc. The experimenter can ask a subject to bisect the interval between the zero object and some given object, and this is fractionation.

Procedurally, there is little difference between bisection and fractionation although they give different data. One characteristic of fractionation is that it cannot lead to the unsolvable problem of bisection. In fractionation the zero stimulus is fixed and always involved, whereas the troubles in forming a bisection scale arose in bisecting A and E, and then also B and D.

This means that fractionation is always possible and that self-consistent judgments can be made. It is still possible that fractionation judgments are not at the actual half-stimulus but at some other fraction. Figure 9.8 shows an example of such a biased half-judgment, if A is a zero or base-line stimulus. If the subject sets his fractionation point at some constant fraction, k, of the standard and a fractionation scale is constructed, the plot of the fractionation scale against the true values will describe a well-defined, smooth curve. In fact, the fractionation scale score of a stimulus of (true) value x will be

$$f(x) = ax^{[-\log 2 /\log(k)]} \tag{9.1}$$

i.e., a power function of x. In this case of a constant but invalid judgment of "half," which would arise in the sort of increasing linear array of sets shown in Fig. 9.7, the fractionation scale should be a power function of the physical, or of the actual psychological magnitude of the stimulus as represented by the measure function m. This fact takes on greater significance later in the chapter, for many scales of this type do yield power functions.

Magnitude Estimation

Subjects may be given a range of stimuli, in random order or arrangement, and asked to assign numbers to them. The process is much more complex than the method of triads or even its extension through adjustment to bisection and fractionation, for the subject has a great range of responses. Given a subject who can handle numbers correctly, however, an experimenter can obtain magnitude estimations rapidly and easily (Stevens, 1956). The most consistent and stable results are obtained when there is no restriction on the subject's use of numbers except, at most, one number fixed to represent one stimulus value. Of course, it is understood that if the subject detects no stimulus he will respond "zero," so this is always a fixed point.

A complete analysis of magnitude estimation would require an understanding of how subjects use numbers in estimating. This in turn would depend upon their specific training in elementary mathematics, on the formal characteristics displayed by their numerical reasoning, etc. For the purposes of the present discussion it is assumed that the subjects use numbers with the usual arithmetic rules. The use of numbers in any empirical application involves having some way of putting the objects in question into correspondence with the numbers. There must be some method for comparing numbers as to precedence or equality, some means of combining objects which corresponds to addition, and some empirical operation like multiplication.

The operation of comparing two stimuli is closely related to simple judgments as to which is louder, heavier, etc. The subject is prepared to use such judgments and map them on the concept of "equality" in using his number system. The problem of "addition" is more complicated. The writer's experience is that he can, with some variables, perform a mental combination. He can look at two line segments and imagine them end to end, stably enough to judge the length of their sum. He can pick up two weights separately, and make some estimate of how heavy they would feel together. The variables of brightness and loudness resist such judgments; when a second light bulb is turned on, the illumination of the room does not seem to double, so the method of combination seems obscure.

The process of fractionating finds a stimulus which is half of some other. Essentially the same method can be used for doubling a stimulus—again, there is a zero stimulus, a middle stimulus (now called S), and a larger stimulus X. Again the problem is so to arrange things that S is as similar to the zero stimulus as it is to X, but in this case it is the larger stimulus X which is variable. Judgments are the same as in fractionation, but the adjustment knob is connected to the largest instead of the intermediate stimulus.

Thus the subject can multiply and fractionate stimuli, and these judgmental acts form a basis for division and multiplication of the numerical responses. Although fractionation and multiplication are, in the laboratory, restricted to halving and doubling, the sophisticated subject can extend and complete the gaps by anchoring his number system at critical points. He can then fill in the gaps tolerably well by quite approximate methods without affecting the data of experiments in magnitude estimation, for those data are extremely variable at best.

In conclusion, it seems reasonable to say that magnitude estimation is a technique which uses a complex subjective scale. The scale is based on a mental operation of combination corresponding to addition, or to mental operations of doubling, halving, or both.

Rating Scales

The method of rating involves showing the subject two extreme stimuli, *A* and *B*, and fixing the responses to them at values such as 1 and 11. Sometimes descriptive adjectives are used, such as extremely small, very small, quite small, small, slightly small, medium, slightly large, large, quite large, very large, and extremely large (an 11-point scale). The subject's understanding, when adjectives are used, is that the spaces should be equal.

This method is like bisection in that the location of each stimulus is to be found between two extremes. A system of bisections can produce the desired spacing, as is demonstrated in equisection experiments like Garner's (Fig. 9.10). In the event that the bisections are invalid, biased consistently to one side or the other, there is no possibility of scaling. In a bisection experiment this difficulty will be noticed only by the experimenter, but in a rating scale experiment it troubles the subject who is attempting to develop a consistent structure for his judgments. The structure will require constant readjustment, and will change with each bisection point which is fixed. The highly fluid character of the scale in such experiments has been the subject of a great deal of research which will not be discussed here. Stevens and Galanter (1957) have provided a variety of demonstrations that magnitude estimation and fractionation produce one kind of scale, whereas rating scales produce another. The arrangement into methods, with fractionation and magnitude estimation on one side and bisection and rating scales on the other, is due to Stevens and his collaborators, and represents one of the major advances in our understanding of scaling methods.

The Question of a General Psychophysical Law

A psychophysical law is a function relating the amount of physical energy put into a receptor and the perceived, or at least judged, magnitude of the resulting sensation. In the simplest sense such a law can be used to predict the judgments which will be made of stimuli of various intensities. Provided that the judgments are a simple function of psychological amount of sensation (as they are in the introspectionist interpretation) the psychophysical law can also be used to study the receptor itself.

One major issue in psychophysics is whether there is a general psychophysical law which applies to all or a majority of stimulus dimensions, and what the form of that law (if any) is. Working from discrimination data (summed j.n.d.'s) Fechner arrived at the classic conclusion that there is a general psychophysical law and that sensation varies as the logarithm of superthreshold intensity. Much the same assumption has been used by Michels and Helson (1949) in their studies of rating scales. S. S. Stevens and his associates have argued that there is a general psychophysical law but that it is a power function. Their data are mainly from fractionation and magnitude-estimation studies. Other writers, from time to time, note that the structures of the various receptors and afferent nervous systems differ so greatly that there is probably no general psychophysical law at all, for different receptors will probably show different input-output relationships.

One difficulty in deciding about the existence and form of a psychophysical law is that, along with the receptor and nervous system, the process of judgment, and the experimental conditions within which judgments must be made, can affect the form of the data. Michels and Helson work mainly with rating scales and argue that the judge establishes a central stimulus, the "adaptation level," and judges all other stimuli in comparison with that level. Rating-scale data are generally in accord with the idea that the several rating categories are selected so that the ratio of stimulus energy between any two categories is roughly a constant. Then, by assuming that the ratings represent "perceived amount" they argue that perceived amount is a logarithmic function of intensity. Stevens, using fractionation and magnitude estimation, seems to find that whenever the ratio of stimulus energies forms a certain fraction, the ratio of estimations is some constant. If estimation is a valid measure of perceived amount, perceived amount must be a power function of intensity. Stevens tends to dismiss the contrary findings of Michels and Helson on the grounds that a rating scale limits the choices available to the subject, hence is invalid.

The writer would propose a third way of interpreting these facts. Both Michels and Helson, on the one hand, and Stevens on the other, emphasize the importance of the form of judgment employed. It seems that the results of a psychophysical scaling experiment depend heavily on the psychophysical method used, and therefore the results may usefully be interpreted not as measures of "perceived magnitude," which lead to an input-output relationship, but rather as *judgments* which lead to an understanding of the process of judging stimuli.

This position leads to a reasonable expectation that there is one psychophysical law which cuts across various sense variables and modalities. The introspectionist, or input-output interpretation must, the writer thinks, trust to luck for it offers no strong reason why one psychophysical law should describe the action of various receptors. But if psychophysical judgments and physical measurements of the same object are similar operations, one made under restricted contact between observer and object and the other made with unrestricted opportunity to inspect, and if the psychophysical law is the relationship between such restricted judgments and the results of complete inspection, then it seems quite reasonable that the same sort of restrictions (i.e., the same psychophysical method) may lead to the same relationship.

With this interpretation, one would expect the same psychophysical law for many different variables, but different psychophysical laws for various kinds of judgments. In this view the power function relating perceived magnitude to physical intensity, so often found by Stevens and his associates, is not interpreted to mean that the senses are power-function transducers but instead that the methods of fractionation and magnitude estimation lead to judgments which are a power function of physical values.

In this chapter the author will not try to prove this point, but merely to explore some of its implications and attempt to order available data along the lines suggested. It should be remembered that there are several sensible interpretations of these results and that the arguments put forward here rest on insufficient and somewhat ambiguous evidence.

In Table 9.1 are shown the results of a number of recent studies by S. S. Stevens and his associates at Harvard. In these studies, magnitude estimation and fractionation have been used to derive scales of psychophysical magnitude of various sensory variables. In almost all cases the psychophysical scale is approximately a power function of the physical measurements employed. Since units of measurement are entirely arbitrary, such a scale is characterized by the power. If we call the sensory scale y and the physical measurements x, the power function is $y = ax^b$. In Table 9.1, approximate values of b are reported, either as estimated by Stevens and his associates or as estimated, from the available data, by the writer.

In the discussion of fractionation earlier in this chapter, it was mentioned that a constant (fractional) bias in fractionation will

TABLE 9.1

Dimension	Typical Power (b)	Location of Fractionation Point (k)
Electric shock (60-cycle current)	3.5*	.82
Heaviness of lifted weights	1.45†	.62
Force of handgrip	1.7‡	.66
Numerousness (dots) (fractionation)	1.35†	.60
Magnitude estimation	1.00 (approx.)§	
Thickness of small slabs of wood	1.33‖	.59
(up to about 2 in.)		
Length of lines	1.06†	.52
Duration (burst of white noise)	1.06†	.52
Visual area	(1.00)†	(.50)
Repetition rate	1.00¶	.50
Pressure on hand	1.1‡	.53
Magnitude of vibration	0.95‡	.48
Loudness (against sound pressure level)	0.6†	.32
Brightness		
5° spot, eye somewhat light adapted	0.36†	.15
"Star," dark adapted eye	0.47†	.28
Lightness of neutral gray paper	1.2†	.56

* S. S. Stevens, Carton, and Shickman (1958).
† S. S. Stevens and Galanter (1957).
‡ J. C. Stevens, Mack, and S. S. Stevens (1960).
§ Taves (1941).
‖ S. S. Stevens and Stone (1959).
¶ J. C. Stevens and Shickman (1959).

lead to a fractionation scale with a certain constant power. From Eq. 9.1,

$$b = -\log 2/\log (k)$$

where k is the location of the fractionation judgment. Thus the estimated values of the power b can be transformed into estimates of the location of a fractionation point. In Table 9.1 these theoretical or estimated fractionation points are shown, to serve as a basis for discussion. It should be recognized that in many of the experiments no fractionation was done, and it is not certain that fractionation results would agree with magnitude estimations.

One finds that in three cases, where the subject has little experience or opportunity for direct manipulation or combination of stimuli (electric shock, loudness, and brightness), the powers deviate sharply from 1.0, with fractionation settings being at .82, .32, and .15 or .28 of the standard. The experimenter does not know where "half" should be subjectively, and the subjects have no firm anchors for their judgments. The observation of power functions means that the subject, when fractionating, sets his judgment at some fixed fraction of the physical energy or pressure, to an approximation, no matter what the energy may be, but the fraction bears no obvious relation to physical measures.

The second set of variables are those in which a natural "true" or objective measurement exists and is fairly familiar to the subject. Force of handgrip belongs with loudness, brightness, and electric shock, except that it is so well associated with efforts like opening jars and lifting that the subject probably can imagine operations of measurement. The heaviness of lifted weights, the apparent numerousness of dots in a field, and the thickness of a small slab of wood all belong together in this class. In these cases the typical power is higher than 1 but less than 2, and the fractionation point is set between about .6 to .7 of the standard.

Warren and Warren (1956) seem to have found the key to the fractionation of heaviness. Consider an array of small boxes, all the same size, which differ in weight. These boxes also vary in density, since density equals weight divided by volume and the volume is constant. In physics the distinction between density and weight is completely clear, but in ordinary language the same term applies to both, as when we ask whether lead is heavier than iron and receive a positive answer.

The fact that heaviness and density are not entirely separate in their subjective aspects is shown by the size-weight illusion. If one presents two objects of the same weight and different volumes, then of course they differ in density—the larger is less dense. Subjects quite consistently judge the less dense to be lighter, provided they have visual or tactual cues as to volume.*

What happens when the subject is asked to select a weight X which is half as heavy as another weight B, of say 100 grams? If the subject picks up a weight X of 50 grams, it is in fact half as heavy as the standard but it is also only half as dense. This makes X feel relatively light, and the person chooses a heavier X' to overcome the size-weight illusion, choosing a weight at perhaps 60 or 62 grams. Since the relation of density to weight is constant along the

---

*Unpublished research, S. H. Bartley and F. Colon, Michigan State University, 1959.

continuum of weights, the subject will consistently set his fractionation judgment at .62 of the standard, producing the scale found by Stevens and others.

Warren and Warren (1956) tested this hypothesis by using variable weights of different volumes. When their variable was as large as the standard, fractionation points were at about .65. When the variable was half as large as the standard, density would be equalized by a weight at .50 of the standard, and the choices were at about .53. When the variable stimuli were only one-quarter the volume of the standard, the fractionation point dropped to .41, for now the variables were more dense than the standard, and therefore had to be lightened (made less than one-half the weight of the standard) in order to make a match. In addition, Warren and Warren cite an unpublished study by Joy in which the subjects hefted hidden containers which could be varied in weight by adding or removing water. Joy's results showed almost objective judgments, with median fractionation points at about .51.

Thus it seems that the observed exponent of 1.45 in heaviness data arises from the size-weight illusion, which in turn is possible because of the confounding of two physical variables which are not well distinguished by the average subject. (Warren and Warren had one subject who worked for a firm that ships books, and had to estimate the weights of boxes of various sizes and densities. This subject's half-judgments, k, were near .50 under all conditions.)

The three other variables showing values of k near .60 are also similar in being a confounding of two or more physical dimensions, or in being subject to a known illusion. Force of handgrip is the most doubtful of these, but it is almost certainly compounded of pressure on the skin and muscular effort, along with the felt excursion of the bar of the dynamometer. In the case of numerousness of dots, there is again a kind of density—the smaller fields of dots used (Taves, 1941) were somewhat less in area, and considerably less in dots per unit area (density of dots). The writer in a few informal observations has noticed that 10 dots close together may look about as numerous as 11 or 12 dots spread more widely across a field of the same size. In other words, numerousness and density are somewhat confused, just as are weight and density of objects. However, in magnitude estimation Taves' subjects underestimate the actual number of dots by roughly a constant fraction, which makes $b \cong 1.0$; and if one replots the data from the Mount Holyoke Psychophysical Research Unit report (Reese et al., 1953, p. 72) in the same terms, underestimation becomes proportionally more severe with larger numbers of dots so that $b < 1$. Thus, the value of b is difficult to determine from available data. In the Holyoke report, fields of dots varying separately in density or area were studied. When the area is held constant and the number (hence density) of dots is increased, $b \cong 0.7$, whereas when the density is held constant and the number (hence area) of dots is varied, $b \cong 0.9$, for the range of dots from 10 to 200. These results do not agree with the interpretation given here, but since they do not agree very well with Taves' results either, the writer is not sure what to do about it. Preliminary laboratory studies at Michigan State University suggest that several incidental variables may enter into judgments of number, and that bold theoretical interpretations will be difficult to sustain until the experimental techniques are improved.

The thickness of small slabs of wood is misestimated consistently, producing a phenomenon known as the kinesthetic aftereffect. After feeling a thinner object, a thicker one is exaggerated, and after feeling a thick object a thinner one feels very thin. Thus, in fractionation, after feeling a thick piece of wood the subject would have to choose, as half, a piece more than half as thick, for this second piece would "shrink." The presence of this aftereffect in comparisons requiring matching is well verified, and there is no reason to believe that a similar effect would not occur during fractionation or magnitude-estimation studies. In general, it appears that the relative shrinkage is roughly constant for different absolute sizes, and is nearly maximal when one object is twice as thick as the other.

The other six variables in Table 9.1—length of lines, duration, visual area, repetition rate, pressure on the palm, and magnitude of vibration—all yield essentially accurate judgments of the physical variable. The variability of data in these experiments keeps us from deciding whether there is any systematic distortion of judgments.

The mental operations for combining lengths of line, durations, areas, and pressures on the hand are familiar to the reader. Notice that pressure on the hand, though a component of weight-lifting, is not affected by the size-weight illusion, simply because the device applying the pressure was quite evidently not a weight. Judgment of repetition rate seems to be a sort of combination of numerousness and duration, which produces little distortion.

The distinction between self-evident variables which are judged accurately, and uncertain variables which are judged in peculiar ways, seems fairly clear to the intuition, but it is difficult to state just where the line is drawn. One cannot appeal just to "previous experience," for several reasons. First, there is no clear evidence that most people have much relevant experience with judgments of numerousness, weight, short durations, or the thicknesses of thin slabs of wood (blindfolded). If it were necessary to find the relevant experience and show its sufficiency to support the argument, one would be thrown into an unproductive form of psychoanalysis. Besides, experience with loudness and brightness is at least as extensive as experience with visual areas or amplitudes of vibration. Finally, if past experiences are sufficient, how does it happen that the size-weight illusion, illusions of numerousness, and satiation effects on thicknesses are not overcome by experience? Clearly, the naïve empiricist interpretation in terms of previous experience will not suffice.

It seems to the writer that some related previous experience is necessary for judging these variables, but that the important factor is the kind of experience the subject has had. Even if a person has had no specific past experience with the judgments required, it is the possibility of certain manipulations which is critical. What is more, the structure of the judgments depends more on formal relationships than on the concrete details of the stimuli.

When a person makes a fractionation judgment, he says that X is half as large as B. This can be accomplished by ordinary comparison if B can be divided into parts and those parts can be consistently discriminated. The subject divides B into two parts, say, B_1 and B_2, and adjusts this division until $m(B_1) = m(B_2)$. The adjustment is one of simple comparison. He then compares B_1 with X, adjusting X until it matches B_1. This value of X is the proper fractionation point. If B cannot be divided into parts, or if these parts do not have stable and distinguishable identities, fractionation is not reducible to simple comparison.

When comparing lines of several lengths, the standard line B can be divided into equal-sized parts and the parts are discriminable through their location. It is no surprise to discover that this can be accomplished quite accurately, with no important constant error. Visual area and the thickness of small slabs of wood are closely related to length, and should behave similarly (except for the after-effect found in judgments of thickness).

Even more elementary is the operation of counting, by which the subject can separate a set of discrete elements into a "first half," a "second half," etc. It is probable that length of line reduces, in a sense, to the counting of small segments; but numerousness, duration, and repetition rate clearly belong with this group of mental operations. Whenever the parts of a stimulus are presented in an order or arrangement it may be possible to separate parts and distinguish them by their location in the arrangement. Then fractionation can proceed through mere comparison.

In three cases—loudness, brightness, and intensity of electric shock—the subject is presented with a stimulus which is entirely homogeneous. In these cases, even the experimenter himself cannot divide a given stimulus into parts and produce a fractionation by comparison. There is no reason to suppose that the subjects are endowed with intuition superior to the experimenter. It must be supposed, therefore, that they establish a loudness relationship which they "define" as half loudness. This relationship will differ from subject to subject (Garner, 1954a) and can depend heavily on any suggestions from the experimenter, such as the range of variable stimuli first presented to the subject (Garner, 1954b, 1958). Although there is no way to determine an actual ratio like 1/2 without dividing the standard stimulus, it is perfectly possible to identify a particular ratio between tones by a direct comparison or "contrast": degree of attenuation is itself an aspect of a situation which includes two tones. Brightness (especially when confusion exists between the intensity of a luminous source and the whiteness of a reflecting surface) is even more complicated than loudness. Considering the complex interrelationships of illumination, whiteness, and contrast (Woodworth and Schlosberg, 1954), it must be expected that further studies of magnitude estimation of brightness will have to cope with discontinuities and context effects. Notice that the three powers given in Table 9.1 for brightness do not agree at all.

In this account it has been argued that the existence of a power function is almost predetermined by the method of constructing a fractionation scale. The same point does not hold for magnitude estimation. The connection between the two, and the general agreement between findings of the two methods, has been attributed in this discussion to the possibility that magnitude estimation is a complication of fractionation and multiplication. In other words, it is assumed that the subject, by a process of fractionation and multiplication, computes his magnitude estimates by a process similar to that used by Stevens in constructing a fractionation scale. It was stated previously that fractionation can be reduced to comparison whenever a stimulus can be divided in half and the subject can compare the halves. When this is possible, it may also be possible to divide a stimulus into smaller parts than halves. In this case, if the subject can establish stable units, he can judge stimuli directly by counting the number of unit parts. The ease with which magnitude estimations are made, along with the tendency to use numbers which represent some modest number of units, suggest that this more complex technique is used by many subjects. Since psychophysical experiments often use psychologists, graduate students, and laboratory employees as subjects, it is sensible to attribute this intellectual feat to the source of data.

Whenever fractionation and magnitude estimation can actually be carried out, the number scale itself plays no intrinsic part in the process. The subject can report the effect of matching or counting numerically, or he can use some other, equally divisible scale as a marker. The recent studies of cross-modality matching have demonstrated that people can match vibration amplitude with loudness, strength of handgrip with heaviness of lifted weights, etc. (J. C. Stevens, Mack, and S. S. Stevens, 1960). This ability establishes that the judgments do not depend on the use of numerical judgments. It cannot be concluded that the judgments actually reflect a purely subjective experience, for any factors which affect the judgment of loudness as compared with numbers will also affect the same judgment when compared with strength of handgrip.

One last question is, How does the subject establish a self-consistent scheme for judging a variable like loudness of pure tones, when he cannot break the tone up into parts and use the methods of comparison? One suggestion, due to Warren (1958), is that the subject may employ a correlated dimension which *is* divisible into parts. The subject may be able to judge the apparent distance of the source of sound on the basis of its loudness. Whether such judgment is learned or innate is a question which cannot be answered here —but there is some evidence that visual judgments of distance need not be learned at all by animals (Gibson and Walk, 1960), and one could imagine that relative distance as a function of loudness ratios is also unlearned. In one study, Warren, Sersen, and Pores (1958) showed that judgments of "twice as far away" corresponded quite well to "half as loud" under conditions of normal reverberation. Since distance, a variety of length of line, can be divided into parts, it would provide a basis for estimations of loudness. It is too early for the present writer to conclude that Warren is or is not right in his particular proposals of the basis of fractionation of variables which cannot be divided up by the subject, but there is every possibility of finding such techniques underlying the more difficult judgments.

One further fact requires explanation. Stevens has shown that, when the subject uses a rating scale with a fixed number of alternatives, the mean category plotted against the intensity of the stimuli produces a scale which is quite unlike the ratio scales.

Systematically, the middle of the rating scale is used for stimuli which are smaller than the middle of the available range. Furthermore, the category scale is much more sensitive than magnitude estimation to context effects, i.e., to the sequence of stimuli presented.

If the subject is given enough categories to prevent artificial bunching, if he judges a dimension which can be estimated quite accurately (length of line, duration, visual numerousness, area of rectangles, and even lifted weights; Stevens and Galanter, 1957), and if the stimuli are spaced equally in physical amount to minimize distortions from context, one finding is quite consistent—the middle category is used for a stimulus which is almost exactly one-third of the way from the smallest to the largest stimulus. Table 9.2 gives

TABLE 9.2

LOCATION OF THE MIDDLE CATEGORY IN PHYSICAL UNITS,
RELATIVE TO THE LARGEST AND SMALLEST STIMULI USED

Dimension	Location
Length of lines	.35
Duration (white noise)	.33, .44, .35
Visual numerousness	.31
Area of rectangles	.32, .27
Lifted weights	Nine cases ranging from .30 to .40

some "locations of the middle category" estimated from the curves given by Stevens and Galanter.

These very consistent results suggest that the subject, in using a rating scale, is trying to bisect stimuli which are not divided into parts but taken as wholes. The lightest stimulus is composed solely of "lightness" aspects relative to the rest of the series, and the heaviest stimulus is composed solely of "heaviness" aspects. However, an increase in physical amount not only increases the difference between the stimulus and the lightest stimulus, but it also increases the total measure of the set of aspects relative to the general background of "zero" stimulus. It seems likely that the smallest stimulus has as great a measure of "smallness" aspects as the largest has of "comparative largeness" aspects, and if to these comparative aspects are added further aspects due to the absolute size of the stimulus, it might well follow that the total set of "largeness" aspects is about twice the total set of "smallness" aspects.

One would then have a situation like that diagramed in Fig. 9.7, where the bisection point would be at $t = \frac{1}{3}$, the value approximated by all the data reported in Table 9.2. The writer is not able to see why the instructions of a rating-scale experiment should produce just this method of comparison, but the results are consistent enough to be suggestive. Clearly, the whole mass of data on rating scales cannot be reduced by so simple a formulation. However, the present hypothesis makes it possible to investigate the process of judgment by ratings with somewhat more precision than has been employed heretofore. In some ways this idea is similar to that used by Helson and his associates in studying the adaptation level. Notice that in the present scheme the extreme stimuli are of more importance than any others, whereas Helson uses the geometric mean of all stimuli. The geometric mean of an equally spaced set of numbers starting with a low number is relatively close to one-third of the range, so that the Helson theory and the present one will make similar predictions.

In the present theory the extreme stimuli are the most important ones in rating because they serve as ideal stimuli for largeness and smallness. If a large stimulus is much more frequent than any other, it should have a disproportionate effect in establishing the set of schemata against which other stimuli are compared. As we saw just above, the center judgment depends on the end stimuli when stimuli are shown equally frequently, but it can also depend upon the distribution of stimuli.

In a very recent study, Parducci, Calfee, Marshall, and Davidson (1960) have studied ratings of numerals. In this case the numeral stimuli do not differ in sensory measure and the only judged aspects are likely to be differential, so that we should expect veridical judgments. However, the restrictions of a rating experiment still move the judgments about relative to the numbers used. The Parducci et al. experiments will not be described here. Suffice it to say that they used a great many different ranges and distributions of numerals, giving the subject a sheet of numerals and having him rate each numeral on a five-point scale. Large numbers of subjects could be studied in this way. The results were summarized by multiple correlations and analysis of variance in which the effects of the midpoint of the range of stimuli, the median, and the mean were evaluated. The center of the judgments (adaptation level) was quite accurately predictable from these descriptions of the set of numerals, as one would expect. However, it was found that the mid-point of the range was by far the most important factor, that the median (which is sensitive to uneven frequencies of presentation of stimuli) was also useful, and that if one knew the mid-point and median no significant improvement in prediction occurred when the mean was also known.

Of the three predictors, mid-point, median, and mean, the mid-point plus median combination was sufficient to predict and the other combinations, mid-point and mean or median and mean, were not sufficient.

One may have some reservations about judgments of numerals as not reflecting a genuinely psychophysical variable; and there is some difficulty in being entirely clear about how to describe the distributions of stimuli used; but the general results of the Parducci et al. experiments are in good accord with the interpretation given in this chapter.

Remarks

In this chapter it has been argued that psychophysical judgments, by bisection, fractionation, magnitude estimation, or rating, are to be thought of as judgments of the situation by the subject, and are as near to objective correctness as the subject can manage with limited access to the objects. Discrepancies between judgments and objective measurements of the objects represent, in this view, systematic errors arising from the various limitations of the observer in precision and purity of sensation, lack of sufficient commerce with the object, or lack of a suitable operational definition of amount of the quality in question.

If the above detailed discussion of psychophysical judgments is analyzed, it can be seen that the whole theory, given in earlier chapters, has been used. It is supposed that the subject responds on the basis of aspects of the situation, adjusting his response on the basis of "ideal situations" which are parts of schemata established by instructions. The judgmental methods are built from the analysis of bisection and fractionation, which in turn relate to the method of adjustment discussed in Chapter 8. Adjustment, in turn, is thought of as a "random walk" in which the probabilities of adjustments up and down are equivalent to probabilities of choices in simpler, one-response situations. The probabilities of these responses are assumed, throughout the discussion of judgment and rating, to depend upon those aspects of the present situation which are in one ideal situation and not in the other: largeness and smallness aspects.

The "line" on which the random walk is performed, and in fact the whole idea of a dimension which can be judged or rated, is in this chapter based on the concept of an ordered array of sets, as developed in Chapter 3.

Finally, and briefly, there was some discussion of how rating scales would be modified by presenting various stimuli with different frequencies. This general problem, only touched upon in Chapter 9, is the problem of "context" in psychophysical judgments. The theoretical background for analyzing context is quite thoroughly developed in Chapters 5 and 6, so that the reader may be able to make useful applications of the general schema theory to psychophysics.

Not only does the theory of psychophysical judgment depend upon the rest of the book, but in fact each chapter can be enriched by references to each of the others. The main point of the theory of preferential choice was that the probability of a choice depends upon how different the alternatives appear. The necessary measurements can in principle be made by psychophysical methods, and if the approach of the present chapter is used such measurements are directly relevant to predictions of preferential choice, since both problems are embedded in the same mathematical structure. Similarly, the theory of choices in risky or uncertain situations depends upon the effects of frequency, and requires for its solution the results of Chapters 5 and 6, which are devoted to schemata and the accumulation of experience.

In the discussions of preferential choice and the effects of frequency, the experimental cases used involved only elementary and discrete responses. The same problems arise when compound or complex responses are required, so that one would use the last two chapters for the analysis of problems like those discussed in Chapters 4, 5, and 6.

The most nearly separate application of the theory is to detection, for the notion of homogeneous classes of aspects is used only in Chapter 7. However, the problem of the limitation of the senses is embedded in the context of the remainder of the book, and a theory of such limitations is essential because the rest of the book assumes that aspects are discriminable. Whenever one uses stimuli that are too small, too dim, or too similar, the results of the other chapters must be qualified by noting the subject's inescapable limitations.

In summary, this essay has attempted to give an integrated and coherent, if grossly incomplete, account of some problems in the psychology of judgment and choice. The arguments have been conducted within elementary probability theory, and a serious attempt has been made to keep various applications consistent and connected with one another. Though the theory is quantitative the writer has, as much as possible, refrained from postulating empirical laws directly.

Instead, each proposal of an empirical regularity has been argued from first principles or from simplifying assumptions. In a sense, the aim has been to construct a quantitative theory which has, as assumptions, only qualitative or categorical statements. The author is not sure whether this program can, even in principle, be carried through. However, it has the strategic advantage that any theoretical discussion about the form of a quantitative law can be reduced to a discussion about ordinary sentences, and thus to a real psychological question. Furthermore, the translation from ordinary language to mathematics makes it possible to draw on the insights of nonmathematical psychologists when attacking a problem in quantitative theory. With such a technique, and the broad base of verbal theory and detailed experimentation available, it may be possible to write a useful mathematical theory of psychology in the near future.

References

Adams, E. W., and R. F. Fagot. 1956. A model of riskless choice. *Tech. Rept. 4,* Applied Mathematics and Statistics Laboratory, Stanford Univ.

Anderson, N. H. 1960. Effect of first-order conditional probability in a two-choice learning situation. *J. exp. Psychol.,* **59,** 73–93.

Audley, R. J., and A. R. Jonckheere. 1956. The statistical analysis of the learning process. II. Stochastic processes and learning behaviour. *Brit. J. stat. Psychol.,* **9,** 87–94.

Békésy, G. v. 1959. Similarities between hearing and skin sensations. *Psychol. Rev.,* **66,** 1–22.

Binder, A., and S. E. Feldman. 1960. The effects of experimentally controlled experience upon recognition responses. *Psychol. Monogr.,* **74,** No. 9 (Whole No. 496).

Bruner, J. S., L. Postman, and F. Mosteller. 1950. A note on the measurement of reversals of perspective. *Psychometrika,* **15,** 63–72.

Burke, C. J., and W. K. Estes. 1957. A component model for stimulus variables in discrimination learning. *Psychometrika,* **22,** 133–145.

Bush, R. R., and W. K. Estes (Eds.). 1959. *Studies in mathematical learning theory.* Stanford Univ. Press.

Bush, R. R., and H. C. Morlock. 1959. Test of a general conditioning axiom for human two-choice experiments. *Memorandum MP-1,* Psychological Laboratory, Univ. Pennsylvania.

Bush, R. R., and F. Mosteller. 1951. A model for stimulus generalization and discrimination. *Psychol. Rev.,* **58,** 413–423.

Casperson, R. C., and H. Schlosberg. 1950. Monocular and binocular intensity thresholds for fields containing 1–7 dots. *J. exp. Psychol.,* **40,** 81–92.

Chocholle, R. 1940. Variation des temps de réaction auditifs en fonction de l'intensité à diverses fréquences. *L'Année Psychologique,* **41,** 5–124.

Coombs, C. H. 1958. On the use of inconsistency of preferences in psychological measurement. *J. exp. Psychol.,* **55,** 1–7.

Coombs, C. H., and D. G. Pruitt. 1960. Components of risk in decision making: Probability and variance preferences. *J. exp. Psychol.*, **60,** 265–277.

Cotton, J. W., and A. Rechtschaffen. 1958. Replication report: Two- and three-choice verbal conditioning phenomena. *J. exp. Psychol.*, **56,** 96

Engler, J. 1958. Marginal and conditional stimulus and response probabilities in verbal conditioning. *J. exp. Psychol.*, **55,** 303–317.

Estes, W. K. 1950. Toward a statistical theory of learning. *Psychol. Rev.*, **57,** 94–107.

Estes, W. K. 1957. Of models and men. *Amer. Psychologist,* **12,** 609–617.

Estes, W. K., and P. Suppes. 1959. Foundations of linear models. In R. R. Bush and W. K. Estes (Eds.). *Studies in mathematical learning theory.* Stanford Univ. Press.

Feller, W. 1950. *An introduction to probability theory and its applications.* New York: Wiley (2nd Ed., 1957)

Gardner, R. A. 1957. Probability-learning with two and three choices. *Amer. J. Psychol.,* **70,** 174–185.

Gardner, R. A. 1958. Multiple-choice decision-behavior. *Amer. J. Psychol.,* **71,** 710–717.

Garner, W. R. 1954a. A technique and a scale for loudness measurement. *J. acoust. Soc. Amer.,* **26,** 73–88.

Garner, W. R. 1954b. Context effects and the validity of loudness scales. *J. exp. Psychol.,* **48,** 218–224.

Garner, W. R. 1958. Half-loudness judgments without prior stimulus context. *J. exp. Psychol.,* **55,** 482–485.

Gibson, E. J., and R. D. Walk. 1960. The "visual cliff." *Scientific Amer.,* **202,** 64–71.

Goodnow, J. J. 1955. Response sequences in a pair of two-choice probability situations. *Amer. J. Psychol.,* **68,** 624–630.

Goodnow, J. J., I. Rubenstein, and A. Lubin. 1957. Response to changing patterns of events. *Memorandum 4:* Problem solving project. Washington, D. C.: Walter Reed Army Institute of Research.

Guthrie, E. R. 1946. Psychological facts and psychological theory. *Psychol. Bull.,* **43,** 1–20.

Jarvik, M. E. 1951. Probability learning and a negative recency effect in the serial anticipation of alternative symbols. *J. exp. Psychol.,* **41,** 291–297.

Kemeny, J. G., J. L. Snell, and G. L. Thompson. 1957. *Introduction to finite mathematics.* Englewood Cliffs, N. J.: Prentice-Hall.

Lamperti, J., and P. Suppes. 1959. Chains of infinite order and their application to learning theory. *Pacific J. Math.,* **9,** 739–754.

Lorge, I., and H. Solomon. 1955. Two models of group behavior in the solution of Eureka-type problems. *Psychometrika,* **20,** 139–148.

Luce, R. D. 1959a. *Individual choice behavior.* New York: Wiley.

Luce, R. D. 1959b. On the possible psychophysical laws. *Psychol. Rev.,* **66,** 81–95.

Michels, W. C., and H. Helson. 1949. A reformulation of the Fechner law in terms of adaptation-level applied to rating-scale data. *Amer. J. Psychol.,* **62,** 355–368.

Mosteller, F., and P. Nogee. 1951. An experimental measurement of utility. *J. Pol. Econ.,* **59,** 371–404.

Nicks, D. C. 1959. Prediction of sequential two-choice decisions from event runs. *J. exp. Psychol.*, **57**, 105–114.

Overall, J. E. 1960. A cognitive probability model for learning. *Psychometrika*, **25**, 159–172

Parducci, A., R. C. Calfee, L. M. Marshall, and L. P. Davidson. 1960. Context effects in judgment: Adaptation level as a function of the mean, midpoint, and median of the stimuli. *J. exp. Psychol.*, **60**, 65–77.

Penfield, W., and L. Roberts. 1959. *Speech and brain mechanisms*. Princeton Univ. Press.

Popper, K. R. 1959. *The logic of scientific discovery*. New York: Basic Books.

Reese, E. P. (Ed.). 1953. Psychophysical research summary report, 1946–1952. *USN Spec. Dev. Ctr. Tech. Rept. No. SDC-131-1-5*, Psychophysical Research Unit, Mt. Holyoke College.

Restle, F. 1959a. A metric and an ordering on sets. *Psychometrika*, **24**, 207–220.

Restle, F. 1959b. A survey and classification of learning models. In R. R. Bush and W. K. Estes (Eds.). *Studies in mathematical learning theory*. Stanford Univ. Press.

Restle, F., J. Rae, and C. Kiesler. 1961. The probability of detecting small numbers of dots. *J. exp. Psychol.*, **61**, 218–221.

Schlosberg, H. 1948. A probability formulation of the Hunter-Sigler effect. *J. exp. Psychol.*, **38**, 155–167.

Schoonard, J., and F. Restle. 1961. Comparison of two methods of teaching double-alternation. *J. exp. Psychol.* (in press).

Schrödinger, E. 1950. What is an elementary particle? *Annual Report of the Smithsonian Institution*, 183–196.

Stevens, J. C., J. D. Mack, and S. S. Stevens. 1960. Growth of sensation on seven continua as measured by force of handgrip. *J. exp. Psychol.*, **59**, 60–67.

Stevens, J. C., and G. M. Shickman. 1959. The perception of repetition rate. *J. exp. Psychol.*, **58**, 433–440.

Stevens, S. S. 1951. Mathematics, measurement, and psychophysics. In S. S. Stevens (Ed.). *Handbook of experimental psychology*. New York: Wiley.

Stevens, S. S. 1956. The direct estimation of sensory magnitudes: loudness. *Amer. J. Psychol.*, **69**, 1–25.

Stevens, S. S. 1957. On the psychophysical law. *Psychol. Rev.*, **64**, 153–181.

Stevens, S. S., A. S. Carton, and G. M. Shickman. 1958. A scale of apparent intensity of electric shock. *J. exp. Psychol.*, **56**, 328–334.

Stevens, S. S., and E. H. Galanter. 1957. Ratio scales and category scales for a dozen perceptual continua. *J. exp. Psychol.*, **54**, 377–411.

Stevens, S. S., and G. Stone. 1959. Finger span: ratio scale, category scale, and JND scale. *J. exp. Psychol.*, **57**, 91–95.

Tanner, W. P., Jr., and J. A. Swets. 1954. A decision-making theory of visual detection. *Psychol. Rev.*, **61**, 401–409.

Taves, E. H. 1941. Two mechanisms for the perception of visual numerousness. *Arch. Psychol.*, N. Y., **37**, No. 265.

Torgerson, W. S. 1958. *Theory and methods of scaling*. New York: Wiley.

von Neumann, J., and O. Morgenstern. 1947. *Theory of games and economic behavior* (2nd Ed.). Princeton Univ. Press.

Warren, R. M. 1958. A basis for judgment of sensory intensity. *Amer. J. Psychol.*, **71,** 675–687.

Warren, R. M., E. A. Sersen, and E. B. Pores. 1958. A basis for loudness-judgments. *Amer. J. Psychol.*, **71,** 700–709.

Warren, R. M., and R. P. Warren. 1956. Effect of the relative volume of standard and comparison object on half-heaviness judgments. *Amer. J. Psychol.*, **69,** 640–643.

Woodworth, R. S., and H. Schlosberg. 1954. *Experimental psychology* (2nd Ed.). New York: Holt.

Index

Absolute and comparative magnitude, 216
Absolute and differential thresholds, 139, 179
Absolute largeness, 197
Abstract utilities, 67–68
Access to schemata, 104
Adams, E. A., 84
Adaptation level, 207
Adding out, of sets, 8
Addition, 205
Additivity of distances, 46, 49–50
Additivity of utilities, 83
Adjustment, method of, 37, 136, 165, 179–187
Algebraic theory of utility, 83
Algebra of sets, 8
Alternation, 109
    effect, 130
    of sequence, 128
Alternatives, 25
    compound (utility of), 66
Ambiguous figures, reversal, 37, 172–175
AND (the logical word), 6
Anderson, N. H., 110, 130
Appearances, 190

A priori probabilities, 85
Aptitude, 42
Arbitrary constant, 65
Arithmetic reasoning, 205
Arrays of sets, see Linear array of sets
Ascending method of limits, 137–138
Aspects, 26–28, 141, 188
    common, 32
    differential, 43
    disjoint pools of, 49–50
    gamble, 90
    homogeneous, 140 ff.
    inhomogeneities as, 30
    relevant, 29, 34
    suppression of, 33
    valued, 64, 74, 82
    weighted, 35
Associativity of addition, 40
Asymptotic distribution of adjustments, 181–182
Asymptotic response frequencies, 123
Attenuation, 214
Audley, R. J., 123
Average error, method of, see Method of adjustment
Averaging ratios, 89
Avoiding an alternative, utility of, 66

225

Axioms, measure function, 10
  set theory, 8

Background, contrast with, 30
Background stimulation, 29, 147
Bartley, S. H., 210 n.
Basic methods of psychophysics, 136
Behaviorism, 189
Behaviorist psychophysics, 190–191
Békésy, G. v., 179
Bet, see Gambling
Betweenness, of sets, 46
Bias, method of limits, 159–162
  response, 156 ff.
Bilateral pairs, 81
Bilateral triples, 79
Binder, A., 97, 97 n., 98–101, 103, 152
Binomial distribution, 154–155, 178
Bisection, method of, 188, 197–203
  uniqueness, 197–199
  validity, 197–203
Boltzmann statistics, 143
Boze-Einstein statistics, 144
Brightness, 42, 54, 214
Bruner, J. S., 173
Burke, C. J., 97
Bush, R. R., 104, 108, 111, 117, 128

Calfee, R. C., 217
Cancelling, of double negatives, 9
Capacities (mental), 106
Cardinal utility of money, 83
Carton, A. S., 209
Casperson, R. C., 154
Catch trials, 138
Category scales, 206, 215
Causal relationships, 21
Cell of a partition, 11, 28–30
Chocholle, R., 168–172
Choice, 25, 31–32, 59
  among disjoint sets, 69
  inconsistency of, 61 ff.
  in ordered situations, 51
  transitivity of, 73
  utility, 60
  voluntary, 67
Circle (color), 49
Circle of sets, 48
Classes of indistinguishable elements,
  146 ff.

Classifying situations, 27
Class-valued function, 146
Closeness, of sets, 45
Cognitive Probability Model, 123
Cognitive theory, 189
Cohesiveness of a group, 42
Collection, 3
College students as subjects, 133
Colon, F., 210 n.
Color circle, 49
Combinatorial analysis, 85–86
Common aspects, 28, 32
  and probability of response, 35
Common overlap, 69
Communication (of situations), 27
Commutativity, of addition, 40
Comparative and absolute magnitude,
  216
Comparative judgments, 179
Comparison of stimuli, 188, 213
Complement of a set, 6
Complexity of situations, 29–30, 54
  possible paradox, 30
Complicated decisions, 70
Component events in reaction time,
  169–170
Compound alternative (utility of), 66
Compound events, 12 ff.
Compound responses, 36, 164 ff., 167–
  168, 180
Conditional probabilities, 19, 128
Conditioning, 23, 97
Conflict, 33, 136
Conscious experience, 189
Consequences of choice, 31–32
Constant stimuli (method of), 136–137
Contained (one set in another), 4
  see also Subset
Context effects, 214–219
Continuity, 144
Continuous time, 166–169
Continuous variable, 180
Contours, 190
Contradictions, 11
Convergence, in neural tract, 145
Convolution, 155
Coombs, C. H., 75–76, 79–82, 90–93
Correct detection (probability of), 149
Correction for guessing, 149
Correlated dimension, 215

Correlation, of discriminal dispersions, 82
Correlation, of fluctuations of utility, 63
Cotton, J. W., 126
Counting, 213
  as measurement, 12
Criterion for response, 148–150
Criterion set, 192
Cross-modality matching, 215
Crossover, method of limits, 137
  as threshold, 159–162
Cross partition of situations, 29
Crucial experiment, 100 ff.

Darkness aspects, 30
Davidson, L. P., 217
Davis, J. H., 176–179
Death, utility of, 66
Decay of schemata, 105
Decision maker, rational, 60
Decisions, 25, 70
Decision theory, 60, 90, 149–151
Defining property, 4
deMorgan's rules, 9
Density of weights, 210–211
Derks, P., 117
Desaturation of a figure, 175
Descending method of limits, 137
Detection, 135, 137, 147, 219
Determinant, 194
Determinism, 21, 23
Deterministic theory of utility, 83
Difference between sets, 43, 44
Difference equation, linear, 108
Differential aspects, and learning, 95
  measure of, 43
Differential thresholds, 156 ff., 179
  and absolute thresholds, 139
Dimensions, physical, 39
  psychological, 39
Discrete responses, 136
Discriminable stimuli, 30
Discriminal dispersions, 81
Discriminal processes, 80, 80 n.
  theory of, 149 ff., 179
Discrimination, theory of, 188
Discrimination learning, 194
Discrimination methods of psychophysics, 136
Disjoint pools of aspects, 49–50

Disjoint sets, choice among, 69
  of valued aspects, 74
Disregarding aspects, 33
Dissimilarity, 82
Distance, 219
  additivity of, 46, 49–50
  between points, 42
  between sets, 198–199
  between situations, 43
  index of, 43
  judgments of, 215
Distribution of ideals, 81
Distributive axioms of set theory, 8
Domain, 3
Dots, detection of, 154–155
Double negatives, cancelling, 9
Doubling a stimulus, 205
Dualism, 191
Dynamic process of adjustment, 179

Economics, 60
Edwards, W., 113 n.
Electric potentials, at synapses, 145
Electric probe in brain, 105
Element of a set, 5
Emergent aspects of a gamble, 90
Empirical vs. normative theory, 60
Empiricism, 213
Empty set ($\emptyset$), 7
Engler, J., 128–230
Enumeration, of elements in a set, 4
Epistemology, of quantum physics, 144
  of situations, 27
Epsilon ($\in$), (member of set), 5
Equal appearing intervals, method of, 189
Equality judgment, 180
Equality of sets, 4
Equal probability hypothesis, 24
Equisection, 203
Equivalence, of elements, 142
  of stimuli, 95
Equivalence class, 43
Ergodic, 182 n.
Error, experimental, 41
  margin of, in choice, 61
  of observation, 22
  time-order, 157 ff.
E-space, 47

Estes, W. K., 23, 97, 104, 108–109, 121–122
Estimation of stimuli, 37, 88
Euclidean space, 46–47
Eureka problems, 175 ff.
Events, homogeneous runs of, 111
Events and responses, 107
Events in probability theory, 16
Exhaustive subsets, 11
Expected utility, 60
  in detection, 151–152
Experience, conscious, 189
  previous, 213
Experimental errors, 41
Experimental measurements of utility, 73
Exponential distribution, 166, 173–175
Extrapolation, 47

Face validity of responses, 137
Factor analysis, 39
Factoring, of sets, 8
Fagot, R. F., 84
False alarm responses, 138, 147, 154
  and reaction time, 172
  probability of, 149
Family, 3
Fechner, G. T., 207
Feldman, S. E., 97–103, 97 n., 152
Feller, W., 155–156, 167, 180
Figure ground, loss of, 175
  reversal, 172 ff.
Fine adjustment, 181
First response (method of limits), 159–162
Fixed aspects and guessing, 130–133
Fractionation, 203–204, 207–213
  bias, 208–209
  context and, 214
  method of, 188
Frequency, 219
  of target, 152–153
  relative (probability), 13
Friedman, M., 121–122
Function, 146
Functional calculus (logic), 11
Fundamental measurement, 41

Galanter, E. H., 117, 206, 209, 216
Gambler's fallacy, 111

Gambler's fallacy, and past experience, 112–113
Gambles, 85
  emergent aspects of, 90
  ideal, 91–93
  skewness of, 91–93
  utility of, 87
  variance of, 91–93
Gambling, specific utility of, 87
Gambling device, 86
Gambling games (mathematical analysis of), 13
Game theory, 90
Gamma distribution, 167, 169–170, 174–176, 178
Ganzfeld, 29
Gardner, R. A., 125–126
Garner, W. R., 202–203, 206, 214
Generalization, 95
  method of, 194
  gradient, 42, 55
General psychophysical law, 206 ff.
Geometric distribution, 166
Gestalt, 28
Gibson, E. J., 215
"Goad," 67
Goodnow, J. J., 111, 118, 128
Gradient, of generalization, 42, 55
  of responses, 55
Group problem solving, 6, 176–179
Guessing, 107 ff., 133
  correction for, 149
Guthrie, E. R., 23

Habit, 31
Half-judgments, 188
Half-way stimulus, 96
Helson, H., 207, 217
Homogeneous classes of aspects, 140 ff., 219
  algebra of, 162–163
  magnitude of, 163
Homogeneous linear equations, 194
Homogeneous nerve tissue, 145
Homogeneous runs of events, 111
Hoppe, R., 174
Hues, 190

Ideal gamble, 91–93
Ideal gray, 75

Ideal object, 75
Ideal point, 80
Ideals, 80
  distribution of, 81
Ideal situations, 30 ff., 36, 94, 139, 218
  discrimination of, 139
Ideal stimulus, 78, 82
Identity of objects, 144
Illusions, 190
Impossible properties, 11
Incommensurable objects, 65
Inconsistencies of choice, 61 ff.
Independence, 19, 24
  of events, 38
  of partitionings, 71
Independence-of-path assumption, 104
Independent judgments, 184
Indirect evidence, 165
Indistinguishability, 142
Indistinguishable aspects, 146, 159
Indistinguishable elements, 157, 185, 188, 195, 219
Indistinguishable particles, 142
Individual differences and reaction time, 172
Inequality, triangle, 44
Infinitely fine adjustments, 184
Infinite sets (measures of), 9
Inhomogeneities, and aspects, 30
Instincts, 31
Instructions, 31
"Integrator" in adjustment, 186
Interference in groups, 178
Interpolation, 46
Intersection of sets, 6
Intersubjective aspects, 190
Interval scales, 42
  of utility, 65
Intransitivities, 78
Introspectionism, 189, 206
Irrelevant elements, 183

Jarvik, M. E., 111, 119–121
Jonckheere, A. R., 123
Joy (initials not known), 211
Judgments, 187
  in measuring threshold, 136
  of stimuli, 188
  of variable, 180

Judgments, systems of, 37, 188 ff.

Kemeny, G., 8
Kiesler, C., 155
Kinesthetic after-effect, 212

Labeling, arbitrary, 42
Lamperti, J., 182 n.
Leaks of probability, 182
Learning (models), 107 ff.
Lengths of objects, 40
Lightness aspects (of weights), 30, 196
Limits, 184
  method of, 137
Limits of a sense, 136
Linear array of sets, 49–50, 75, 180, 195–203, 218
Linear difference equation, 108
Linear equations, 194
Linear model, 123, 128
Linear plot, 171
Location of the middle category, 216
Locke, J., 104
Logarithmic law, 207
Logic, 6 ff.
Logically false sentences, 11
Logically true sentences, 11
Long runs of events, 119
Lorge, I., 6, 176–177
Loudness, 42, 54, 196
Lubin, A., 118
Luce, R. D., 69–70, 70 n., 87 n., 147, 150, 156, 170
Luce's model, 74

m (measure function), 9
Mack, J. D., 209, 215
Macroscopic evidence, 165
Magnitude, absolute and relative, 197
  of classes of homogeneous aspects, 163
  of sets, 9
Magnitude estimation, 189, 204 ff., 209, Maltese cross, 172–175
Manipulation of stimuli, 209–210
Map, of observations, 39
Margin of error, in choices, 61
Markovian learning models, 104
Markov Process, 104, 182 n.
Marshall, L. M., 217
Massed practice, 134

Matching, with runs, 114
  with schemata, 31, 94–95
Mathematical models of learning, 107 ff.
Mathematical reasoning, 205
Matrix, 194
Maximizing success, 123
Maximum expected utility, 60, 151–152
Mean, of reaction times, 168–172
  of stimuli, 217–218
  of waiting times, 168
Measure, of a set, 9
  of differential aspects, 43
  of indistinguishable elements, 146
  probability, 12
Measure function, 141
  axioms, 10
Measurement, as theory, 40 ff.
  definition, 42
  of physical variables, 56
  of utility, 59
  principles of, 40
  psychological, 40
Measure theory of utilities, 65
Median of stimuli, 217–218
Member (of a set), 4
Memory, 128
  by redintegration, 105
  of specific past events, 105
"Mental" as abstraction, 191
"Mental attributes," 190
Mental operations, 212
Metaphysics, 191
Metathetic scale, 50
Method of adjustment, 37, 136, 165, 179–187
Method of average error, see Method of adjustment
Method of bisection, 188, 197–203
  uniqueness, 197–199
  validity, 198–203
Method of constant stimuli, 136–137
Method of equal-appearing intervals, 189
Method of equisection, 203
Method of fractionation, 188, 203–204, 207–212
Method of generalization, 194
Method of limits, 137, 159–162
  crossover point, 137

Method of magnitude estimation, 189, 204 ff., 209
Method of multiplication, 189
Method of paired comparisons, 136–137
Method of triads, 33, 188, 192
Metric axioms, 43
Michels, W. C., 207, 217
Microelectrodes, 164
Microneural events, 170
Midpoint of stimuli, 217–218
Missed stimuli and reaction time, 172
Model of a response, 168
Models of learning, 107 ff.
Momentarily perceived utilities, 61
Momentary perceptions, 80
Money, 83
  utility of, 83
Monotone sequence of sets, 49
Monotonicity, 80
"More of the same," 142
Morgenstern, O., 84
Morlock, H. C., 111
Mosteller, F., 85, 108, 128, 173
Motivation, 59
Multiple-choice decisions, 69 ff.
Multiple-choice guessing, 123, 127–128
Multiple ideal situations, 36
Multiple targets, 153 ff.
Multiplication, method of, 189
Multiplication, process of, 205
Multiplying out, 8
Multistage choosing, 73
Mutually exclusive categories, probability of, 18
Mutually exclusive subsets, 11
Myotatic reflexes, 29

Necker cube, 172–174
Negation, 6
Negative binomial distribution, 167
Negative recency, 111, 124
  and random sequences, 116
Negative stimuli, 30
Negative utility, 65–66
Nervous system, 189
  and reaction time, 170
Nested sets, 49
  of valued aspects, 82
Neural events and reaction time, 170
Neural network, 145

Neurons, 145
  combinations of, 106
  number of, 106
Nicks, D. C., 111
Nogee, P., 85
Noise, 140, 159
  background, 29
  indistinguishable, 147
Nonsequential stimuli, 132
Nonsolvers, 178
No response, 147 ff.
Normal curve theory, 61, 69
Normalized distribution, 183
Normative vs. empirical theory, 60
NOT (logical word), 6
Notation, sets of aspects and situation,
  32
Number of elements in a set, 9
Number of stages, 176
Numerals, assignment of, 41
Numerical reasoning, 205
Numerousness, 211–212

Objective aspects, 189
Objective phenomena and physics, 190
Objective world, 189
Objects, partitioning of, 70 ff.
Object-subject system, 190
Observer, training of, 27
Odds, 86, 91–93
Omega, 15
One-to-one correspondence, 10
Optic tract, 145
Optimal behavior in detection, 151–153
Optimal psychophysical method, 138
OR (logical word), 5
Ordered sets, 44–45, 49–50, 218
  of valued aspects, 74
Ordering, 39–42
Outcomes, partitioning of, 70 ff.
Overall, J. E., 105, 123, 134
Overlap of sets, 6
Overshooting of event probabilities, 123

Paired comparisons, method of, 136–137
Paradox of complexity, 30
Parameters of choices, 90
Parducci, A., 217–218
Parentheses, 8
Part-events, 166

Particles, physical, 142
Partitions, 38
  by similarity, 73
  independence of, 71
  of objects, 70 ff.
  of sets, 11
Parts of a stimulus, 213
Parts of responses, 164 ff.
Past experience, 31
Patterns, and guessing, 109
Patterns of responses, 110
Penfield, W., 105
Perceived magnitude, 82
Perception, reversal of, 172 ff.
Perceptual defense, 138
Perceptual vigilance, 138
Perseveration of response (in method of
  limits), 138
Personality attribute, 42
Perspective reversal, 172–174
Photons, 142
Physicalism, 189 ff.
Physical variable, measurement of, 56
Physics and psychology, 189
Physics as abstraction, 191
Pitch, 42
Point of subjective equality, 179
Poisson approximation, 155
Poisson distribution, 173
Polymers, and memory, 106
Pooling of abilities, 176
Popper, K., 14
Pores, E. B., 215
Positive recency effect, 121 ff.
Possible targets, 154
Postman, L., 173
Potter, L., 174
Power function, 170–171, 204–208
Precedence, 205
Prediction experiments, 107 ff.
Preference scale, 78
Preferential choice, 219
Previous events, as stimuli, 110
Previous experience, 213
Primate Laboratories, 29
Primitive concepts, 50
Probabilities, a priori, 85
  direct presentation of, 86
  learned through experience, 85
Probability, conditional, 19

Probability, subjective, 86
Probability matching, 100, 109, 123, 127, 129, 131, 133
Probability of an individual occurrence, 15
Probability of a set, 14
Probability of response, 33–34
  and common aspects, 35
Probability (theory of), 12 ff., 219
  and determinism, 21
  classical, 12
  relative frequency, 13
  set-theoretic, 14
  subjective, 14
Problem solving, 175 ff.
Product (of sets), 6
Properties, logic of, 11
Proportion of solvers, 177
Prothetic scales, 49
Pruitt, D. G., 91–93
PSE, 179
Pseudometric, 43
Psychophysical law, 206 ff.
Psychophysical methods, 135, 218–219
  discrimination, 136
  importance of, 207–208
Psychophysical theories, 189 ff.
Punishments and rewards, 134
Pure alternatives, 85
Pure quantity, 140 ff., 147
"Purified" events, 21

Qualitative variables, 159
Quanta of light, 135
Quantitative dimension, 188
Quantitative scales, 49
Quantitative variables, 159
Quantity (pure), 140 ff., 147
Quantum physics, 190
Quietness (aspects), 30

Radar watching, 153
Rae, J., 155
Random access hypothesis, 94–95
  and response, 96
"Randomness," 20
Random perturbations of situations, 140
Random reinforcement schedule, 102
Random sequence, 126

Random stimulation, 140
Random walk, 180, 186, 218
Range, 3
Ranking of alternatives, 70
Rank orderings, 42
Rate (lambda), 167
Rate of learning, 133
  and recognition, 99–100
Ratings, 37, 189
Rating scales, 206–207, 217, 219
Rational choice, 61
Rational decision-maker, 60
Rationality, 93, 151–153
Ratios, average of, 89
  of utilities, 65
Ratio scales, 42, 215
  of utilities, 65
Reaction time, 36–37, 164
  and intensity of stimulus, 170–172
  and missed stimuli, 172
  simple, 168 ff.
Receiver Operating Characteristic function, 150
Recency effect, negative, 111 ff.
  positive, 121 ff.
Receptors, 136, 189, 206
Rechtschaffen, A., 126
Recognition, 94 ff.
  and learning rate, 99–100
Redintegration theory of memory, 105
Reese, E. P., 211
Reflection (thought), 31
Reflexes, myotatic (balancing), 29
Reinforcement, 128
Reinforcement schedule, 102
Reinforcing events, 108
Relative frequency, approach to probability theory, 13
  of trials, 96
Relative magnitude, 197
Relevance to choice, of aspects, 29
Relevant aspects, 34
"Representative gray," 75
Resolution of conflict, 33
Resolving power of senses, 135
Response and events, 107
Response and random access, 96
Response bias, 156 ff., 179, 186–187
  in method of adjustment, 181, 186–187
Response frequencies, asymptotic, 123

Response gradient, 55
Response patterns, 110
Response perseveration in method of limits, 159–162
Responses, compound, 36, 167–168
  discrete, 136
  parts of, 164 ff.
  probability of, 34
Response strengths, 39
Response time, 36
Restle, F., 39, 50, 109, 134, 155
Restrictions on sequences and guessing, 111 ff.
Restructuring of ambiguous figures, 37
Reversal of transitivity, 77
Reversible figures, 172
Rewards and punishments, 134
Risky situations, 60
Roberts, L., 105
ROC function, 149 ff.
Rubenstein, I., 118
Rubin, H., 182 n.
Runs, distribution of, 111 ff.
  matching, 114
  of events, homogeneous, 111

Samples, 15
Sample space, 15
Sampling rate, 110
Satiation, 213
Saturation, 42
Scale, metathetic, 50
  of preference, 78
  prothetic, 49
  quantitative, 49
  substitutive, 50
Scaling methods, 189
Schemata, 30 ff., 94, 133, 218
  access to, 104
  and method of limits, 138
  and training, 94
  matching, 31, 94–95
  multiple, 36
  random decay of, 105
  theory, 100 ff., 127, 130, 134, 219
  unique elements in, 95
Schlosberg, H., 154, 170–171, 214
Schoonard, J., 109
Schrödinger, E., 143–145
Sensationalism, 189 ff.

Sensations, 190, 206
Sensitivity of senses, 135
Sensory transmission system, 136
Sequential restrictions and guessing, 111 ff.
Serson, E. A., 215
Set, 3
Set difference, 44
Set product, 6
Sets, monotone sequence of, 49
  nested, 49
  ordered, 49–50
Sets of aspects, 188
  and utility, 64
Set theory, 3
  and homogeneous aspects, 162–163
  approach to probability, 14
Several ideal situations, 36
Shickman, G. M., 209
Short runs of events, 119
Similarity, 32, 192
  partitioning by, 73
Simple reaction time, 168 ff.
Simplifying assumptions, 181
Sinking traces, 158
Situational aspects, 28
Situational variables, 26
Situations, 26 ff., 191
  classification of, 27
  communication of, 27
  cross partitioning of, 29
  distance between, 43
  epistemology of, 27
  ideal, 30 ff.
  past, present, 133
  risky, 60
  unique, 26–27
Size, of stimuli, 54
Size-weight illusion, 210–211, 213
Skewness of a gamble, 91–93
Snell, J. L., 8
Solomon, H., 6, 176–177
Solution times, 175 ff.
  group, 177
  individual, 177
Solvers, 177–178
Sources of energy and aspects, 163
Space, 3
Specific utility of gambling, 87
Split triple, 79

Spurious responses, 138
  see also False alarm responses
Stages of a problem, 175 ff.
Stages of reaction time, 170
Standard, 181
Standard deviation, minimum, 172
  of reaction times, 168–170
Standard stimulus, 136–137, 157 ff.
Statistical decision theory, 149–151
Statistical learning theory, 129, 133
  see also Stimulus-sampling theory
Statistical methods, 74
Statistics, 60
Stevens, J. C., 209, 215
Stevens, S. S., 40, 41, 49, 50, 157, 170, 204, 206–209, 214–216
Stimulus aspects, 28
  and neural paths, 145
Stimulus element, 23, 97, 129
Stimulus error, 189–190
Stimulus-response theory, 105
Stimulus-sampling theory, 97, 100 ff., 123, 129, 133
Stimulus traces, 128
Stimulus variable, 27
Stirling's formula, 185
Stochastic transitivity, strong, 77 ff.
  weak, 76
Stone, G., 209
Storage capacity, 104–105
Straight line, 42, 46
Strength of responses, 39
Strong stochastic transitivity, 77 ff.
Subatomic particles, 142
Subjective, 189
Subjective probability, 14, 86, 92
Subsets, 4
Substitution of elements, 50
Substitutive scale, 50
Suppes, P., 109, 182 n.
Suppression of aspects, 33, 140, 147
Swets, J. A., 149–151, 153
Symmetry of adjustments, 181
Synaptic connections, 170
Synaptic stimulation, 145
Synthesis, problem of, 21
System, observer-object, 189

Tanner, W. P., 149–151, 153
Targets, for detection, 147

Targets, frequency of, 152–153
  multiple, 153 ff.
  "possible," 154
Tautologies, 11
Taves, E. H., 209, 211, 212
Temporal lobe of cortex, 105
Test stimulus, 33
Theory of choice, 51
Theory of games, 90
Thermal noise, 135
Thompson, G. L., 8
Three-choice guessing, 125
Thresholds, 135, 186
  differential, 156 ff.
Threshold theory of choices, 61
Thurstone theory, 76, 80, 80 n., 81, 123, 134
Time, to choose, 36
Time-order error, 157 ff., 187
Torgerson, W. S., 179, 192
Traces, of runs, 114
  sinking, 158
Training and schemata, 94
Training of observers, 27
Transformations of energy (psycho-physical), 189
Transformations of expressions, 7
Transition probabilities, in adjustment, 181
  in guessing, 126
Transitivity, of choice, 73
  of equality, 40
  strong stochastic, 77 ff.
  weak stochastic, 76
Triads, method of, see Method of triads
Triangle inequality, 44
Trigonometry, 46
Triples of stimuli, 79
"True" scale, 201–206

Uncertainty, 136
Unfolding, 76
Unilateral pairs, 81
Unilateral triples, 79
Union of sets, 5
Unique elements in schemata, 95
Uniqueness of bisection point, 197–199
Unitary events, 166
Universal property, 11
Universe, 6

Urn model, 123
Utility, 42, 59, 134
    additivity of, 83
    avoiding an alternative, 66
    choice behavior and, 60
    compound alternative, 66
    death, 66
    detection, 151–152
    employees, 84
    experimental measurements of, 73
    gamble, 87
    gambling (specific), 87
    interval scale of, 65
    maximum expected, 60
    measurement of, 60
    measures of sets, 65
    measure-theory of, 65
    money, 92
    negative, 65–66
    ratio scale of, 65
    ratios of, 65
    sets of aspects and, 64

Vacations, utility of, 62
Validity of bisection, 198–203
    of responses, 137
Valued aspects, 64
    disjoint sets of, 74

Valued aspects, nested sets of, 82
    ordered sets of, 74
Values of a variable, 28
Variables, situational, 26
Variables, values of, 28
Variable stimulus, 136–137, 157 ff., 181
Variance, of a distribution of ideals, 81
    of a gamble, 91–93
    of waiting time, 168
Visual fatigue, 175
Voluntary choices, 67
von Neumann, J., 84
v-Scale, 70

Waiting-time theory, 165 ff., 180
Walk, R. D., 215
Warren, R. M., 170, 210, 211, 215
Warren, R. P., 210, 211
Weak stochastic transitivity, 76
Weight, 196
    of an aspect, 35
Weighted sum of traces, 114
Weights (of elements of sets), 9
Whole-part relationship, 27–28
Whole (psychophysical) system, 189
Woodworth, R. S., 170–171, 214

Yes response, 147 ff.